John Dalton

& the
progress of science

John Dalton

John Dalton
& the progress
of science

*Papers presented
to a conference
of historians
of science
held in
Manchester
September 19–24
1966 to mark
the bicentenary
of Dalton's birth*

Edited by
D S L Cardwell

Manchester University Press
Barnes & Noble Inc, New York

© 1968 Manchester University Press
Published by the University of Manchester
at THE UNIVERSITY PRESS
316–324 Oxford Road
Manchester 13

GB SBN 7190 0301 6

U.S.A.
1968
BARNES & NOBLE, INC.,
105 Fifth Avenue, New York, N.Y. 10003

Printed in Great Britain by
Butler & Tanner Ltd, Frome and London

641756

Contents

		Contributors

D S L Cardwell (editor) — *Reader in History of Science and Technology, University of Manchester Institute of Science and Technology*

William H Brock — *Lecturer in the History of Science, University of Leicester*

Archie Clow — *Director of Science Talks, British Broadcasting Corporation*

M P Crosland — *Lecturer in the History and Philosophy of Science, University of Leeds*

Kathleen R Farrar — *Special Lecturer in Chemistry, University of Manchester*

W V Farrar — *Nuffield Research Fellow in the History of Science and Technology, University of Manchester, Institute of Science and Technology*

Robert Fox — *Department of History, University of Lancaster*

Frank Greenaway — *The Science Museum, London*

Henry Guerlac — *Goldwin Smith Professor of the History of Science, Cornell University*

A Rupert Hall — *Professor of History of Science and Technology, Imperial College, London*

Marie Boas Hall — *Reader in the History of Science and Technology, Imperial College, London*

The late Sir Cyril Hinshelwood FRS — *Senior Research Fellow, Imperial College, London, from 1964; formerly Dr Lee's Professor of Chemistry, University of Oxford*

B B Kelham — *University of Manchester Institute of Science and Technology*

Gordon Manley — *Professor of Environmental Studies, University of Lancaster*

L P Petrov — *Trade Delegation to the USSR, London*

C A Russell — *Harris College, Preston*

E L Scott — *Deacon's School, Peterborough*

Yu I Solov'ev — *Professor, University of Moscow*

Arnold Thackray — *Churchill College, Cambridge*

Harold C Urey — *Professor of Chemistry, University of California*

W D Wright — *Professor of Applied Optics. Department of Physics, Imperial College of Science and Technology, London*

List of Plates

The papers which form this volume were read before a conference of historians of science convened by the Manchester Literary and Philosophical Society, the Royal Society, the Chemical Society and the Society of Chemical Industry to commemorate the bicentenary of John Dalton's birth.

The arrangement is simple: as far as possible the papers are set out in a chronological sequence; thus the first papers deal with the eighteenth-century background, with the development of the concept of element and with atomic speculations after the 'scientific revolution', the next papers examine the life and works of John Dalton together with the achievements of his contemporaries, while the final papers discuss the elaboration of the atomic theory in the nineteenth century.

It was not, of course, possible to cover all the important aspects of such a remarkable achievement as Dalton's. For this reason contributions 'from the floor' have, where they supplement the papers presented, also been included.

I am very grateful to my friend and colleague Wilfred Farrar for much help and valuable advice in preparing these papers for publication. I wish also to express my thanks to the Council of the Literary and Philosophical Society for permission to include as a paper ('The Qualitative and the Quantitative') the address given by Sir Cyril Hinshelwood on the occasion of the award to him of the Society's Dalton Medal.

D S L Cardwell

D S L Cardwell

Introduction

The name of John Dalton is as closely associated with the scientific atomic theory as that of James Watt with the invention of the steam engine, or that of Charles Darwin with the doctrine of evolution by natural selection. Dalton's atomic theory did, in fact, usher in a change in physical science as revolutionary in its way as the innovations of Darwin and Watt were in their respective fields. There can, then, be no doubt of the magnitude of Dalton's contribution to science and in this Introduction I shall try to summarize his achievements as they were revealed in the papers presented to the conference.[1] I shall also try to supplement these papers by outlining some aspects of his life and work which, because time was necessarily limited, were not discussed at the conference.

Dalton, like Newton and Faraday, came of humble stock, being born in 1766 in Eaglesfield in Cumberland where his father was a smallholder and weaver; like Faraday he had a mother who was an exceptionally intelligent woman. Dalton's first regular job was that of village schoolmaster and his first scientific interest was in meteorology; he was to remain a teacher and to retain his interest in meteorology for the rest of his active life. In his early days he was considerably helped by John Gough, a blind amateur scientist and mathematician who gave him some training in mathematics and introduced him to experimental science. In 1793 Dalton moved to Manchester where he was to spend the remaining fifty-one years of his life. This move brought him into contact with the select group of men who had formed the Manchester Literary and Philosophical Society, an institution with which his name came to be closely linked and which he served as Secretary and as President.

Although Dalton was a devout and conscientious member of the Society of Friends all his life[2] he does not seem to have expressed any notable views on religious questions, nor does he appear to have taken part in any of the social work characteristic, then and now, of Friends. He kept his political, social, intellectual and aesthetic opinions to himself. It seems that he liked music but his colour-blindness, which by a remarkable scientific inquiry he himself diagnosed, must have limited his appreciation of the visual arts. It has even been suggested that his character may have been influenced by his colour-blindness: certainly it is surprising that he never commented on the radical transformation which he must have witnessed when Manchester ceased to be a country town and became a grimy industrial city.

He never married; teaching, research, religious observance, the well-regulated life of a scholarly bachelor gifted with a mind of great power and insight, were the dominant features of John Dalton's career. By all accounts he was reserved, quite unaffected and spoke with a marked regional accent. This then was the man who was to leave an indelible impress on physical science and who, in several ways, determined the broad strategy of nineteenth-century chemistry and, to some extent, physics too.

Dalton's generation of scientists was heir to a number of important advances in scientific knowledge and to some important scientific traditions. In the first place there had been a great increase in empirical chemical knowledge during the eighteenth century: many new substances had been discovered and new reactions studied. Joseph Priestley[3] in particular had made important contributions of this sort, he had pioneered the new techniques of pneumatic chemistry and he had made brilliant discoveries about the earth's atmosphere, identifying the two main constituents as two 'airs' with very different properties. These 'airs' had different specific gravities yet they remained homogeneously mixed. Priestley was puzzled by this, for according to established principles they should separate out into layers: the heavier 'air' (oxygen) at the bottom, the lighter 'air' (nitrogen) at the top. Besides important advances of this sort, Dalton's generation benefited from the cumulative knowledge and experience gained by practical chemists like assayers, with their developed notions of 'pure' substances and their progressively refined techniques for using the balance.

The second major inheritance of Dalton's generation was that of the established sciences: in particular mechanical science in its triumphantly successful Newtonian form; an achievement that could be taken as an exemplar, showing what all sciences might hope to attain. Associated with the mechanical philosophy of men like Boyle and Newton was the doctrine, then hardly more than a metaphysical notion, of atomism. In Proposition 23, Book 2, of *Principia mathematica* Newton had tentatively suggested that *if* an 'elastic fluid' be composed of atoms, and *if* the atoms repel one another with a force proportional to the reciprocal of the distance, and *if* this repulsion acts between immediately adjacent atoms only, then such a model would obey Boyle's law. The reservations put forward by Newton were formidable, his intellectual caution and modesty are apparent. But by Dalton's time Newton's authority was such that his merest suggestion could be—and frequently was—taken as certain truth.

We should, however, remember that Newtonianism was susceptible of different interpretations and was logically consistent with other systems of chemical quantification besides that put forward by Dalton.[4] On the other hand there were non-Newtonian versions of atomism, like the kinetic theory of the gifted Daniel Bernoulli,[5] which, had Dalton known of them, might have been of equal value to him.

Finally, Dalton was indebted to the great French chemist, A. L. Lavoisier. The nature of this debt can best be explained by demonstrating the relationship between atomism and the theoretical foundation of chemistry. One ambition of the seventeenth-century mechanical philosophers had been to ascribe suitable mathematical and arithmetical properties to the atoms and then to discover mathematical laws which the atoms would obey and thus account for the chemical and physical properties of macroscopic bodies. But the mechanical philosophers, like all their predecessors, had only the haziest ideas about atoms. They were supposedly common to all material things, the universal building blocks of nature, and in themselves entirely elusive. On the other hand the variety and complexity of material things were enormous and, in the course of the eighteenth century, were ever increasing. Thus between the complexity of the chemical world and the elusiveness of the atoms no simple bridge could be built.

To the chaos of chemical knowledge Lavoisier ultimately brought simplicity and order. His well-known definition of an element—a substance that cannot be analysed into, or synthesized from simpler constituents —was, of course, empirical and in its reservation—that any designated element might by further research be shown to be a compound—logically unsatisfying. However, with increasing success and acceptance Lavoisier, like Newton before him, was elevated to the status of authority and his reservations could be forgotten by his followers. Whatever Lavoisier's personal views, his reorganization of chemistry was the most important step forward in the history of the science; and acceptance of his element theory in its unqualified form ultimately carried profound implications for the atomic theory too; in effect, and unconsciously, *Lavoisier transformed the ancient atomic theory as decisively as he reordered the world of macroscopic chemistry.* Dividing a lump of gold indefinitely you must at some stage or other reach the level of the constituent atoms and finally the last atom. By Lavoisier's unqualified theory this last atom cannot be just a vague, undefined universal building block of nature, it must be specific and definite, an atom of gold; and similarly for all the other elements. In other words the old question—what is an atom?—now admits of a new and fruitful answer: an atom is the smallest possible particle of gold, lead, oxygen, hydrogen. . . . Thus, for the first time, atoms were brought within experimental range and though it may not have been consciously recognized before Dalton, a really scientific atomic theory became possible. Indeed, it may not be immodest to claim Dalton as Lavoisier's greatest disciple.[6]

We have now assembled the main developments in knowledge, thought and techniques that made the scientific atomic theory possible. It seems a fairly obvious development now; it can hardly have been obvious at the time. At the beginning of the nineteenth century the choice of possibilities in chemistry must have seemed bewildering. There was certainly no consensus that an atomic theory on Dalton's lines was inevitable, or even desirable. On the contrary, public opinion might well have favoured the concept of affinity as offering the best prospects for advance, possibly in conjunction with studies in electricity and heat. It is, of course, wrong to suppose that in any given age the really important problems, as revealed by later developments, are clearly recognized as such by the general scientific community. Often the innovator is the only person to recognize the importance of a problem and the opportunity which its solution will give him. Such seems to have been the case with Dalton.

The actual course of Dalton's inquiries is, in outline, easy to understand. His interest in meteorology led him to speculate, like Priestley before him, on the anomalous mixing of oxygen and nitrogen. A similar line of inquiry led him to ponder the reasons for the fact that different gases are differently soluble in water, generally the heavier the gas the more soluble it is. It seems most likely that he first used atomic ideas in his attempts to solve problems like these, thrown up by his detailed studies of the physics of gases. Two atomic dimensions which might determine gaseous diffusion and differing solubilities are size and weight; thus, for example, if gaseous atoms are free to move then it is not difficult to imagine that small atoms might percolate among big atoms, so explaining how a light gas may diffuse into a heavy gas. For Dalton the size of an atom includes its surrounding atmosphere of 'caloric', or the self-repellent matter of heat and the atoms of a gas are to be imagined as touching one another like hard-cored rubber balls packed into a box. (These are not, of course, the same as Newton's atoms, with their short range *forces*; they are at best derived from Newton's ideas.) One cannot measure the actual diameter of Dalton's atoms but, if one knows the volume and density of the gas and can measure the *relative* weight, one can easily calculate the *relative* atomic diameter. Relative atomic weight thus appears to be of fundamental importance both in its own right, as a determinant of solubility, and as a simple measure from which to compute relative atomic size. By making certain assumptions we can easily determine relative atomic weights from the study of chemical combinations. The recognition that this concept of atomic weight was immensely important in the science of chemistry must have followed fairly quickly, possibly with the encouragement and help of Dalton's Manchester friends. The task for atomism had in fact changed; no longer was the prime object to explain the distinctive properties of (say) sulphur and mercury, these properties could be imputed to the ultimate units, the sulphur and mercury atoms, but to rationalize and quantify the combination of sulphur atoms with mercury atoms, or either with other elements. This was a much more manageable task, well within the scope of early nineteenth-century knowledge and techniques.

Now Dalton had not merely to hit on the atomic theory in this, its viable form but to demonstrate the fact to the world, to convince the Senate and the Plebs of science. This is usually a difficult enough task. A genius like Sadi Carnot failed to do it in his lifetime, Joule had to be 'discovered' by the successful and personable young William Thomson (Kelvin) while the unhappy Waterston failed altogether; on the other hand it must be confessed that there have been scientists who have succeeded beyond their deserts and whose scientific reputations have stood much higher than they warrant. That Dalton succeeded comparatively easily must be ascribed to that intangible factor, the character of the man himself, to the fact that he had already established a reputation for himself as a physicist in both Britain and France and, lastly, to his good fortune, or good sense, or both, in finding a powerful and eloquent supporter (Thomas Thomson) in Scotland. It was a good thing to be well thought of in Paris or in Scotland in those days; and Dalton acknowledged this when he dedicated the first volume of the *New system of chemical philosophy* to the members of the Universities of Edinburgh and Glasgow.

The development of the atomic theory and its reception in Britain, Europe and America are topics which are important and interesting enough to merit a volume to themselves.[7] At first sight it would seem to be a truism to say that no one could regard the atomic theory in quite the same way as Dalton and yet it is much more than a truism. For Dalton was a meteorologist and physicist as well as a chemist. Accordingly we must suppose that for him, at any rate, the atomic theory must throw light on important problems of the physics of gases and on some puzzling facts of meteorology (the composition of the atmosphere). As a chemist he had inferred from the atomic hypothesis certain quantitative laws which were found to hold for chemical combinations. But even those chemists, like Gay-Lussac and Wollaston, who were also physicists were not compelled to sympathize with Dalton's idiosyncratic interpretation of the atomic theory; after all there were many problems, even in the physics of gases, on which the atomic theory could throw little or no light. In brief, very few men of science were in a position to view the new theory in the way that Dalton did.

This last point is important. Positivists in every generation of science have argued that the difficulties of science can be resolved and undesirably speculative statements eliminated if we reduce our claim that science can tell us about the structure of the world to the more modest assertion that science is merely concerned with finding convenient short-hand expressions (usually mathematical in form) for the relations between phenomena (Mach, Duhem). Entities like 'atoms' are therefore merely convenient fictions which enable us to set up equations to account for the experimental facts of chemical combination. We are not therefore surprised that Dalton's theory, while its practical value was fully realized, was treated with reserve in its more speculative reaches. For the positivists of the day argued that some such word as 'equivalent' or 'ratio' or 'proportion' was much more suitable than 'atom'; after all you did not require the concept of the minute billiard ball in chemistry; you could get all the benefits of Dalton's new methods and rules without making any assertions, implicit or otherwise, about the ultimate structure of matter. Indeed, it seems likely that the positivists were in a majority at that time. 'The particles of bodies', wrote one careful critic, 'are objects of science and not of sense, yet we speak of them as if they were as palpable and visible as the masses they comprise.'[8]

Dalton would have none of this; there was nothing imaginary about atoms, they really exist.[9] 'Equivalent' or 'ratio' might preserve the anti-metaphysical purity of a cautious chemist but they are no help at all when, like Dalton, you ponder the physics of gases. You cannot talk sensibly about 'ratios' diffusing among one another, or 'equivalents' dissolving in water!

It seems likely therefore that there were few who could put themselves in the cross-bench position of Dalton. And, in the event, Dalton was fully justified: the realist view of atoms proved immensely fruitful in nineteenth-century chemistry and physics[10] and the positivist view—whenever it became dominant— equally obstructive. Positivists might do well to recall that when science is in a healthy and progressive state there is usually a crisis somewhere within its frontiers; and furthermore that when new concepts arise in science they are rarely if ever clearly defined: indeed the progress of science is, in some respects, a process of refinement and clarification of concepts.[11]

If, then, Dalton's realism had a sound rational basis there may also have been a personal factor to influence his judgment. Dr Kathleen Farrar has made what seems to me to be a most important point: Dalton was a born teacher.[12] It has commonly been asserted by historians that Dalton's teaching activities were a chore which, it is implied, was a heavy burden on the great man. Some have gone further, to draw inferences about the lowly status of science in England at that time and to compare the 'neglect' of Dalton with the honours and pensions bestowed on scientists in foreign countries. Mrs Farrar's point is simply that Dalton seems to have liked teaching; why, for that matter, should he not have done so? If we accept this interpretation then one or two aspects of his character become much more easy to understand. He thought in simple, concrete terms as one might suppose would suit a teacher; and this would be consistent with his simple and realistic view of the atomic theory. He liked playing with models, both as aids to teaching and as representations of physical reality. His character in fact is coherent: he dislikes reservations, ambiguities and sophistries; he ignores Newton's qualifications about the famous Proposition 23 and he disregards Lavoisier's caution in the matter of the ultimate status of elements. Who can blame him? One cannot really advance science if one is doubtful of one's premises. Similarly one cannot teach science if one hedges every statement with reservations and qualifications. Herein perhaps lies a key to Dalton's nature and to his success both as scientist and, on a humbler but not less worthy plane, as teacher.

The Daltonian phase of the atomic theory was in fact a transient one: an anomalous period in the long history of atomism. In its classical statement Daltonian atomism denies that there are *universal* building blocks. Daltonian atoms are unique: no hydrogen atom occurs in any substance that does not contain hydrogen. The doctrine of specific atomism collapsed by the end of the nineteenth century when the first genuine universal building block—the electron—was discovered. What the exact status of this and the other 'fundamental particles' is in the light of modern research and modern thought is a question that lies outside the scope of John Dalton studies.

It is a fact that practically all the details of Daltonian atomism, as he advocated and taught it, have been superseded: we no longer accept the material, or caloric theory of heat, we no longer believe that one atom of hydrogen combines with one atom of oxygen to form a compound atom of water, we accept Avogadro's hypothesis, we explain diffusion by means of the kinetic theory, we know to our cost that the atom is eminently *divisible*, we do not even take the atomic weight of hydrogen as 1. When everything he taught has been so modified why do we still continue to honour Dalton? Because, in simple terms, he indicated the way ahead; he made progress possible on a wide, a very wide, front. That progress had modified most of his ideas and superseded the rest, but this does not detract from the honour of the man who first showed the way.

Notes

1 For a scholarly and very readable account of the life and work of John Dalton see F. Greenaway, *John Dalton and the atom* (London, 1966).

2 J. T. Marsh, 217 below.

3 There is a perceptive account of Priestley's career in R. Schofield, *The Lunar Society of Birmingham* (Oxford, 1963) 193 et seq.

4 A. W. Thackray, 92 et seq below.

5 Daniel Bernoulli, *Hydrodynamica* (Basle, 1738) 200 et seq.

6 Thus Dalton accepted and apparently never queried Lavoisier's 'caloric' doctrine; characteristically he ignored the reservation that Lavoisier attached to it.

7 C. A. Russell, 259 et seq below; M. P. Crosland, 274 et seq below.

8 Marshall Hall, 'On Chemical Attraction', *Nicholson's Journal*, xxx (Nov. 1811) 193.

9 See, for example, John Dalton, 'Inquiry Concerning the Signification of the Word "Particle" as used by Modern Chemical Writers', *Nicholson's Journal*, xxviii (Feb. 1811) 81.

10 W. V. Farrar, 290 et seq below. For a recent critique of the effects of positivism in nineteenth century physics see J. W. Herivel, 'Aspects of French Theoretical Physics in the Nineteenth Century', *British Journal for the History of Science*, iii (Dec. 1966) 109.

11 D. S. L. Cardwell, 'Reflections on Some Problems in the History of Science', *Manchester Memoirs*, cvi (1963–4) 108.

12 K. R. Farrar, 159 et seq below.

D S L Cardwell

John Dalton and the Manchester School of Science

The Manchester in which Dalton settled in 1793 was, by modern standards, a small and relatively pleasant country town. Its history was much less distinguished than those of towns like York, Bristol, Plymouth and Durham, while the scientific record was, with two or three exceptions, uninspiring: John Dee (if one can count him as a scientist), the seventeenth-century astronomers Horrox and Crabtree together with a few minor figures had been born or had lived in the district. And that was about all. Indeed the Manchester area was about as far away as it was possible to get from a university. Only the peripheral counties of Kerry, Cornwall, Pembrokeshire and Caernarvonshire were further from seats of higher learning. Although this may not have been wholly a disadvantage and there was, after all, the excellent Chetham's Library, it is fair to conclude that Manchester was not a particularly promising town for the development of a notable scientific school. An observer of the scientific scene in 1790 might well have predicted the imminent rise of a scientific school in Birmingham which had long been ornamented by the Lunar Society whose membership included Boulton, Watt, Priestley, Wedgwood and Erasmus Darwin; but unless he had made an unusually perceptive survey of the leading manufacturers of the district he would hardly have held out much hope for bucolic Manchester.

The new and revolutionary textile industries were well represented in the surrounding districts; and it has been claimed, rightly I think, that there was a fairly general awareness among manufacturers of the importance of relating science to industry.[1] When, however, we examine this 'science' more closely a good deal of it seems disappointing. The books in circulation, William Emerson's *Mechanics*, John Banks' *Treatise on Mills*, Olinthus Gregory's *Mechanics*, were rather shoddy imitations of Desaguliers' famous earlier work, but without the latter's originality and stimulation. We need do no more than contrast these books with their French contemporaries—Prony's *Nouvelle architecture hydraulique*, and the treatises of Guenyveau, Lazare Carnot, Borgnis, etc., to confirm the point. And how shall we interpret George Atwood's caustic comments that the science of mechanics could be of little help to the practical engineer and that improvements in machinery resulted from experience and invention, not from applied science?[2]

Atwood was, of course, a sophisticated thinker who understood the science of mechanics as well as, and perhaps better than, any other man in England. Yet it does not seem to me that these facts refute the thesis in question. What, after all, was happening at that time was that, in the continuing revolution a new form of science was being born. The old orthodoxy, against which Atwood seems to have been reacting, was being swept away and, much broader in scope, the science of the nineteenth century, concerned with 'transformation'—to use Clausius' expressive word—was being established.

For these reasons Dalton was of supreme importance. He was the first great Manchester scientist and the first of a recognizable school of scientists. As we have seen he established his reputation in, significantly enough, more than one subject, being recognized in Paris, in Scotland and in London. In his maturity he was elected to learned academies and awarded honorary degrees by the universities of Oxford and Edinburgh. He was a teacher but not a polemicist; indeed his quietude was such that he remained silent when persistently and even bitterly attacked by William Higgins and his partisans in the *Philosophical Magazine*.[3] (This seems to have been one of those situations in which one can have some sympathy with both parties.) Yet despite this lack of assertiveness it seems clear that he must have acted as a kind of magnet, drawing men to science and scientists to Manchester. One might add that at this time the Literary and Philosophical Society together with the great Mechanics Institute, founded in 1824, formed a kind of loose, informal university.

Dalton dedicated the second volume of his *New system of chemical philosophy* to two of his friends, John Sharpe, F.R.S., and Peter Ewart. In Ewart's case an additional motive, besides friendship, is given:

... more especially for the able exposition and excellent illustration of the fundamental principles of mechanics in his essay on the measure of moving force.

Evidently then it must be of some importance to understand the scientific work of these two men.

John Sharpe was a solicitor by profession, a member of the firm of Sharpe, Eccles and Cririe, of Red Cross Street (now Cross Street) and King Street. Later he moved to London where he died in 1834.[4] In 1806 he gave an account to the Literary and Philosophical Society of some experiments he had carried out to determine if the force of steam was proportional to the generating heat.[5] The motive for these researches was the realization at about that time that the high pressure steam engine, introduced from about 1800 onwards, was much more economical than the low pressure, or Watt type. Just why this was was hard to see, in the then state of knowledge. Sharpe showed, clearly enough, that the latent heat certainly did not increase with the pressure and therefore the temperature but his experiments were otherwise inconclusive. Indeed the correct explanation was not understood until the acceptance of Carnot's ideas and the establishment of thermodynamics in the 1850's. Nevertheless, Sharpe was one of the first experimenters in the field and deserves great credit for opening up what was to be a fundamental branch of knowledge. In fact his experiments must have been carried out simultaneously with those of John Southern, the employee of Boulton and Watt.[6]

Even more importance in our view attaches to the work of Peter Ewart. Ewart was one of several brothers, sons of a Dumfriesshire Manse, all of whom had distinguished careers. Trained as an engineer under

Rennie, he had been employed as a representative of Boulton and Watt and his acquaintances included Benjamin Gott of Leeds, Samuel Oldknow, Samuel Greg, the Strutts, Murdoch and many other leaders of the industrial revolution. For a long time he was Vice-President of the Literary and Philosophical Society. In 1813 the *Manchester Memoirs* published Ewart's long paper—virtually a small book—which so aroused the admiration of Dalton, and indeed many others. Entitled 'On the Measure of Moving Force', the paper is in essence a long, detailed and scholarly examination and advocacy of the utility and correctness of the vis-viva and work doctrines as put forward by John Smeaton in the previous century.[7] Indeed it was by far the best and most comprehensive account of this theory to have appeared in English, going far beyond the outline sketches provided by Smeaton and those like Wollaston who later adopted his views. This is not the place to go into the details of the paper, a paper which shows considerable familiarity with the writings of French and Swiss scientists: d'Alembert, Euler, Borda, etc., and which is only occasionally marred by lapses of understanding. Nevertheless, one example of his reasoning may be given. He argues that ideally a given amount of heat must yield a given amount of work and that this cannot vary with the time or any other circumstance:

... although the whole heat, or the whole force, can in practice never be completely transferred from one given object to another, yet there can be no doubt of the real exist- ence of both the heat and the force in their full quantities, and we can form no idea of the portion of time being limited in which the one must be evolved or the other transferred.

This is not, of course, the doctrine of the mutual convertibility of heat and energy—Joule's doctrine— but it is an essential step in that direction.

Ewart also published papers on the pressure and temperature of steam and he tried to relate these measures to the atomic structure of the vapour. But these papers are not, in the view of Dr A. J. Pacey and myself, as important as the one on the moving force of bodies. This latter in fact marks the real beginnings of the doctrine of energy in Britain. It had the supreme assets of detailed and sound scholarship backed by clear argument. It could not be ignored.

There is, I suggest, a pattern in the works of Dalton, Ewart and Sharpe in which we can detect some essential components of Joule's doctrine of the mechanical equivalence of heat. The question of the relationship between the heat in steam and the power, or duty, it can yield, discussed by Sharpe; Ewart's excellent exposition and defence of the concepts of vis-viva and work and, finally, Dalton's picture of matter as composed of discrete atoms each of which has a definite weight and therefore mass: all of these are, if we throw out 'caloric', consistent with Joule's ideas about the nature of heat and his acceptance of the kinetic theory.[8] I do not, of course, mean to imply that these ideas were unique to the Dalton group; they were indeed being pursued elsewhere in this country and in Europe. The point is that they were under active and urgent consideration in Manchester and Joule can hardly have failed to have been influenced by his mentors of the Dalton school. Support for this view can be found in the writings of Robert Angus Smith, a biographer of Dalton and an historian of the Literary and Philosophical Society.[9] We must not forget that in Joule's young days there were no hierarchies of national institutes and of international journals; there was no national system of education and no rationalized—or depersonalized—science degree courses. There were two or three journals devoted to science, a few books and practically no textbooks. It follows that the influences of the teacher and of his associates must have been much more pervasive than they could possibly be today.

The subsequent development of the Manchester school of science was rather curious. Scientific engineering, as Ewart had practised it, found its disciples in Eaton Hodgkinson—whose obituary notice of Ewart has a prominent place among the complimentary papers presented to Joule[10]—and by Osborne Reynolds and his successors at the Owens College, founded in 1851. In physics Balfour Stewart made notable contributions to the study of heat while Manchester and Owens College can claim some share in a younger generation of 'atomic' physicists, men like Arthur Schuster, J. J.

Thomson and C. T. R. Wilson. But perhaps the most interesting development took place in 1907 when Rutherford came to Manchester. He was then at the height of his powers and the years that followed were perhaps among his most creative. It is an interesting reflection, as Professor Hall points out, that if Manchester was, thanks to John Dalton, the birthplace of the absolutely indestructible billiard ball atom it was also, a century later but still within the Daltonian tradition, the place where the atom was deprived of its elemental simplicity and provided with components and a structure when the Bohr-Rutherford atom was postulated just before 1914.

In a strange way the Mantle of John Dalton seems to have fallen rather more on the physicists than on the chemists. In spite of Dalton's great contribution to the quantification of chemistry and in spite of the contributions of local chemists like the Henrys; in spite, too, of local interest in chemistry as practical art and as academic discipline—witness the foundation of the Mechanics Institute and the inauguration of public instruction in chemistry—the first influx of 'new men' brought in personalities from a very different background. The young Lyon Playfair went to Clitheroe when Dalton was still alive and a prominent Manchester figure. But Playfair came from a Scottish university and, more significantly from Liebig's laboratory at Giessen. From that time onwards most, if not all the notable chemists who worked in this area—academic, industrial or amateur—were trained in German universities. Such was the case with, for example, Roscoe, Frankland, Robert Angus Smith, Schorlemmer etc. up to the moment when the 1914 War turned the tap off.

What were the causes of the dramatic development of the Manchester School of Science? The more one considers it, the more one realizes that this was a new and unprecedented phenomenon in British and European cultural history. The sociology of science is an ill-developed subject with very limited powers of explanation; it is still in the natural history stage. Yet I suppose we can all agree that from the seventeenth century onwards the advance of science was, with some brilliant exceptions, fostered in and by 'schools' of science working in internationally recognized centres.

To adapt a famous epigram: all universities are as men make them, and very often worse. Their periods of decadence are, if respectably in the past, well known. But there are also times when they can provide exactly the right stimulus and milieu for scientific work—security and protection for the scholar; libraries and laboratories for his work; congenial company for the stimulation of his mind; and so on. Such we may assume was the state of the Scottish Universities in the eighteenth and nineteenth centuries; of Cambridge since 1851 and of most German universities in the nineteenth century. For important periods it has also been true of Padua and Bologna, of Basle and Geneva, of Leyden and Utrecht. On the other hand capital and metropolitan cities can provide a suitable stimulus through the provision of national libraries and observatories and the functioning of national academies. These and other, less tangible factors, account for the scientific achievements of London, Berlin, St Petersburg, Moscow, the Scandinavian capitals, Vienna, Prague, Budapest and, above all, Paris.

But none of these factors apply to Manchester: no university, no academies, no sophisticated society, no history, no traditions. A parvenu industrial city created a scientific intellectual tradition of its own. The comparison with Birmingham is no doubt odious but instructive and perhaps inevitable. The latter city had its famous eighteenth-century Lunar Society; the Soho Foundry was described by a contemporary as 'a great science school';[11] it had a great diversity of industry and skills, it was not too far from London and Oxford and the population had a rich levening of non-conformists including some notable Quaker families. All the recognizable sociological features favourable for scientific development were present. But no scientific tradition worthy of the name developed in Birmingham until the end of the nineteenth century. And much the same can be said of the other great English industrial cities: Liverpool, Leeds, Sheffield, Bradford, Bristol.

Dr Clow stresses the important rôles played by Scotsmen in the rise of science and applied science, or technology, in Britain. Certainly I support his argument: I have just emphasized the importance of men like Peter Ewart, Lyon Playfair and Robert Angus Smith. Two other Scottish names that must be included on the civic roll of honour are those of Sir William Fairbairn and James Nasmyth, mechanical engineers both. The record, then, is impressive and later on Manchester extended its catchment area when it acted as a magnet for Germans, Swiss and other central Europeans. Schorlemmer, Schunck and Dittmar are good examples, as are the technologists Ferranti, Renold and Simon. What brought these men to Manchester and what stimulated them so successfully when they got here? No doubt many and detailed answers can be given; and from the point of view of scientific success we are far from an understanding of the mechanism. But one thing does seem clear: in any general explanation of the rise of science in Manchester we should be unwise to neglect the dominating personality and rôle of John Dalton. A science school would no doubt have been founded in Manchester even if John Dalton had never settled in the city, but it would, I suggest, have been a much more parochial affair. His national and international reputation was established well within his lifetime; his standing in the city was demonstrated by his civic funeral and confirmed by many other gestures of public respect. Indeed he seems to have achieved a kind of lay-canonization. Thus the curiously named Mr Slugg, writing (in 1881) his reminiscences of Manchester fifty years earlier had this to say:[12]

I occasionally saw him, the last time being about a year before his death, when I met him with his attached friend Peter Clare, in York Street, as though they were proceeding from the Literary and Philosophical Rooms in George Street to Clare's house in Quay Street. They were walking at a slow pace owing to the Dr's feebleness, his arm resting on that of his friend. He had a beautifully calm and placid countenance, expressive of gentleness, thoughtfulness and intelligence. . . .

And he adds somewhat inconsequentially '(he) was generally dressed in black'.

The eulogy is not, perhaps, to the taste of the modern age. But one must reflect how rare it was (and is) for a distinguished scientist to be treated with such great respect. It is, I argue, reasonable to take him as the venerated teacher and inspirer of later generations of scientists. He was one of those who, in A. W. Williamson's words, lived for science and not by it.

1 A. E. Musson and E. Robinson, 'Science and Industry in the late Eighteenth Century', *Economic History Review*, 2nd Series, xiii (1960) 238.

2 George Atwood, *A treatise on the rectilinear motion* (London, 1784) 380.

3 See *Philosophical Magazine*, xlviii (1816) 363, 408; xlix (1816) 241; i (1817) 406; li (1817) 81, 161.

4 W. E. A. Axon, *The annals of Manchester* (Manchester, 1886) 190.

5 J. Sharpe, 'An Account of Some Experiments to Determine whether the Force of Steam be in Proportion to the Generating Heat', *Manchester Memoirs*, 2nd Series, ii (1813) 1.

6 J. Farey, 'John Southern's Experiments on the Density, Latent Heat and Elasticity of Steam', *Philosophical Magazine*, xxx (1847) 113.

7 Peter Ewart, 'On the Measure of Moving Force', *Manchester Memoirs*, 2nd Series, ii (1813) 105.

8 An indirect link between Joule and Ewart is provided by the apparatus used by Joule but adapted from that designed by George Rennie—John Rennie's son—to measure the friction of liquids. See George Rennie, V.P.R.S., 'On the Friction and Resistance of Fluids', *Phil. Trans. Roy. Soc.*, Part 2 (1831) 423.

9 R. A. Smith, 'A centenary of science in Manchester', *Manchester Memoirs*, ix (1883) 233.

10 Bound in one volume in Joule's personal library, now in the possession of the University of Manchester Institute of Science and Technology library.

11 Conrad Gill and Asa Briggs, *A history of Birmingham* (Oxford, 1952) i, 109.

12 J. T. Slugg, F.R.A.S., *Reminiscences of Manchester fifty years ago* (Manchester, 1881) 107. I am very grateful to Mr T. G. Warburton, of the Department of Building, the University of Manchester Institute of Science and Technology, for bringing this very interesting book to my attention.

The Qualitative
and
the Quantitative

The precise train of thought which led John Dalton to the atomic theory for which he is chiefly famed is not exactly known, and was perhaps not a clearly defined trail at all. No doubt ideas at first misty gradually took shape during his long preoccupation with the behaviour of gases and vapours in which meteorological studies had engaged him. All of which means incidentally that he would almost certainly have been rejected had he had to apply for support to the highly organized and admirably rational bodies upon whom most researchers have to rely today. Fortunately, however, the most original things are not necessarily costly and the atomic theory came. Looking back and leaving origins aside we can see that what was so very convincing about the theory was the quantitative side of it. The laws of constant, multiple and reciprocal proportions became obvious in the light of it and there was a sound basis for the great quantitative science of analytical chemistry, every advance in which strengthened the basis itself.

The ancients had their atomic theories. In the hands of Lucretius they gave beautiful qualitative descriptions of much that went on in Nature. Yet, somehow, the doctrines remained fanciful and never really penetrated deeply or conclusively behind the façade of appearances: never found a route by which further progress could be made.

Men of science have on the whole very rightly emphasized that the element of quantification has been one of the greatest strengths of the scientific view of the world. The thesis is strengthened by all that happened in chemistry itself after Dalton. During most of the nineteenth century the Daltonian atoms remained indivisible: they had their own characteristic masses and in them resided individual properties to which in major part all the significance of chemistry in the scheme of things was due. For further penetration into the nature of things fresh stages of quantification had to come. Of this story there is no need for me to try and trace the steps in detail. Certain roughly whole number relations between atomic weights suggested the idea of atoms built from smaller units. Then followed the discovery of these units and eventually of the laws according to which the sub-units are patterned into atoms. The whole system of the chemical elements in all its vast variety is now in principle predictable from the laws of physics, and in particular from the strikingly simple prescription that of four quantum numbers no atom possesses all the same. The interpretation of chemistry in terms of physics is a truly wonderful achievement. Yet, let us pause for a moment to ask ourselves a simple question. Would we be happy entirely to abandon our concern with the variegated disorder of chemical *phenomena* for the austere mathematics of quantum physics? I doubt it. These phenomena themselves have interest and beauty. The strange structure of sub-atomic reality which seems gradually to be revealing itself in terms of geometry and number, fascinating as it is, seems filled with a slightly eerie emptiness of anything else.

There is no doubt about the power of the methods which the mathematical analysis of nature employs. Some ancient thinkers may easily have read the picturesque imaginings set forth by Lucretius and wondered sceptically how any of them could ever be tested, verified or developed further. We now know that measurement, quantification, numeration and mathematical analysis have provided the Ariadne thread to the centre of the mystery. But are we wholly satisfied when we arrive? Have we not perhaps been so impressed with the triumphs of quantitative science that we deprive ourselves of some things which only the qualitative can offer at all? Because, in the last analysis would it not be fair to say that it is only the qualitative for which we really live? The question might be rather summarily dismissed by some men of science. They might point out, for example, that biology is rapidly yielding to the processes of quantitative analysis: the chemical structure of biological materials is largely known, the conception of genetic information inscribed in chemical codes which are just permutations of chemical units, the understanding of replication, of adaptation and of cybernetic adjustments all do for the living organism what the Daltonian laws originally began to do for chemical substances themselves. But does this foreshadow an end of the story in which everything else yields to the same kind of analysis? Let us reflect.

May I return to Dalton. Throughout his life Dalton remained deeply interested in the phenomena of meteorology. We all remain interested in *phenomena* as such and only a small minority would be content to transfer this concern to the ultimate laws of physics to which the phenomena are referable. The question, moreover, goes deeper. How far, indeed, does our quantitatively based analysis of things really penetrate after all, behind the world of appearances from which we have to start?

Dalton, apart from his chemistry, would be remembered in science for his work on colour vision. His own perceptions of colour were abnormal, a fact of which he became aware and into which he made some shrewd investigations. He discovered his own abnormality by noticing discrepancies between the ways in which he would have used certain colour terms and the ways in which the generality of people appeared to use them.

There was and is no conceivable way in which Dalton could have compared the experience which he called seeing blue with that of anyone else. The element of absolute privacy in such experiences, commonplace as it is, is one of the major facts about existence. What Dalton could do and in effect did was to institute an elaborate series of comparisons and to ascertain that *coherence* could be established among them if he made the assumption that most people had colour experiences of one sort and that at the same time he (and his brother) deviated in certain ways from a norm. Although a coherent pattern could indeed be established in this way, the essence of colour, as distinct from its physical correlates of the wavelength of light and so on, remained and still remains private to each individual. At any rate even if it seems reasonable to assume that the normal individuals who make coherent statements about colour do have similar experiences, it nevertheless remains true that there is no possible means of conveying to someone who has no colour sense what the experience of seeing blue would be like. Try and imagine what we should see if some suddenly operating mutations of our body cells made our sight respond to radiation in regions of the spectrum outside the present visible range.

And so it is with large tracts of our experience whether in respect to colour, sound, smell, or various emotions. Our scientific analysis gets to grip with the qualitative aspects of these things only in so far as it shows that in certain physical and physiological circumstances large groups of individuals, who in virtue of their size count as normal, make intelligible and consistent statements about their experiences. To this extent the experiences themselves are for practical purposes shareable, and they are translateable in terms of wave lengths, ionic movements, chemical and physical changes in blood, nerves, and brain cells, and yet in their essence they are irreducible and incommunicable to anyone who does not already know what kind of things they are.

Does this perhaps mean that the qualitative and subjective aspect of things is unimportant? A detailed account could certainly be given in purely behaviourist terms of a large part of human life. Electrons, neutrons, protons, themselves analysed according to the recondite schemes of subatomic physics, can give us chemistry: chemistry can provide genetic codes and cell mechanisms. Natural selection can guide the emergence of organized creatures which perform their actions in the ways best adapted to survival. What then is the need to introduce into the description any of the language of human experience, consciousness, emotions, sensations and the content of that inner world which we know that we inhabit ourselves, and which we believe other people to inhabit too because our communications with them make some kind of sense?

The plain fact, of course, is that this inner world of human experience is the only one which has any direct importance to us at all. Biologically we could be enormously efficient as behaviouristic automata. But we should be utterly uninterested in what was happening. We should not even have any concern with the laws of science and we should certainly have no urge to discover them nor any delight in the contemplation of their beauty.

Could we then do what plenty of people have tried to do, go to the other extreme and express all we have to say about existence in terms of what is known to our immediate consciousness? Much has indeed been achieved in this way and it represents our heritage of art, literature and history, more or less what we group together as the arts. But by confining ourselves to the methods of the arts and foregoing the quantitative analysis practised in the sciences we sacrifice entirely any satisfactory account of the external world itself or of ourselves regarded as parts of that world. We are back at pre-Galilean and pre-Newtonian physics, at pre-Daltonian chemistry, and thereby abandon not only a tremendous potential of human achievement, but a magnificent empire of human understanding.

Thus we cannot escape from the admission that there is one mode of description, largely quantitative, which is applicable to a world outside ourselves, and another, essentially qualitative, which is applicable to an inner world of consciousness. We can often, in principle, perhaps always, express the *concomitance* of what happens in the two worlds—or more carefully expressed, make equivalent statements in two different languages. What we cannot, however, do is to convey, describe or express the essence of qualitative experiences to any to whom they are not already familiar. This is really a very peculiar limitation. To an intelligent man the principles of the most abstruse scientific arguments can sooner or later be conveyed. A man born deaf could master the theory of acoustics: he could no doubt come to understand erudite discussions on the structure of Bach's music, even to enjoy this music as an intellectual pattern but he could not gain the faintest inkling of what the hearing of music meant, or even the hooting of an owl.

The two worlds to which reference has been made are in some degree the respective domains of the arts and of the sciences, though to be sure the arts make much use of scientific analysis and the sciences do not dispense with the qualitative, quite apart from the fact that they would not be pursued at all if they did not provide satisfactions belonging to the qualitative world.

And the peculiar relation in which these worlds stand is closely connected with what we call the problem of mind and matter. I do not want to enter into philosophical discussions and I know that philosophers are apt to tell us that the mind-matter problem is an unreal one created by an improper use of language. This view is one which I can never bring myself to share. The relation between what is described by the quantitative language of science and the qualitative statements which we make about ordinary experience appears to me, as it did to Sherrington, an inscrutable mystery. It seems to me that you can escape from it only by disregarding as an unimportant abstraction the vast power and coherence of the scientific description, or by being so unselfconscious about experience as to draw no distinction between mental experience itself and the scientifically describable events which accompany it. At any rate, what can surely be said is this: if there is in the strict sense no mind-matter problem, there are two related ones. Why do descriptions in qualitative nonscientific terms so signally fail to do justice to attempts to analyse the external universe? And correspondingly what is lacking in the scientific description of reality which leaves out the qualitative essence of our experiences? If a philosopher would answer the first question, or a man of science the second the mind-matter problem would look less formidable. Until then the two aspects of reality look distinct, and existence seems to involve a wonderful dialogue between them.

There is at the present time some danger of a serious confusion in which people, impressed with the power of the scientific method, but having little intuitive feeling for the practice of true men of science try to impose criteria of measurement and quantification upon qualitative matters to which they are not applicable. If a quantitative measure is in fact assignable, well and good. But the ever present temptation is that where this can not be found, a good but subjective and qualitative criterion is arbitrarily replaced by a downright bad one simply because this can be given a numerical measure and juggled with mechanically. The pressure to do this kind of thing is increased by the fashion of feeding information into computers. Computers are wonderful products of human ingenuity and certainly not distracted by the perplexities of the mind-matter problem nor the perversities of qualitative judgments. Thus if you feed sense into them you get sense out. But unfortunately if you feed nonsense you get out nonsense which may have become even worse for no longer being immediately recognizable for the rubbish it is. To pronounce on the relative merits of Mozart and Beethoven would be a subtle and difficult task. If we agree to relate their merit to the number of symphonies produced we arrive at the neat result that Mozart is 4·55 recurring times as good as Beethoven, that is 41/9. Nobody would accept this absurdity but there is quite a danger that support for education may soon be assessed on considerations of a comparable order. We hear much talk of creativity in universities and such places, and many people have a shrewd working knowledge of how to size it up intuitively in particular examples. But since much money is now involved and public authorities come on the scene, methods of quantitative measurement are demanded. So we enter the questionnaire age. Total number of students processed per annum? But are they good or bad? Never mind, that probably averages out. But does it? Well, work out the total hours worked by the staff. Yes, but how do they use their time, well or ill? Is not much of the best work subconscious? Never mind that, take the number of published papers. They may be long or short: well, count the words. And so on.

The administrative mind easily sweeps away objections as merely captious and perverse. When I once explained to the operator of one of the famous questionnaires that the questions I was asked were ambiguous to the point of meaninglessness I received a patient letter, humouring me by conceding my points but adding: would I none the less please answer the questions.

I have no wish merely to poke fun, merry or sour, at those who struggle with intractable practical problems, and evidently some statistics must be collected. Nevertheless there is a very real and very serious danger that we are trying in the name of objectivity, efficiency and even of fairness and justice to eliminate from our judgments an element which just simply can not be and should not be eliminated.

Accountants sometimes demand from scientists numerical measures of quite imponderable things, like probability of success, and they sometimes try and force upon them in the interest of tidy accounting practices which in themselves are highly undesirable. The administrators of questionnaire operations want us to divide into numerical fractions things of which the parts are inextricably blended, like teaching and research. It is sometimes claimed that the results even if rough will be useful statistically. There can be no more dangerous doctrine than that based upon the idea that a large number of wrong or meaningless guesses will somehow average out to something with a meaning. If enough ignorant people guess the date of the Creation, will the result really be worth much even after treatment by a million pound computer? The most serious damage is done when different sets of meaningless guesses are compared and conclusions are drawn about relative merits of institutions, procedures and practices. Of course in real life people tend to fill up the questionnaire in the way which is calculated, they think, to lead to actions which they would welcome. But is this really a very good thing?

Nor is it any defence of spurious quantification to say that we often know of no better alternative. If you do not know how to reach a correct judgment, best admit the fact and not make things worse by pretending.

The plain truth, I believe, is that the replacement of difficult qualitative judgments by inadequate mechanical counterparts is not rationalization or efficiency, or impartiality or objectivity but just simply a deplorable evasion of responsibility.

This brings us to a very deep question. Is there not in the most important kind of judgments an essentially creative element? And can the qualitative and the quantitative be sharply separated one from the other?

Consider even within the bounds of science itself some of its great theories: Newtonian mechanics, the electromagnetic theory of Faraday and Maxwell, the quantum theory, the theory of evolution. These have all helped us to penetrate behind the crude appearances of things, and in this respect they have fared much better than the Lucretian doctrines precisely because they permit quantification at the appropriate stage. But genius entered at two stages of their development: the quantitative working out was essential, but so also was the original conception of the appropriate qualitative substratum on which these quantitative methods could operate. The Newtonian conceptions of mass and force, the idea of electromagnetic and electrostatic fields, the notion of discretely divisible phase-space, the pictures of selection and of genetic determinants have an inherent rightness and appropriateness about them without which their quantitative development would be fruitless.

The train of thought set up by the reference to Newton and his fellow philosophers of Nature might, I suppose, encourage the high priests of the questionnaire era to imagine that they too can introduce concepts suitable for the quantization of such matters as originality creativity, desirability, beauty and even goodness. Some plausibility might seem to be lent to this kind of venture by the amazing achievements of electronic computers, which can make fairly convincing guesses as to which of the writings commonly attributed to St Paul came from the Apostle himself.

This feat, which is certainly remarkable needs to be looked at coolly. It consists basically in the recognition of numerical patterns among grammatical and linguistic elements and in the comparison of various works in respect of the presence or absence of these. The patterns are, as it were, finger-prints or signatures of the author's style, but they are *not* the style itself.

No doubt the recognition and comparison of numerical patterns among the physical elements of musical composition would lead to the discovery of a characteristic signature of Beethoven, and possibly allow the signature to be plausibly forged. Yet the outcome, good, bad or indifferent would still be a forgery. It would not be based upon the conscious experience of the composer and would resemble that experience only as physical measurements resemble a human personality or a man may be identified by his fingerprints, by which, however, he is not made known.

We are faced once more with the old antithesis of conscious experience and of its physical concomitants, and with the inescapable truth that the former alone gives to living any significance it may have.

The man of science is right in his quantization and numeration of physical Nature because he has found that these procedures open paths to progressively deeper understanding. His imitators are wrong if they pervert these methods in an attempt to apply them to human experience itself, which resolutely refuses to conform to them. Is not every human judgment which affects conscious life itself, on however small a scale and whether for good or ill, in a sense a creative act? And is not all life itself an interplay of innumerable small creative acts?

The idea that the exercise of scientific or artistic imagination or of choice or judgment in complex human situations has this creative element may shock some, even perhaps those who are prepared to work with physical theories about the continuous creation of matter in the physical universe. Perhaps the very success of the quantitative methods in the analysis of the physical world has made people reluctant to admit elements in existence to which these methods are, according to our present lights, inapplicable. But to deny these elements is to commit the classical error or indeed dishonesty of discarding data which do not fit a preconceived scheme.

Despite all attempts to talk it out of court the mind-matter problem remains intractable—or if you object to this use of language the intractable problem remains of relating satisfactorily what we can say about the external world with what we can say about the world of experiences and their qualities.

Does this not mean that our knowledge and understanding of the ultimate structure of reality is as incomplete as was that of people of the past ages about chemistry and physics? Will new Galileos, Newtons and Daltons appear in due season?

There are still vast and strange seas of thought for the lone voyager. Many great developments are more or less foreseeable by extrapolation from present trends. Some are heartening, some appalling, but none contain anything really new. Our extrapolations are essentially

C N Hinshelwood

*The Qualitative
and
the Quantitative*

quantitative: the really new things involve new qualitative elements. How, when and whence these may come is not predictable and not even clearly understandable. The question presents a slightly disturbing mystery to much of our present philosophy. Let us hope, however, that despite all difficulties the independent thinkers like Dalton will continue the quest.

3

Marie Boas Hall

The History of the
Concept of Element

The phrase 'chemical element' has a long, active and tangled history; although it may be found embedded in the texts of late Greek alchemy in the second or third centuries, it is equally fundamental to the chemistry of the periodic table in the mid-nineteenth century. Yet though the *word* 'element' is the same, the concept of what the *thing* was changed radically in the course of the centuries and even in a definable period, that between Boyle and Dalton. I think every historian of chemistry would agree that Dalton necessarily subscribed to the 'modern' (or at least the nineteenth century) definition of the chemical element, because otherwise he could not have formulated his atomic theory as he did. His atoms necessarily presuppose the existence of certain substances not further decomposable by any experimental means, and indeed this is how he thought of matter. As he wrote casually in the *New system of chemical philosophy*,[1]

In order to convey a knowledge of chemical facts and experience the more clearly, it has been generally deemed best to begin with the description of such principles or bodies as are the most simple. . . . By elementary principles, or simple bodies, we mean such as have not been decomposed, but are found to enter into combination with other bodies. We do not know that any one of the bodies denominated elementary, is absolutely indecomposable; but it ought to be called simple, till it can be analyzed.

Dalton here (and elsewhere) used the term 'element' without qualification or justification, rightly assuming that his readers would be familiar with this usage which had been sanctified by Lavoisier's employment of it in the *Traité élémentaire de chimie* of 1789, twenty years before. But this usage had been unknown a hundred years before Dalton; at that time the word 'element' meant something quite different, something much closer to its original Greek meaning. It is my intention here to try to trace the way in which the meaning of the word element, stable from late antiquity until the seventeenth century, changed rapidly with the rapidly expanding chemistry of the mid-eighteenth century. In making this attempt I shall, I know, be retracing much familiar ground, but I believe that there has been sufficient misunderstanding of the problem to justify my doing so, in order to emphasize the precise and often subtle changes of meaning that profoundly affected chemical theory.

To begin, if not at the beginning, at least as far back as may be, let us consider the definitions offered by Aristotle. In his *De caelo* he gave two definitions that are relevant here, one of *simple bodies* and the other of *elements.* The first (simple bodies) he defined as 'all bodies which contain a principle of natural motion, like fire and earth and their kinds, and the other bodies of the same order',[2] a characteristically Aristotelian definition in terms of motion. Of elements he said:

> Let us then define the element in bodies as that into which other bodies may be analysed, which is present in them either potentially or actually (which of the two is a matter for future debate), and which cannot itself be analysed into constituents differing in kind. Some such definition of an element is what all thinkers are aiming at throughout. . . . Now if this definition is correct, elemental bodies must exist,[3]

Aristotle's further discussion makes it clear that this generative form of definition is fundamental to both his theory of matter and his cosmology. In considering the problem historically, Aristotle found no disagreement among previous philosophers on the definition of an element (he appears to take it for granted that all previous materialistic philosophers had the same definition in mind); disagreement arose only over the number and nature of elements. There is no need here to consider in detail the arguments which led Aristotle to conclude in Book III of *De caelo* that there were a finite number of elements, in fact precisely four, which were not immutable and eternal but could be generated one from another.[4] Earth, air, fire and water are elements, because they are the substances into which all bodies can be resolved; but they are differentiated only by their 'properties, functions and powers'. That is, universal, unformed matter takes on the nature of earth, air, water or fire depending upon the forms impressed on it, and by a change of form one element can be changed into another. In the normal way, however, they remain distinct, and if any one substance is examined it will be found to contain, in varying proportions, all four elements. And it seems clear that nearly all Greek philosophers did indeed agree with Aristotle about the definition of element—the simple substances of which all bodies were composed and into which they were resolved—except perhaps the atomists; they had no need of this concept, since they were concerned only with atoms which were in every sense the fundamental building blocks of nature.

The Aristotelian theory of elements was essentially a physical theory, and its mode of entry into chemistry is obscure, chiefly because we lack detailed study of the texts. But it has been plausibly argued by A. J. Hopkins in a book that deserves to be better known,[5] that Aristotelian physics provided the theoretical basis for the more rational and philosophic side of late Greek alchemy, and that the interconvertibility of the four elements provided the rational framework for the theory of transmutation: just as earth became water by a change of form, so mercury and sulphur could become gold. All that was required was a correct balance of the elements. Certainly, as alchemical theory was elaborated and became sophisticated, the Aristotelian correlation of form and element played an ever-increasing rôle in the explanation of chemical change and in the fifteenth and sixteenth centuries alchemists often employed Aristotelian terminology in much the same way as the contemporary Peripatetic natural philosophers. By the sixteenth century, indeed, elements began to take an important place among alchemical concepts, as alchemy became sophisticated and theoretical and its practitioners sought for the explanation of simple chemical changes in terms of the substances involved rather than in symbolic terms. This is the first (though admittedly confused and obscure) step along the road that was to convert alchemy into a physical science in the course of the next century and a half; for this the fusion of the alchemical and technological traditions must be in large part responsible.

The technological tradition was concerned with techniques and effects and had little or no theoretical substructure. Alchemy had, besides its basic mystic tradition, a certain substructure of explanation in terms either of the Aristotelian elements or the Islamic salt, sulphur and mercury, the *tria prima* of the Renaissance. The adoption of the *tria prima* by Paracelsus as the basis of matter caused his followers to adopt them also, and the Paracelsans or Spagyrists of the seventeenth century were more concerned with analysis and explanation in terms of composition than their master himself. Every Paracelsan felt obliged to state his belief that analysis of bodies produced certain chemical elements or principles, a paradoxical situation, indeed, for the works in which this doctrine is most clearly expressed are usually textbooks designed either to teach pharmacists how to prepare chemical drugs or to instruct and exhort physicians to use such chemical remedies. Needless to say, the chemists' belief in the existence of elements had no practical application whatever, a fact tacitly recognized by most authors, who carefully divided their books into a theoretical section and a practical one, with virtually no connection between the two parts. It is, however, not the case that chemical theory was without any empirical basis; on the contrary, most writers endeavoured to demonstrate the existence of their chosen elements by experiment, usually the well-known 'analysis by fire' in which the elements were apparently shown to exist by destructive combustion of a chosen substance. Thus, in a famous example, Jean Beguin, a popular and influential teacher of Paracelsan iatrochemistry, 'demonstrated' the pre-existence of the *tria prima* in all substances by the combustion of a green stick in the fire, the ashes, flame and sap corresponding to salt, sulphur and mercury.[6] Others, with the same sort of evidence, sought for and found other elements. Thus Lefebvre, professor of chemistry at the Jardin des Plantes, brought into England by Charles II to teach the English apothecaries how to prepare the fashionable French chemical remedies, claimed to find five elements in all bodies: phlegm or water, spirit or mercury, sulphur or oil, salt, and earth;[7] and Christopher Glaser, another popular textbook writer, opted for three 'active' elements (salt, sulphur, mercury) and two 'passive' ones (earth and water).[8] Though some chemists combined Aristotelian and Paracelsan elements by addition, some chemists coalesced them into three or fewer: thus the highly original chemist Glauber, who was interested in chemical theory as much as he was in the discovery of new compounds, declared that there were three elements only, water, salt and sulphur, mercury being only another metal (and therefore, like all metals, a compound).[9] Van Helmont's insistence that there was only one element—water—was also supported by empirical evidence which appeared to be unanswerable: his famous willow-tree experiment. In all these cases chemists appeared to be able to offer empirical demonstration of their claim that all elements were to be found pre-existent in all substances, although in fact they nearly always chose organic substances as analytical material.

A curious variation of the usual view of chemical elements or principles was embodied in a series of theoretical works by the German physician Daniel Sennert; convinced that all great men must equally share in the claim to have discovered the truth, Sennert with impartial eclecticism tried to reconcile Galen, Paracelsus, Aristotle and Democritus, declaring that the four Aristotelian elements were indeed elementary, but were themselves composed of atoms.[10]

Seventeenth-century chemists tended to regard all bodies as made up of a limited number of elements whose nature and number were empirically determinable; all chemists mentioned or even discussed this theory in prefatory matter, but few felt inclined to try to utilize it in practical discussions, and while analysis was technically the determination of the proportions of the elements in a body, in fact much analysis in terms of practical chemical substances was performed. The only case of which I am aware, of a chemist's seriously studying the elementary composition of bodies in any systematic way is to be found in the work of the first chemists to be appointed to the Académie Royale des Sciences. Bourdelin and Du Clos during the years after 1666 laboured prodigiously at the analysis by fire of an enormous series of plants, carefully noting in each case the relative amounts of oil, phlegm, spirit and so on found in a fixed quantity of a wide variety of plants. Needless to say their results as entered into the Registres of the Académie have, rightly, remained unstudied from 1699 to the present day.

At this point it seems advisable to consider the definitions given to the term element by the seventeenth-century chemists who employed it. Allow me to quote two definitions, written very near the middle of the century. First:

[principles or elements are the] simple bodies, which enter originally into the composition of mixts and into which these mixts resolve themselves or may be finally resolved.[11]

second:

[elements or principles are] certain primitive and simple, or perfectly unmingled bodies; which not being made of any other bodies, or of one another, are the ingredients, of which all those called perfectly mixt bodies are immediately compounded, and into which they are ultimately resolved.[12]

I believe it is fair to say that these two definitions, published exactly twenty years apart, sound remarkably similar and have almost exactly the same meaning. Yet the first was written by an obscure French chemist who held that the true principles or elements were spirit, oil, salt and earth (but not air, because he held that air merely mingled with bodies and did not enter into the composition of mixts); his name was Estienne Clave. The second was written by a well-known English chemist who recognized no elements except the ultimate physical properties of matter; as you may all have perceived, this is part of Robert Boyle's famous definition. To strengthen my contention that there is nothing new in what Boyle was saying, I should like to quote the words which Boyle prefixed to his definition. He said:

to prevent mistakes, I must advertize you, that I now mean by elements, as those chymists that speak plainest, do by their principles . . .

26 It is, therefore, not surprising that Boyle's definition

agrees with Clave's; it would be strange if it did not, for the force of Boyle's argument would be lost if he had tried to find a new definition. For his aim in the *Sceptical chymist* was to cast doubt on the existence of elements as commonly defined. And he was therefore, like his chemical predecessors, thinking of elements as substances necessarily present in all bodies. This becomes plain if one notes Clave's rejection of air as an element: it was not resolvable into other elements, and was therefore simple and uncompounded; yet it did not, he thought, enter into the composition of bodies, but was merely mixed into some. An Aristotelian or Spagyrical compound was always held to be resolvable into the four elements or three principles, and the only difference between different compounds was the proportion in which the elements and principles existed in it. A modern compound, on the other hand, is resolvable into some few of the large number of elements recognized. We do not expect to find our mercury in all compounds and the Spagyrists did; we do not expect to find hydrogen or oxygen or even carbon in *all* compounds, but the Aristotelians did expect to find earth, air, fire and water in all compounds. Modern scholars have been curiously blind to this difference in regarding Boyle's definition of an element as 'modern'. He did not have the modern concept, and therefore recognized no real elements except perhaps the corpuscles which were the physical elements of all bodies, including those regarded by others as elementary. As he wrote:

I see not, why we must needs believe that there are any primogeneal and simple bodies, of which, as of pre-existent elements, nature is obliged to compound all others. Nor do I see, why we may not conceive, that she may produce the bodies accounted mixt out of one another, by variously altering and contriving their minute parts, without resolving the matter into any such simple or homogeneous substances, as are pretended.[13]

And again, in the essay 'Of the Imperfection of the Chymist's Doctrine of Qualities' he said:

the chymist's salt, sulphur, and mercury themselves are not the first and most simple principles of bodies, but rather primary concretions of corpuscles, or particles more simple than they . . .; by the differing conventions or coalitions of which minutest portions of matter, are made those differing concretions, that chymists name salt, sulphur, and mercury.[14]

J D—D

By repeated experiment, by an immense effort of empirical demonstration that the supposed elements and principles were unstable, inter-convertible, and not by any means universally pre-existent in all bodies, Boyle strove at one and the same time to demonstrate the existence of his corpuscles and invalidate the concept of the elementary composition of bodies. And having eliminated elements, Boyle was free to begin looking at chemical composition in an equally empirical and far more useful manner, in terms of definite entities like sea salt, vitriol, nitre, animal alkali, spirit of salt, sal ammoniac, etc. In fact (though not yet in name) Boyle was beginning to develop the concept of 'simple substances' which was ultimately to lead to the modern concept of element. Boyle's emphasis upon composition in terms of identifiable entities, coupled with the increasing knowledge of simple inorganic chemical compounds produced by the great increase in practical (and especially in medical) chemistry, began to lead to a more fruitful type of analysis than the old analysis by fire could ever be. He himself assisted by his interest in the use of chemical reagents to identify classes of substances (like the use of syrup of violets to determine whether a substance was acid, alkali or neutral) or specific substances (like the blue-green colour of copper ions in solution). And whatever chemists might think of Boyle's attempt to amalgamate chemistry and physics by elaborating a chemical theory of matter that was physical because it was based upon the corpuscles of the mechanical philosophy, while rejecting the truly chemical theory in terms of elements, they all recognized the utility of Boyle's methods and even while retaining elements they spoke at the same time of composition on the empirical level of definite, simple chemical entities.

In the early eighteenth century various new attitudes towards elements emerge, more or less derived from earlier conceptions. Those chemists most deeply influenced by Boyle, who adopted a particulate theory of matter, seem most clearly to have sought to avoid at least some of the pitfalls pointed out by him. An interesting and insufficiently known example is the theory sketched by Guillaume Homberg; he, though of Dutch extraction, spent a good deal of time working with

Boyle in England and was, after the reform of the Académie Royale des Sciences in 1699, both a leading figure in the Académie and a strong influence upon later French chemists like Rouelle. Homberg wrote no book and his writings (in the form of essays, perhaps because of Boyle's influence) survive either in manuscript or in the printed Mémoires of the Académie.[15] Homberg, very remarkably for his time, thought of the organic and inorganic realms as being composed of different chemical principles. And among inorganic substances he distinguished between 'minerals' which he thought did contain mercury and 'fossils' and 'salts' which did not, the earliest case of which I am aware in which an element is not taken to be a universal constituent of all matter. For Homberg, mercury the principle was beginning the slow journey which should dethrone it from its regal position of universal element and declare it just another metal. Homberg's principles are not yet simple substances, but they are approaching that status. An even more curious compromise was that of the great Dutch chemical teacher Boerhaave, who respected Boyle extremely; Boerhaave in his lectures taught a completely particulate structure of matter but also emphasized the four elements by dividing his lectures (and hence his book) into four headings corresponding to Earth, Air, Fire and Water. These, he held, occupied a special position in chemistry by virtue of their ability to act as chemical 'instruments', and he stressed their powers as solvents.[16]

Boerhaave's views, especially his insistence upon the importance of fire as a chemical agent, seemed to many eighteenth-century chemists to be quite consistent with the increasingly influential doctrines of the German chemists, J. J. Becher and G. E. Stahl.[17] (As Becher's views were and are mainly known from his posthumous *Physica subterranea* (Leipzig, 1738) edited by Stahl, it is difficult to tell how much master and pupil differed in their views, particularly since Stahl's theory is avowedly an extension of Becher's.) Both Becher and Stahl thought of matter as particulate; Becher initiated the view accepted by Stahl that matter was formed from particles by aggregation: thus, Becher said, *mixts* were made up of corpuscles, themselves formed from smaller particles; *compounds* were made up of different mixts;

and *aggregates* were combinations of different compounds or of mixts and compounds, only aggregates being discernible by the senses. This is in no way inconsistent with Stahl's theory that earth and water were the two material principles of mixts, and that phlogiston was a particulate material principle present in all bodies. The views of Becher and Stahl on the structure of the elements themselves are more confusing; it was their theory of chemical combination that their successors found most interesting.

It is perhaps difficult to see precisely why this should be so, for the mechanism proposed by Becher and Stahl is still a long way from presenting a picture of chemical composition in terms of actual analysis. But even in the middle of the eighteenth century chemists still clung to the notion that they needed some unifying theory of matter different from the physicist's constructional particles, and at the same time they were in some confusion over what true chemical analysis was. The traditional 'analysis by fire' still persisted although it was known to produce results different from those obtained by solution or chemical reaction; at the same time heat was recognized as an active promoter of chemical reaction, and calcination and combustion were beginning to be regarded as 'type' reactions. All this perhaps explains why heat—whether fire, phlogiston, caloric or plain heat—became a chemical substance and remained so well into the nineteenth century. At the same time the connotations of words began to change; 'element' connoted primarily simplicity, while 'principle' was taken either to be an active agent ('principle of fire', 'acidifying principle' and so on) or the last product of non-destructive analysis, the mixts or compounds of Becher and Stahl. At the same time the new pneumatic chemistry seems to have suggested to some, at least, that the element air (as the common principle of all the new non-atmospheric airs) was, like fire, an immutable element, while earth and water also seemed necessary parts of chemical composition.[18]

How confused, and indeed how fluid the situation was in the face of changing chemical knowledge may be perceived in the writings of that industrious, capable, useful but unoriginal French chemist P. J. Macquer. Macquer was initially inclined to accept the Aristotelian elements as the ultimate chemical building blocks, physically composed of particles, because this is how they appeared to chemists.[19] Twenty-five years later in his *Dictionnaire de chymie* (Paris, 1766), trying to set out the opinion of the generality of chemists, he wrote:

In chemistry the name of elements is given to bodies so simple that every effort of the chemical art is insufficient to decompose them or even to bring about any sort of alteration, and which, on the other hand, enter in the form of principles or constituent particles into the combination of other bodies, which are therefore called compound bodies.[20]

Thus, as late as 1766, elements were still *both* the last product of analysis and the 'principles' (to be defined elsewhere) of mixts or compound bodies. Macquer still regarded Fire, Air, Water and Earth as the true elements, never decomposed, and always present in analysis, though not necessarily all present in the analysis of every body. But Macquer went on cautiously to say that:

It is very possible that these substances, although taken to be simple, are not really so; that they may even be highly compounded and that they are the result of the union of several other simpler substances. But as experience teaches us absolutely nothing on this point, it is possible without inconvenience, and is even proper in chemistry, to regard fire, air, water and earth as simple bodies, since indeed they act as such in all the operations of chemistry.

So far Macquer's opinions do not seem inconsistent with his earlier views. But his theory was complicated by his belief that there were principles of various kinds to be reckoned with, and that these were the working basis of chemical compounds. Under the heading 'Principes'[21] Macquer wrote, somewhat confusedly, that physicists and chemists all held and had held that chemical substances were all composed of simpler bodies, 'The name of principle is given to substances extracted from compound bodies upon analysis or chemical decomposition.' While he held it 'generally taken as demonstrated' that water, earth and fire enter as principles into bodies, and that chemists have shown that air enters into many others, he somewhat destroyed the force of this statement by speaking of various sorts of principles, some primitive and some (among them chemical agents, like acids and alkalis) more complex, more nearly simple bodies. Further (under 'aggregation') Macquer admitted as principles 'parties constituant', constituent parts of particles which are the units into which a compound may be divided, when it loses its character. (Thus acid and alkali are the principles (in this sense) or constituent parts of common salt). The compound formed by two constituent particles is a *molecule* or 'partie-intégrant'—two terms with a long subsequent history.

Thus while Macquer regarded *elements* in the same light as they had always been held, *principles* were both elements and the chemical components of compounds, a confusing view amply demonstrating the confusion which then prevailed, and which continued to prevail, for Macquer did not alter his statements in the second edition of his dictionary which appeared in 1777.

By this time, however, there was an increasing amount of scepticism among chemists, especially theoretical chemists. Scheele, although, like Lavoisier, he had demonstrated that Boyle had not really converted water into earth, and recognized that there were many who doubted whether the true elements of bodies could ever be discovered, thought that air and fire were compound bodies. Only phlogiston was a 'true element and simple principle'.[22] Bergman, the great proponent of Newtonian attraction (in the form of elective attractions), was even more emphatic; in an introduction to Scheele's treatise he flatly proclaimed that though the elements had not so far been analysed, they were far from homogeneous.[23] This scepticism combined with the dichotomy proclaimed by Macquer—the division between chemical elements, thought of as uniquely necessary to the chemical point of view, and chemical principles and simple bodies—was first extended, and then coalesced. Thus Guyton de Morveau, the same chemist who first demonstrated that phlogiston must have negative weight because all metals gained weight on calcination, and who later became one of the first converts to the anti-phlogistic chemistry, nicely presented this dichotomy in the lectures he gave in Dijon in the 1770s and published in 1777.[24] He first defined *simple bodies* as those not susceptible of further analysis, and then characterized these as either 'natural elements' (earth, air, fire and water), or 'chemical elements'

(Macquer's constituent particles, the units which make up chemical substances).

It was such views as this which led to the reform of chemical nomenclature which, though Lavoisier's antiphlogistic chemistry made it peculiarly apposite and valuable, did not owe its origin to Lavoisier's new chemistry. Lavoisier himself thought that Macquer and Baumé were 'among the first to distinguish each metallic salt by the name of the acid and the metal which enter into its composition. . . . Of late years, Mr Bergman, Mr Bucquet and Mr de Fourcroy have carried the application of the same principle to a much greater length.' [25] But it was Guyton de Morveau who was the leading spirit, and who, according to Lavoisier, conceived the notion of reform in 1782, in the course of composing an article on chemistry for *Encyclopédie méthodique*.[26] And this chemical nomenclature, determined upon in 1787 when it was presented to the Académie Royale des Sciences, could never have been conceived without a real scepticism about the nature of elements. I do not know how far Guyton achieved this scepticism himself, and how far he was influenced by his co-authors, Lavoisier, Berthollet and Fourcroy. Certainly Lavoisier had no doubts; in a passage which foreshadows the more famous statement in the *Traité élémentaire de chimie*, he wrote:

We should be in contradiction with ourselves, were we at present to enter into great discussions of the constituent principles of bodies and of their elementary particles. We shall content ourselves here with regarding as simple all the substances which we cannot decompose; all such as we obtain in the last result from chemical analysis. Without doubt, in time to come, these substances which appear to us to be simple, will in their turns be decomposed, . . .; but our imagination ought not to anticipate the facts, and we must not take upon us to say more than nature presents to our understanding.[27]

This is not very different (though more emphatically expressed) from the ideas of Lavoisier's contemporaries, and it must be remembered that Lavoisier retained many principles: caloric replaced phlogiston, and oxygen was so named as the acidifying principle. Guyton's 'Memoir to explain the principles of the methodical nomenclature', which is printed immediately following

Lavoisier's in their *Method of chymical nomenclature,*
puts the case even more simply:

In the order which we have proposed to ourselves, the simple
substances, that is to say, such as chymists to the present
time have not been able to decompose, ought chiefly to fix
our attention, because the denominations of bodies which by
exact analysis can be reduced to their elements are properly
expressed by the re-union of the names of those same
principles.[28]

And in his first class of simplest substances, Guyton
listed light, matter of heat (or caloric), dephlogisticated
or vital air (oxygen), inflammable gas (hydrogen) and
phlogisticated air (nitrogen). This mixture of chemical
substance and chemical principle was to continue, and
remained a commonplace for some time. Thus William
Higgins, the would-be rival to Dalton (but he never
really understood the essence of Dalton's theory, which
must necessarily diminish the seriousness of his claim),
wrote in his defence of Lavoisier against Kirwan:

It is to Mr Lavoisier that we are chiefly indebted for our
present knowledge of the constituent principles of the different acids . . . Mr Lavoisier has shown that dephlogisticated
air is one of the constituent principles of all acids.[29]

Sometime later, in a general work of 1801, Fourcroy
could write:

In the first class I have placed the simple bodies, those at least
not so far decomposed, which in my experience behave as
simple substances. These are, in large part, the constituent
elements of all other bodies. . . . They correspond in some
measure to what the ancient chemists called principles or
elements, because they are not subject to decomposition and
because they are truly the consitituent principles of all compounds. These bodies are at the same time the first and the
most general productions of nature and the last products,
the final terms of decompositions effected by the [chemical]
art.[30]

And yet, almost immediately after this he could firmly
declare that 'in chemistry the name of simple body only
means a substance never decomposed', and this cannot
be applied to the ancient elements, now known to be in
fact complex.[31] Fourcroy listed as certainly simple
about thirty substances: light, caloric, oxygen, nitrogen,
hydrogen, carbon, phosphorus, sulphur, diamond, the
metals—and atmospheric air!

Very similar were Humphry Davy's earliest views as expressed in his 1802 lectures before the Royal Institution, though Davy was also interested in the physical structure of matter. He began by saying that:

The different bodies in nature are composed of particles or minute parts, individually imperceptible to the senses. When these particles are similar, the bodies they constitute are denominated simple, and when they are dissimilar, compound.[32]

This is the concept of a physicist, rather than a pure chemist, and interestingly close to the concept held at this same time by Dalton, still looking at matter from a physicist's point of view. Davy went on further to clarify the *chemical* point of view, saying:

Though the corpuscular theory supposes the existence of bodies composed of similar particles, yet we are not certain that any such bodies have been examined. The simple principles of the chemists are substances which have not been hitherto composed, or decomposed by art; and they are elements, only in relation to other known substances.[33]

This is an uncompromisingly rationalist view, and although not all Davy's forty-two 'acknowledged' simple principles are in fact elementary in the modern sense (he includes earths, like silex and alumine, fixed alkaline substances like potash and lime, and undecompounded acids, like muriatic acid and boracic acid) they are all in fact true chemical substances, and heat is not mentioned among them. A few years later, in his *Elements of chemical philosophy*, Davy took an even more uncompromising stand, using element as a term equivalent to chemical component. He there wrote:

The term *element* is used as synonymous with *undecompounded* body; but in modern chemistry its application is limited to the results of experiments. The improvements taking place in the methods of examining bodies, are constantly changing the opinions of chemists with respect to their nature, and there is no reason to suppose that any real *indestructible principle* has yet been discovered. Matter may ultimately be found to be the same in essence, differing only in the arrangements of its particles; or two or three *simple* substances may produce all the varieties of compounded bodies. . . . By analysis compounded bodies are resolved into their constituents; by *synthesis* they are produced in consequence of the union of these constituents; and when the weight of the compound corresponds to that of the constituents, the processes are considered as accurate.[34]

Davy, partly as a result of his own successful analysis of substances previously considered genuinely simple and elementary, here indeed seems to be the true upholder of what is said to be Lavoisier's concept, both in regard to simple substances and in regard to quantitative rigour. For unlike Lavoisier, Davy admitted only chemical substances as elementary, placing heat, though important to chemical activity, outside the range of elements, principles or simple substances. At the same time Davy began that scepticism concerning chemical simplicity which was to lead to much questioning later in the century and much discussion of the possibility that elements were compounds.[35]

Dalton's own views, as given at the beginning of this paper, were similar to Davy's, since he too regarded 'elementary principles or simple bodies' as purely chemical substances. So did Thomas Thomson, who was the first to introduce Dalton's atomic theory in print. He wrote, as early as 1804:

> By simple substances is not meant what the ancient philosophers called *elements* of bodies, or particles of matter incapable of farther diminution or division. They signify merely bodies which have not been decompounded, and which no phenomenon hitherto observed indicate to be compounds. Very possibly the bodies which we reckon simple may be real compounds, but till this has actually been proved, we have no right to suppose it. Were we acquainted with all the elements of bodies, and with all the combinations of which these elements are capable, the science of chemistry would be as perfect as possible; but at present this is very far from being the case.[36]

Thomson's views, which reached a wide audience, especially after the book was translated into French (Thomson's 1807 edition was the source from which Avogadro drew his knowledge of Dalton, for example), are more historically sophisticated than those of most chemists, for he clearly saw the difference between the old elements and the new simple substances. It appears that this difference was more genuinely maintained among English chemists—whose chemical elements were all true chemical entities—than upon the Continent, where the old confusion between elements and principles continued to reign and produced several anomalous intrusions into lists of simple substances. The most striking example of this latter point of view that I have met with is to be found in Berzelius' Treatise on chemistry, written as late as 1828. In his introductory matter Berzelius expounded the problem in terms not very different from those being used fifty years before (say, in 1785). He wrote:

> The substances found on our globe are divided into *simple* and *compound*.
>
> We call those *simple* which we think are certainly not compound and which we meet on every side as constituent parts of the rest of nature.
>
> Formerly they were called *elements* and all bodies were taken to be composed of four simple or elementary substances, earth, fire, air and water. Today we know that the majority of these so-called elements are components and that, in consequence, the ideas of the ancients were false.[37]

It is certainly odd to find Berzelius harking back to the four Aristotelian elements; it is even odder to find him dividing simple substances into *imponderables* (light, heat, electricity and magnetism) and *ponderables* (fifty-two chemical substances.) But this does not affect the fact that chemical elements had come to be universally accepted as the substances into which chemical compounds were resolvable by chemical means. (It is even arguable that chemical reactions do very frequently produce heat, and sometimes even light, so that these 'imponderables' appear to emerge from chemical compounds.) That Berzelius and others were doubtful of the true simplicity of chemical elements is also readily understandable, in view of the rapid progress in chemical analysis and discovery made by Davy and others in the early years of the nineteenth century. What was quite clear and beyond doubt was that simple substances or elements did exist and, whether compound or not, were useful and manageable chemical entities. When Dalton chose to speak of his atoms as having precise, definite weights he calmly assumed the existence of simple substances or elements composed of atoms; and although he might expect some chemists to deny the existence of the atom, he clearly did not expect, nor need to expect, any controversy over the existence of elements in the modern sense. So far had chemistry advanced in the course of the previous fifty years.

Notes **1** Part II (published in 1810) I, 221–2.

2 *De caelo*, I, ii (268b 28–30), quoted from *On the heavens*, transl. W. K. C. Guthrie (Loeb Classical Library, London, 1939) 11–12.

3 Op. cit., III, iii (302a 16–21) 283–4.

4 Cf. Aristotle, op. cit., III, iv (303a–303b) 291–5.

5 *Alchemy child of Greek philosophy* (New York, 1934).

6 *Tyrocinium chymicum* (Paris, 1610, and many subsequent editions, including an English translation of 1669).

7 *Traité de chymie* (Paris, 1661).

8 *Traité de la chymie* (Paris, 1663).

9 'A Treatise of the Nature of Salts' in *Works*, translated by Christopher Packe (London, 1689).

10 See especially his *De Chymicorum Aristotelicis et Galenis consensu ac dissensu* (Wittenberg, 1619), translated into English as *Chemistry mode easie and useful* (London, 1662); a more detailed discussion of his theory of matter may be found in *Hypomnemata physica* (Frankfort, 1636).

11 Estienne Clave, *Nouvelle Lumière Philosophique des vrais principes et Elemens de la Nature & Qualités d'iceux* (Paris, 1641) 39.

12 Robert Boyle, *The sceptical chymist* (T. Birch, *The works of the Honourable Robert Boyle* (London, 1772) I, 562; hereafter referred to as *Works*).

13 Ibid., 583.

14 *Works*, IV, 281.

15 See especially the *Mémoires de l'académie royale des sciences pour 1702;* Homberg's 'Essais de chimie' will be found in pp. 44–70 of the edition published at Amsterdam in 1702.

16 See his *Elements of chemistry*, trans. by Timothy Dallowe (London, 1735) especially I, 46 and 78 or the version translated by Peter Shaw as *A new method of chemistry* (2nd edn, London, 1741).

17 For Stahl, see *Philosophical principles of universal chemistry* (London, 1730) especially pp. 10–20 and his *Traité des sels* (Paris, 1771).

18 I cannot wholly accept the view of Henry Guerlac (see e.g. Marshall Clagett, ed., *Critical problems in the history of science* (Madison, Wisconsin, 1959) 516–17, that Hales' work alone is responsible for this view. Macquer (see below) found earth, fire and water *clearly* principles, and air less certainly so.

19 P. J. Macquer, *Elémens de chymie théorique* (Paris, 1741) 12–15.

20 *Dictionnaire de chymie* s.v. 'Elémens' (my translation).

21 This is a much longer article than that on elements, and may be supplemented by the articles on *Aggregation, Analyse, Composition des corps* and *Décomposition des Corps*.

22 *Chemical observations and experiments on air and fire* (London, 1780) 3, 95–103; there was a French edition in 1781.

23 Op. cit., pp. xv–xl, especially xxxii.

24 *Elémens de chymie théorique et pratique* (Dijon, 1777) see especially I, 8–20, 50.

25 James St John (trans.), *Method of chymical nomenclature proposed by Messrs. De Morveau, Lavoisier, Berthollet and De Fourcroy* (London, 1788) 2 (from Lavoisier's 'Memoir on the necessity of reforming and bringing to perfection the nomenclature of chemistry' of 1787).

26 Described in 'Mémoire sur les Dénominations Chymiques, la nécessité d'en perfectionner le systeme, & les règles pour y parvenir', *Observations sur la physique*, xix (1782) 370–82.

27 *Method of chymical nomenclature*, 12.

28 Ibid., 21.

29 *A Comparative view of the phlogistic and antiphlogistic theories* (2nd edn, London, 1791) 8; facsimile in T. S. Wheeler and J. R. Partington, *The life and work of William Higgins, chemist (1763–1825)* (New York and London, 1960).

30 *Système des connoissances chymiques et leur applications aux phénomènes de la nature et de l'art* (Paris, 1801) Discours préliminaire, I, xliv, lvi.

31 Op. cit., 'Des corps simples ou indécomposés', III.

32 'A Syllabus of A Course of Lectures' in *Collected works* (London, 1840) II, 330.

33 Ibid., 333.

34 *Collected works*, IV, 132.

35 See W. V. Farrar, 'Nineteenth-Century Speculations on the Complexity of the Chemical Elements', *British Journal for the History of Science*, II (1965) 297–323.

36 *A System of chemistry* (2nd edn, Edinburgh, 1804) 16.

37 J. J. Berzelius, *Traité de chimie* (Paris, 1829) 37.

4

A Rupert Hall

Precursors
of Dalton

John Dalton was born more than two hundred years ago near Cockermouth in Cumberland. His origins were humble, and his education informal. All his life he remained the quiet, modest Quaker, and just as his work displays the force and originality of mind that enabled him to educate himself, so also it shows the weaknesses of one who was self-taught, without early subjection to criticism and discipline.

All his life, too, John Dalton was a teacher, from the age of twelve onwards. In 1781 he moved to Kendal, where he taught school first with his cousin George Bewley and later with his own brother Jonathan. After twelve years of this he was brought to Manchester in order to instruct in mathematics and science at the New College in Mosley Street; from 1799 onwards, however, he lived by giving public and private instruction in mathematics and chemistry without any institutional appointment. He remained in Manchester for the rest of his life, making only occasional excursions to London, and to other cities where the British Association meetings were held, and once in 1822 to Paris. It is not for me to speak of John Dalton's long life in Manchester, of his long connection with the Literary and Philosophical Society, and of the scientific distinction he brought to this city. But I cannot refrain from remarking on the strange coincidence that Dalton, who founded the atomic theory of nineteenth-century chemistry and Ernest Rutherford who destroyed it, were both associated with Manchester. How vivid a

picture of the development of science during this
century—and of this city too—is conveyed to us by
reflecting on the very different circumstances and researches of Dalton on the one hand and Rutherford on
the other.

Sixty years ago it was possible to write of Dalton's
theory of chemical atomism:

it is certain that the ages to come will reckon it as the central,
dominating conception which has actuated the chemistry of
the nineteenth century. The characteristic feature of the
chemistry of our time is, in a word, the development and
elaboration of Dalton's doctrine; for every great advance in
chemical knowledge during the last ninety years finds its
interpretation in his theory.[1]

Since the time of Rutherford this has ceased to be true.
We can today no more believe in the reality of Dalton's
atoms than we can in that of Newton's atoms, or
those of Democritus. And even through the nineteenth
century there was a persistent doubt whether atomism
was more than a useful figment. But there is no doubt
that John Dalton made an enormous contribution to
science—for in the long run it was to be virtually as
great in physics as in chemistry—when he, for the first
time, made positive, verifiable statements about the
ultimate structure of things. This had never been done
before. I am going to attempt a brief sketch of the
history of atomic speculations before Dalton, but let me
say here and now that the lesson of this history is that
no one, before Dalton, was able to make any precise,
definite pronouncements about atoms, or indeed to
show in any very clear and compelling way that there
was a direct advantage to be gained by thinking of
matter as having an atomic structure. Dalton did this
by taking the atom out of the speculations of physicists
and making it the foundation of a verifiable theory of
chemical combination. Dalton did not invent the atom,
but he made it scientifically useful. And it strikes me,
by the way, as being one of those steps in intellectual
history that are really idiosyncratic. One can often say
'*This* was bound to be found out by someone very
soon'; not so of Dalton's atomic theory. Few if any
chemists of this time and perhaps long after would have
followed the particular path in thought that John
Dalton took.

Now I do not want to digress into the analysis of the steps by which Dalton—who was an atomist before he ever made a chemical experiment—arrived at the full theory of chemical atomism as first described by Thomas Thomson in 1807, and by Dalton himself in the following year. The fundamental concept of chemical atomism is, of course, that atoms of different substances have different weights, from hydrogen the lightest to gold (in Dalton's day). We know that Dalton applied this idea to questions of chemical combination —that is to the problem of finding the number of different elementary atoms assembled in the compound atom (or as we would say, molecule)—at least as early as September 1804. However, examination of Dalton's notebooks before their lamentable destruction in the last war had demonstrated that in the period before this —before the summer of 1804—he had been little concerned with purely chemical topics; Dalton's interest was in heat, and in the physics of the atmosphere, not at all in chemistry. It was discovered by Roscoe and Harden that Dalton's *earliest* list of relative atomic weights was entered in his notebooks on or soon after 6 September 1803, more than a year earlier, and in connection with a study of the relative solubilities of the atmospheric gases in water. Indeed, if we look at Dalton's published work in the *Manchester Memoirs*, we see this first 'Table of the relative weights of the ultimate particles of gaseous and other bodies' introduced at the end of a paper 'On the Absorption of Gases by Water and other Liquids' read on 21 October 1803. Dalton had wasted no time. Now it is not for me to try to analyse Dalton's intellectual processes in detail, nor to describe the ways in which he derived the numbers in the first table of atomic weights; but I must just explain that Dalton at first subscribed to a simple, naive opinion (as he tells us himself) that the fundamental atomic particles—the ultimate physical building-blocks—of all elements are the same, and therefore of the same weight. What caused him to change his mind? It was a group of experiments on the solubility of gases in water, partly performed by himself, partly by his friend William Henry. First, these confirmed a hypothesis long held by Dalton that when two gases are mixed, the particles of one exert no pressure on the particles of the other. Second, they showed that different gases fell (as regards their solubility by volume in water) into distinct classes; the relative absorbed volumes being as the series $1/1^3$, $1/2^3$, $1/3^3$, etc., and thirdly they showed that solubility depended upon pressure. Accordingly, Dalton formed the view that there was no *chemical* action between dissolved gases and water, but a *mechnical* interspersion of the particles of the one among those of the other. Then, he asked (at the end of the paper of October 1803) 'Why does water not admit its bulk of every kind of gas alike?'; and he answered his own question thus:

> Though I am not yet able to satisfy myself completely, I am nearly persuaded that the circumstance depends upon the weight and number of the ultimate particles of the several gases: Those whose particles are lightest and single being least absorbable, and the others more according as they increase in weight and complexity.

Then, introducing his table of atomic weights without further elaboration, he adds, with modest satisfaction: 'An enquiry into the relative weights of the ultimate particles of bodies is a subject, so far as I know, entirely new; I have lately been prosecuting this enquiry with remarkable success.'[2]

Several years later, near the end of January 1810, when Dalton was giving his recollections of his earliest ideas about the differences between the atoms of the various elements in a lecture at the Royal Institution, he himself linked them with his interest in the atmosphere.[3] The problem he there mentions is this; if the atmospheric gases oxygen, nitrogen and carbon dioxide have (as we know) different densities, why do they not settle out in layers with the heaviest at the bottom? How do they continue uniformly dissolved? It is true that Dalton in this narrative speaks of the different *sizes* of atoms, rather than weights, and also that he makes no mention of the effect of particle size on solubility in water, but the general effect is much the same. We thus learn that Dalton grafted the notion of chemical differentiation by size or weight to the clear concept of a physical atom that he already possessed: an atom consisting of a small, hard spherical nucleus surrounded by a large sphere or atmosphere of heat. The weight or mass of the atom was in its solid nucleus: the atmosphere of heat was weightless (at least, so far as instruments could detect). This heat surrounding the nucleus was, however, highly elastic: it resisted the compression involved in trying to make two atoms approach each other. Thus a gas was like a number of lead bullets symmetrically embedded in sponge rubber. To make the bullets closer you have to squeeze up the rubber; conversely, a compressed gas escapes into the atmosphere with expansion of the heat surrounding the atomic nuclei.

There is no question but that in holding this physical atomic theory, and what is more, in actually making it *work* by giving it an explanatory function in physics, Dalton regarded himself as following faithfully the teachings of Isaac Newton, and the classical eighteenth-century tradition. For example, in the lecture of 1810 I mentioned above, Dalton says that

Newton had demonstrated clearly, in the 23rd Prop. of Book 2 of the *Principia*, that an elastic fluid is constituted of small particles or atoms of matter, which repel each other by a force increasing in proportion as their distance diminishes.

And in the same lecture he illustrated Newton's ideas upon the atomic structure of matter by quoting from the famous Queries in *Opticks*, notably Query 31:[4]

It seems probable to me that God in the beginning formed matter in solid, massy, hard, impenetrable, movable particles, of such sizes and figures, and with such other properties and in such proportion to space as most conduced to the end for which he formed them . . .

And again:

I had rather infer from their cohesion [wrote Newton] that their particles attract one another by some force, which in immediate contact is very strong, at small distances performs the chemical operations above mentioned, and reaches not far from the particles with any sensible effect.

Now it may occur to you that there is one significant difference between Newton's physical atomic theory and Dalton's: Newton did not assert that the atomic nuclei are surrounded by atmosphere of heat, nor did he attribute to this elastic heat the effect of repulsion between particles. Finally, Newton did not ever conceive of heat as a material fluid, for his notion of heat was kinetic.[5]

44   To trace the evolution of the theory of heat from

Newton to Dalton would lead us far astray: let me only indicate now that it was only towards the mid-eighteenth century that the idea of aether, electricity, phlogiston and heat as impalpable substances, weightless fluids, was definitely accepted by most scientists. The discoveries and teachings of Scottish chemists particularly seemed to endorse the material conception of heat. For it was clear that heat was not only intimately connected with matter in the chemical ways revealed in endothermic and exothermic reactions, but in other ways shown by the latency and specificity of heat. Seeing no intrinsic difficulty in this fluid conception of heat, Dalton could justify its amalgamation with the Newtonian atomic theory thus: may we not, he says, look forward to the time when the three related agents in Nature, light, heat and electricity 'shall be shown to arise from one and the same principle?' (This is the idea later given more specific form as the 'correlation of physical forces').

And in the mean time (he goes on) is it not most consistent to conclude that these agents are of the same nature? If any one of these three, *heat, light* and *electricity* be deemed a *fluid*, then the other two must also be deemed *fluids*. If any one of these three be deemed *powers* or *properties*, then all three must be deemed *powers* or *properties* of matter. Now with regard to *light*, our knowledge concerning it remains nearly the same as it was in the time of Newton. His decided opinion concerning light was that of its being a body . . . May it not then be argued that the notion of heat and electricity being also *bodies*, is more conformable to the Newtonian philosophy than the opposite doctrine, which considers them mere *qualities* or *properties* of bodies?[6]

This one passage alone tells us so much about Dalton as a physical atomist that we hardly need more. As a chemical atomist Dalton had no precursors worth speaking of; as a physical atomist he placed himself firmly in the Newtonian tradition, as enriched by the progress in physics that the eighteenth century had made. He was unaffected by the more sophisticated atomistic speculations of Boscovich and Le Sage. However, it is not my province at this point to investigate Dalton's early thoughts about the nature of matter in detail; let it suffice to say that they seem not to have changed at least since he wrote his *Meteorological observations and essays* in 1793.[7] It is for me rather to describe now the evolution of the physical atomism from which Dalton took his departure.

Let us begin with Dalton's authority, Isaac Newton, who died almost forty years before Dalton was born. Now we commonly think of Newton as a mathematical physicist, the author of the *Mathematical principles of natural philosophy*, the first celestial mechanician. And this indeed provides Newton's title to his extraordinary eminence. But Newton was also an experimental scientist, the fruits of this side of his work being reflected in his second major work, the *Opticks* of 1704. This was a work that Newton had long matured, since the time of the first publication of his optical experiments in 1672; and to it he appended in successive re-editions of 1706 and 1717 his final thoughts about physics. If we examine *Opticks* we discover that it is a strange work, and that these final thoughts take a strange form. *Opticks* is in part a straightforward book of experimental science, in part an exposition of applied mathematics, but in part also a statement of some peculiar and necessarily hypothetical ideas about the nature of things. These are largely (but not wholly) to be found in the total of thirty-one *Queries* appended to the last editions of the book. This last section is called 'Book III, Part I' (there is no Part II); in it Newton described a group of experiments on diffraction—an optical effect discovered long before by an Italian, Grimaldi. When he has done with these descriptions, evidently at the end of a draft he left off about 1690, Newton's book goes on:

> When I made the foregoing observations, I designed to repeat most of them with more care and exactness, and to make some new ones. . . . But I was then interrupted, and cannot now think of taking these things into farther consideration. And since I have not finished this part of my design, I shall conclude only with proposing some Queries, in order to a farther search to be made by others.

In the group of queries proposed with the first edition of *Opticks* Newton confined himself to uncertain issues in that science, but as he enlarged their number in later editions of the book, so his range widened to include the theory of matter, physics and chemistry. The *Opticks* was very widely read in the eighteenth century; indeed it was the only scientific work of Newton's that could be thoroughly appreciated by non-mathematicians. Many whose own interests led them to experimentation there studied attentively the example of Newton as an experimental scientist, and there found in the *Queries* (as John Dalton did) an eloquent, impressive view on what they took to be Newton's insight into some most obscure corners of Nature.[8] (Whether Newton believed everything he proposed as a question is, however, open to doubt.) The *Queries*—some passages from which, as extracted by Dalton, I have already read—made it clear beyond controversy that Newton believed in atoms. The phenomena of Nature are caused by the changes in things brought about by the forces existing between the particles, which set these in motion. For it is not only a property of these fundamental particles that they are endowed with inertia and otherwise obey the laws of motion, says Newton, 'but that they are moved by certain active Principles, such as is that of gravity, and that which causes fermentation, and the cohesion of bodies'. Newton's is a highly kinetic world; the laws of mechanics are the fundamental prescripts of this world, and the only permanently enduring entities in it are the indestructible atoms.

Such ideas expressed in the *Queries* were by no means fresh in the mind of the ageing Newton, indeed it is easy to show that the *Principia* fits perfectly into the same scheme of things.[9] Gravity was always treated by Newton as only *one* of the interparticulate forces—one that is more important, in general, at long distances than at molecular ones; and in the third of his Rules of Reasoning in Philosophy, in Book III of the *Principia*, Newton explicitly asserted the principle of homogeneity in physics: What is attributed to wholes must be attributed to parts, that is to say, if there is a force of gravity between macroscopic bodies it can only arise from a force of gravity between their component particles. This leads Newton in the Preface to the *Principia* to express the wish that:

we could derive the rest of the phenomena of Nature [those not connected with gravity] by the same kind of [mathematical] reasoning from mechanical principles, for I am induced by many reasons to suspect that they may all depend upon certain forces by which the particles of bodies, by some

causes hitherto unknown, are either mutually impelled towards one another, and cohere in regular figures, or are repelled and recede from one another.

Actually Newton gives in the *Principia* two examples
of the mathematical investigation of forces other than
the gravitational. One is a derivation of the ordinary
optical law of reflection and of Snel's law of refraction.[10] It involves the assumption—and we must recall
Newton's avoidance of a positive declaration that such
an assumption is justifiable—that light consists of a
stream of fine particles attracted by dense material substances. The other example is that instanced by
Dalton,[11] Newton's demonstration that if an elastic
fluid (gas in our language) consists of spaced-out particles repelling each other inversely as the distance
between them, it will obey Boyle's law, that is, its
resistance to compression will increase in proportion to
its diminution of volume. But as Newton pointed
out, this demonstration was defective to the extent that
it considered only the repulsion between immediately
adjacent particles. So that neither of these excursions
from gravitational mechanics gave an unequivocal,
wholly satisfactory exemplification of the mathematical
investigation of forces, though their weakness in this
respect was generally overlooked by Newton's successors, including Dalton.

It would be easy to ramify this account of Newton's
atomic theory of matter with the aid of unpublished
material from his papers, which of course were not
available to Dalton. But I hope that what has already
been said will indicate that there was more than enough
evidence in the *Principia* and the *Opticks*, taken together,
for Dalton to feel that he knew Newton's mind on these
matters very well.

It is interesting to note that Dalton must also have
read, in the *Queries* in *Opticks*, Newton's specific ideas
concerning chemical atomism. I will not elaborate this
point, merely pausing to remind you that Newton
clearly contemplated the existence of a chemical force
of cohesion between particles, of varying strength depending on the substances thus combining into compounds. So Newton wrote:

And is it not from the like attractive Power between the
Particles of oil of vitriol and the Particles of Water, that oil

of vitriol draws to it a good quantity of Water out of the Air [sulphuric acid is hygroscopic, we say] and after it is satiated draws no more, and in Distillation lets go the Water very difficultly?[12]

In the same way he instanced the formation of a succession of salts of metals by replacement, the metal added to the solution in each case having a greater attraction for the acid particle, and so precipitating the metal in the former salt. But this is a chemical atomism very different indeed from Dalton's, since it is concerned with a differential attractive power qualitatively linked with substances, whereas Dalton was concerned solely with different weights of atoms. Newton's theory related to chemical kinetics, Dalton's to chemical statics. It is perhaps not surprising, therefore, that Dalton seems not to have mentioned *these* ideas of Newton.[13]

As Dalton was heir to Newton, so Newton succeeded to the seventeenth century mechanical philosophy, his own chief contribution to that philosophy being the concept of *force*, as the cause of the motions of particles, and hence of gross phenomena. Newton was educating himself in science at a time when Descartes was already long dead, when Boyle was acquiring his high authority, and John Locke was still young. The 'mechanical philosophy' that was common to them all, and which more or less consistently supplied the whole seventeenth century with its conception of Nature, had two chief aspects. On the one hand it approached what philosophers call 'mechanism'—the idea that all the events and processes in Nature can in the final analysis be reduced to phenomena of mechanics, amenable to the simple laws of motion; but the 'mechanical philosophers' of the seventeenth century were chary of applying such a principle all along the line, while they were by no means confident of its ability to embrace living things, and were certain of the impropriety of excluding God from his creation. Accordingly, if they spoke of 'the grand machine of the universe', comparing it to a most complex clock or automaton, they also had no doubt of the rôle played by the Grand Clockmaker; in Boyle's words, the mechanical philosophy taught

that the phenomena of the world are physically produced by the mechanical properties of the parts of matter, and that they operate upon one another according to mechanical laws, but it asserted no less strongly an assurance that the universe was framed by God, that he had settled the laws of motion, and that all was 'upheld by his perpetual concourse and general providence'.[14] Modern science was not to be accused of introducing atheistic principles.

In the second place, the mechanical or corpuscular philosophy signified more particularly the interpretation of this metaphysics by means of a theory that all material bodies are composed of particles, the kinetics of these particles being the ultimate cause of phenomena. For example, on the kinetic or mechanical theory of heat, it was regarded not as a quality of bodies, nor as a material entity infusing them to various degrees, but as the manifestation to our senses of an intense vibratory motion in the particles of the so-called 'hot' body. Some philosophers like Robert Hooke thought that if this vibration were intense and quick enough it would also become manifest to our eyes as light—though it was of course also well known that light does not always originate in heat. But if the particulate structure of things was inseparable from mechanism, its details could be regarded in two principal ways: from the point of view of the strict atomists, matter was composed of tertiary, secondary, primary corpuscles (or molecules) composed of true, hard, unalterable atoms. All else was vacuum, emptiness, and the atoms could only act upon each other by contact. According to the Cartesians, on the other hand, the notion of vacuum is absurd; to say that omnipotent God could empty a vessel of all matter is only to say that he could collapse its walls into perfect contact. So that for them matter consisted not only of corpuscles and fundamental particles (not *atoms*, for Descartes also scorned the idea of an indestructible atom) but of an aether as well, filling all space, and indeed also the active source of most of the movement of matter in it, and so of phenomena.

Now it is not hard to see that the incompatibility of these ideas, as viewed by a man interested in plausible explanations of things rather than in metaphysical disputation, might seem more illusory than real. Such a man was Robert Boyle, who held that

notwithstanding these things, wherein the Atomists and the

Cartesians differed, they might be thought to agree in the main, and their hypotheses might be looked on as one philosophy.[15]

For the speculations of the working scientist it was unnecessary to ask the question: Can God split an atom? Secondly, it was perfectly possible to combine with the notion of atom (if one wished) the Cartesian idea of aether. One can even give the aether a special kind of atomic structure. Of course the philosopher must pay a price for doing this: he destroys the beautiful, stark simplicity of the original Greek atomic concept—the notion that if we only have a proper idea of *matter* (just that, nothing besides, no other machinery or forces or spirits or fields) we have enough to account for the whole universe. The aether is a complication to the atomic ideal. It is even an incomprehensible complication—for as a matter of principle if we transfer to an aether all the difficulties and complexities we find in material things so that it becomes their 'cause' how can we in turn explain all these marvellous properties in the aether except by making *it* complex, so that we must devise a second-order aether to be the 'cause' of the properties in the first, and so on *ad infinitum*? But the idea of aether has seemed at many stages of science to offer a short-cut to insight. Robert Boyle was unwilling to pronounce decidedly in favour of either vacuum or aether. Newton pronounced in favour of both—though the aether he held to be physically possible is a strange, contradictory beast, and it is not really clear that he was sure of it. Newton's successors were firmly pro-aether, and, as we have seen already, elaborated the idea into the special 'subtle fluids' of electricity, phlogiston, and heat. To this post-Newtonian tradition Dalton belonged.

Thus, for the proximate origin of the 'atmosphere of heat' surrounding the hard nucleus of the Daltonian atom we must look to Descartes, though it was not what Descartes himself conceived. Both before and after Descartes this was in turn associated with the notion of 'insensible effluvia', an emission of material particles so tiny as to be effectively weightless, or perhaps the radiation of something immaterial that is yet capable of affecting material bodies. The notion of 'effluvia' was long associated with the perplexing appearances of magnetism and electricity, where in the former case especially the ability of the 'cause' (whatever its nature) to pass through dense obstructions is very conspicuous. Here again Newton speaks:

> let anyone who denies the existence of rare media tell me how an electric body can by friction emit an exhalation so rare and subtle, yet so potent, as by its emission to cause no sensible diminution of the weight of the electric body, and to be expanded through a sphere whose diameter is above two feet, and yet to be able to agitate and carry up leaf copper or leaf gold at the distance of above a foot from the electric body? And how the effluvia of a magnet can be so rare and subtle as to pass through a plate of glass without any resistance or diminution of force, and yet so potent as to turn a magnetic needle beyond the glass?[16]

Like Newton, Boyle spoke of electrical and magnetic effluvia; the English father of studies in these fields of physics, William Gilbert, in *De Magnete* (1600) distinguished firmly between magnetic and electric attraction, asserting that the first of these arose from the *forma* of the magnetic body, the second from its *materia*. Obviously he related these Aristotelian categories to the fact that the magnet is always unchangingly active, while the 'electric body' (in his sense) 'has to be awakened by friction till the substance [amber, jet, etc.] attains a moderate heat, and gives off an effluvium', which is a very subtle matter, distinct from air, having the power of drawing light particles towards the electrified body. Gilbert thus gave strong authority to the notion of an effluvium.

Before this aetherial thread takes us too far from atomism proper, I must amplify a little further Boyle's connection with the mechanical philosophy, which I indicated a moment ago, for it is peculiarly relevant to Dalton's contribution to theoretical chemistry. In a very real sense Dalton accomplished what Boyle had long before visualized as his object in natural science —that is, the reconciliation of chemical experiments with the particulate theory of matter. Chemistry in Boyle's time smacked of the occult; it was his wish to render it as mechanistic as physics. For example, in chemical operations, colour-changes are conspicuous: Boyle wrote a whole book about them. Since, in Boyle's view, colour was an effect upon light of the corpuscular texture of bodies, it was easy to imagine how colour-changes would be brought about through the alteration of the texture of a fluid (for example) by chemical means. As Boyle put it, since various materials differ only in the variety of their 'textures resulting from the bigness, shape, motion and contrivance of their small parts, it will not be irrational to conceive that one and the same parcel of the universal matter may, by various alterations and contextures, be brought to deserve the name, sometimes of a sulphureous, and sometimes of a terrene or aqueous body'.[17] In no more recherché a book than the *Sceptical chymist* we can examine Boyle's association of particulate structure with chemical properties, and discover that (long before Newton) he contemplated a range of orders of compound corpuscles, each larger order being easier to break up by chemical means than the next smaller order.

I cannot tell whether John Dalton understood anything of Boyle's rôle as a mechanical philosopher in chemistry—a chemical atomist Boyle was not. It seems most unlikely. It seems to me that Boyle was read in the eighteenth century purely as a source of experimental information and comment; Boyle's theoretical objective as we see it today was ignored and neglected. It is the more likely that Dalton would have known little or nothing of Boyle's theoretical objective because he came late and hurriedly to chemistry, and because Dalton lived at a time when all chemistry was dominated by the recent transformation of the science in terms of elements. Boyle had never interpreted chemical reactions in terms of analysis and synthesis of the Aristotelian elements, or of the chemical principles; for if, as he said, 'the generality of physicians and other learned men [believed] that the elements themselves are transmuted into one another, and [that] those simple and primitive bodies which nature is presumed to have intended to be the stable and permanent ingredients of bodies may be artificially destroyed, and generated or produced' it was the more likely that lesser changes could 'proceed from the local motion of the minute or insensible parts of matter, and the changes of texture that may be consequent thereunto'.[18] Boyle seems to have believed that only the inaccessible particles of matter were stable and unchanging; chemical permanence existed, probably in nothing substantial. Dalton's discovery was precisely

A Rupert Hall

Precursors of Dalton

53

the opposite of this, that is, the identification of particulate permanence and identity with substantial permanence and identity.

We might perhaps without great loss finish this review of pre-Daltonian atomism here, since there is no reason to believe that Dalton drew on sources before Newton, Descartes and their contemporaries. There are indeed many other ramifications that we might unravel. For example, there is the separate story of the mere survival of atomistic and mechanical concepts in science, against the criticism of those who feared that philosophers with their aid would construct a science without revelation and a universe without a God. Christian apologetics completed what aetherial speculations had begun; they rendered the matter of the universe, with its properties, no longer self-sufficient. So Newton repulsed with horror the attribution to himself of the notion that gravitation is a property of inanimate matter; it must have some *other* cause. Epicureanism in the good sense (atomism) had to be very firmly salvaged whilst Epicureanism in the bad sense —you know what *that* is—had to be consigned to the flames with all the bad language which a well-brought up clergyman can bring himself to utter. Or again we might ask the still more important question: How is it that the thought of Europe leaned so strongly towards atomism in the late sixteenth and seventeenth centuries, after so long contumely and neglect? It is certain that interest was revived, in large part, by one accidental circumstance; the rediscovery in 1417 of Lucretius' *De rerum natura*, the greatest purely philosophical poem ever composed. It was printed and read with avidity. It seemed to sweep away Aristotelian preconceptions in favour of the continuum. It inspired Galileo and Bacon. It caused Gassendi to blow its ideas up into three huge folio volumes. And so on. Now we know what was always held against Lucretius and Epicurus; it was the words attributed to Leucippus, the predecessor of Democritus: 'everything happens out of reason and by necessity'. The atomistic universe was fatalist; it excluded God and free-will; it had no room for parables of creation and salvation. How such a philosophy was naturalized into Renaissance Europe is another story; as we have seen, it was not naturalized without modification. Fortunately, though Dalton was undoubtedly both a philosopher and a Christian, these problems had concern for him no longer. (If he had but known it, Newton himself had declared that the ancient Greek atomists were in truth no atheists.) I do not mean that there was no natural theology in Dalton's day: William Paley would teach us otherwise. But natural theology was demonstrating what all believed; that God was wise and good, and that religion and science must ever agree. The theory of matter had become a docile fragment of physics. The atom could offer no threat to religion.

Notes

1 Sir T. E. Thorpe, *Essays in historical chemistry* (London, 1902) 516.

2 I have summarized the evidence about the origin of Dalton's atomic theory presented in Henry E. Roscoe and Arthur Harden, *A new view of the origin of Dalton's atomic theory* (London, 1896), partially re-interpreted by Leonard K. Nash in 'The Origin of Dalton's Chemical Atomic Theory', *Isis*, xlvii (1956) 101–16. Dalton's two crucial papers 'On the Tendency of Elastic Fluids to Diffusion through each Other' and 'On the Absorption of Gases by Water and other Liquids' were printed in *Memoirs of the Literary and Philosophical Society of Manchester*, Ser. II, Vol. I (London, 1805) 259–87. My quotations are from p. 286; the table is on p. 287.

3 Roscoe and Harden, op. cit., 13.

4 Ibid., 123 ff. Isaac Newton, *Opticks* (Dover edn, 1952 etc.) 400, 389.

5 'Respecting the nature of the principle [heat] there is a diversity of sentiment: some supposing it a *substance*, others a *quality*, or property of a substance. *Boerhaave*, followed by most of the moderns, is of the former opinion; *Newton*, with some others, are of the latter; these conceive heat to consist in an internal vibratory motion of the particles of bodies' (John Dalton, *Meteorological observations and essays*, London 1793, 18). Newton himself wrote: 'Color est agitatio partium quaquaversum' (*De natura acidorum*, see I. Bernard Cohen (ed.), *Isaac Newton's papers and letters on natural philosophy* (Cambridge, Mass., 1958) 256).

6 Roscoe and Harden, op. cit., 13.

7 See Dalton's reference to the mixture of gases problem, ibid., 104–5, and to the particulate form of the atmosphere, ibid., 201.

8 Here I lean heavily on I. Bernard Cohen's monumental treatise, *Franklin and Newton*.

9 Besides A. Rupert Hall and Marie Boas Hall, *Unpublished scientific papers of Isaac Newton* (Cambridge, 1962) see our paper on 'Newton's "Mechanical Principles" ', *Journal of the History of Ideas*, XX, 1959, 167–78.

10 *Principia*, Book I, Section XIV.

11 *Principia*, Book II, Proposition XXIII.

12 Query 31.

13 One wonders whether Dalton was also acquainted with Newton's expression of chemical atomism in *De natura acidorum*; it seems likely, since it was published in a common enough book,

the second volume of John Harris, *Lexicon technicum* (London, 1710). If so, he would have noticed that Newton here spoke of the atoms having different size—but did not attach much importance to the notion.

14 Robert Boyle, *Some specimens of an attempt to make chymical experiments useful to illustrate the notions of the corpuscular philosophy* (*Works*, London, 1772, I, 356).

15 *Some specimens of an attempt*, etc. (Marie Boas Hall, *Robert Boyle on natural philosophy*, Bloomington, Indiana, 1965, 282).

16 Isaac Newton, *Opticks*, Query 22.

17 Thomas Birch, ed., *Works of Robert Boyle* (London, 1772) I, 494.

18 Robert Boyle, *Origins of Forms and Qualities* (Marie Boas Hall, op. cit., 227; compare also ibid., 217–19).

5

Henry Guerlac

The Background
to Dalton's
Atomic Theory

We have been several times reminded of John Dalton's debt to the atomistic speculations of Sir Isaac Newton. And various contributors have made it clear that a corpuscular conception of matter was a commonplace in the two centuries that preceded Dalton's successful application of the atomic theory to a quantitative chemistry. What I shall attempt to do is to contrast the different approaches to the corpuscular view that we encounter in Newton's immediate predecessors, in Newton himself, and in some of those, both in France and in Britain, who were influenced by him and who in differing ways thought of themselves as following the path he had marked out.

Newton is, of course, the culminating figure of what we call the Scientific Revolution of the seventeenth century, an historic series of events, immensely complex, but whose main outlines are surely familiar to everyone. If called upon to single out the enduring discoveries made before Newton set to work, any of us would include without hesitation in his list a series of famous achievements: Galileo's demonstration of the law of falling bodies, Kepler's determination of his three planetary laws, Harvey's painstaking proof of the circulation of the blood, the experiments of Torricelli and Pascal on the properties of air, Snel's discovery of the law of refraction, and similar well-known discoveries by other men.

Now these all have certain features in common: they were investigations into a strictly limited area of experience; and, where appropriate, they were carried out, and their results expressed, in the language of mathematics. But what I wish to stress, however, obvious it may seem, is that these enduring discoveries all concerned the *macroscopic* world, or at least the world of the immediately visible and palpable. They dealt with phenomena directly impinging on the senses. They were *not* carried out to support or illuminate some great system of natural knowledge; they were, in other words, largely independent (except on some deeper psychological level) of any theory about the invisible world, about—for example—the structure of matter, the intimate nature of light, the cause of motion, and so on. These men agreed on one thing: they distrusted the world-view of Aristotle, with its occult doctrines of form and matter, substance and accident, and all the rest. If, as many of them did, they shared the conviction of the mechanical philosophy—that the valid objects of study are material bodies in motion—they held their speculations in check, and confined themselves to what they could observe and measure.

There were, however, others of a different cast of mind for whom this strictly limited, piece-meal investigation of the objects of perception was not enough, and who were anxious to substitute for Aristotle's great ordered picture of nature a new and more satisfying, but equally ambitious, world-image. Influenced by the Renaissance revival of early Greek speculation, by the classical atomic doctrines in particular, they shared with many of the more circumspect scientists the conviction that the real world must ultimately consist in material particles whose motions, shapes, combinations and separations could best account for the differing properties, and the curious behaviour, of the objects perceptible to the senses. Upon this conviction the so-called mechanical philosophers—the French priest, Pierre Gassendi, England's controversial Thomas Hobbes, and the French philosopher René Descartes—erected great systems of natural knowledge, divergent in detail, of course, but having the common object of deducing observed phenomena from the hypothetical behaviour of invisible corpuscles. This, after the middle of the century, was what men commonly meant when they spoke of *physics* or *physiologia*; and it was seen as the task of the natural philosopher, the true physicist, to suggest plausible mechanisms, models— as we should say—of corpuscular behaviour, pictures of what Francis Bacon called 'the secret motions of things'. As Newton put it, in natural philosophy there was 'no end of fancying'.[1]

These great conjectural systems were the subject of keen debate in England when Newton entered Cambridge as a student, and their influence on his first speculations is beyond question. His earliest commonplace book of that period shows his reading of Descartes, of Hobbes, of Walter Charleton, a disciple of Gassendi, and of course of Robert Boyle.[2] Several pages of this notebook are devoted to musings about atoms, and to similar speculations about the nature of light. As early as 1665-6 Newton conceived of light rays as a stream of corpuscles or, as he calls them, of 'globules', and even drew a sketch of one. This view of the corpuscularity of light he never abandoned, any more than he did his firm belief that matter is ultimately composed of 'solid, massy, hard, impenetrable and moveable' particles; though whether the atoms had their abode in empty space, or in a tenuous aether, was a question on which his opinion seems to have varied at different times of his life.

Yet—and this is a point I now must emphasize— though Newton was manifestly influenced by this mechanistic view, it would scarcely be correct to call him a partisan of the mechanical philosophy. He well knew how much of it was sheer 'fancying', and would have agreed with John Locke who wrote that 'most (I had almost said all) of the hypotheses of natural philosophy' are really but doubtful conjectures.[3] Quite early in his career Newton seems to have set himself the task of proving to himself and his critics that natural philosophy, or what we should call physical science, could and should be made, as far as possible, probative and demonstrative. It was against mechanical philosophers of all stripes—as well as the latter-day Aristotelians— that Newton was protesting when, late in life, he wrote the famous words:

I feign no hypotheses; for whatever is not deduced from the phenomena is to be called an hypothesis; and hypotheses,

J D—F

whether metaphysical or physical, whether of occult qualities or mechanical, have no place in experimental philosophy.[4]

By physical and mechanical 'hypotheses' Newton meant precisely those gratuitous, imaginary 'principles'—the figured atoms of Gassendi, the whirling particles of Descartes—when they are taken as the unsubstantiated premises of scientific argument. Instead, under the title of 'Experimental Philosophy', he invoked Galileo's more cautious method. Even as a very young man he saw the necessity of proceeding, as Galileo had urged (though it is doubtful if Newton was well-acquainted with Galileo's books) 'by geometrical demonstrations founded upon sense experience and very exact observations',[5] even when this procedure led to principles, like that of universal gravitation, for which no indisputable cause could be found.

As early as his first scientific paper—the famous memoir of 1672 in which he showed that sunlight is composed of diversely coloured rays, each with its different refrangibility—Newton clearly stated his determination not to 'mingle conjectures with certainties'.[6] In this early paper, though he hinted at it, he did not defend his privately held opinion that light is a stream of corpuscles. For the business at hand he treated light rays, as he said, only in general terms, abstractly, as 'something or other propagated every way in straight lines from luminous bodies, without determining what that thing is'.[7] This point of view his older contemporaries, Robert Hooke and Christiaan Huygens, for example, found difficult to accept, if indeed they understood what he was about.

The same caution pervades Newton's great *Mathematical principles of natural philosophy*. Though the atomic doctrine surely lurks behind the theorems of this historic work, he does not discuss it and nothing that he demonstrates stands or falls as a result of one's believing or disbelieving in the philosophical doctrine of atoms and the void. Nor, to the confusion of his readers, did he try to account for the novel doctrine of universal attraction, insisting instead that it must be understood, mysterious though it seemed, simply as a fact of nature. The same discretion is evident later in the main body of his *Opticks*, where the experimental results do not in any way depend upon what we may believe the intimate nature of light to be.[8] To keep this distinction before us, I shall speak for convenience of Newton's 'Natural Philosophy' when I mean his conjectures about the nature of matter or of light and the cause of attraction, conjectures he kept clearly distinct from his 'demonstrative' or 'scientificall' work. On those speculative matters he was for a long time silent in print, and when later he spoke of them, he deliberately set them apart, in *scholia* added to the *Principia* (notably in the second edition of 1713), or in the famous 'Queries' added to the Latin *Optice* of 1706.

The surprising consistency with which Newton prevented his Natural Philosophy—his conjectures—from intruding on his more rigorous demonstrations, does not in the least imply a lack of concern about the deeper problems. Yet the first order of business was to do what must be done: to give direction and precision to the scientific enterprise, to show the power and scope of a method of inquiry—a blend of observation, experiment and mathematics—which Newton was at pains to describe and advocate. The element of self-discipline and self-restraint is well expressed by Newton in one of his unpublished manuscripts:

> But if without deriving the properties of things from Phaenomena you feign Hypotheses & think by them to explain all nature, you may make a plausible systeme of Philosophy for getting your self a name, but your systeme will be little better than a Romance. To explain all nature is too difficult a task for any one man or even for any one age. Tis much better to do a little with certainty & leave the rest for others that come after you then to explain all things by conjecture without making sure of any thing.[9]

At Newton's hands these canons of scientific procedure yielded remarkable results. But since they depended, in principle as well as in fact, upon sense experience, he could apply them only at the visible or the macroscopic level. Yet he was obsessed by the possibility that this method ought somehow to be applicable for exploring the submicroscopic world with the same rigour and reliability as in the study of the visible universe. Professor Hall has reminded us of that telling, if cryptic, passage in Newton's 'Preface' to the *Principia* where, after informing the reader that the central problem of science 'seems to consist in this—

from the phenomena of motions to investigate the forces of nature, and then from these forces to demonstrate the other phenomena', he adds the significant words: 'I wish we could derive the rest of the phenomena of Nature by the same kind of reasoning from mechanical principles.'[10] If this were to prove possible, then the hidden, invisible world which had so preoccupied the mechanical philosophers, and which held the deepest secrets of nature, might eventually become part of science as Newton conceived science should be. He brooded over this problem throughout his life, for many years confining his thoughts to letters and personal memoranda, or to papers he was reluctant to publish. And when, late in his career, he appended to his *Opticks* the famous Query 31, setting forth his conjectures about the atomic theory of matter (and at the same time reminding his readers of the strict method that must be followed in Experimental Philosophy) he was, in effect, bequeathing this problem to those who came after him as the great unfinished business of science.[11]

Let us now ask what Newton's disciples and followers made of these pronouncements, what interpretations they placed on his scientific work, on his speculations (so cautiously phrased for the most part in the interrogative voice), and on his doctrines of method. The interpretations of his eighteenth-century admirers are surprisingly divergent; they fall rather sharply into two patterns, one best illustrated by his British disciples, the other, at least until late in the century, by the majority of Frenchmen.

In Britain, quite understandably, Newton was the revered sage. His vision penetrated—no one doubted —into the inner reality of nature. One had only to follow him faithfully: in mathematics (by adhering to his fluxional calculus), in celestial mechanics, of course, in optics and in chemistry. Robert Smith, in his massive *System of optics*, published in 1738, made no distinction between Newton's conjectures and his more rigorous discoveries. He adopted and elaborated without hesitation Newton's suggestion that light was corpuscular, that its particles were acted upon by attractive forces in a way that could explain reflection, refraction and diffraction. It is not too much to say that this Master of Trinity was, if not the real author of the corpuscular theory of light, at least its most influential advocate.[12] As for chemistry, to a degree that can scarcely be exaggerated, Newton's Queries left their mark on that science in Britain for more than a century. From the early writings of Keill, Freind, Stephen Hales and Peter Shaw down to Dalton himself, English writers unhesitatingly invoked Newton's atomic explanation of chemical processes.[13]

By contrast, Newton's followers in France were many of them sceptical of his speculations in Natural Philosophy. On the other hand, they were captivated by his statements concerning method, citing repeatedly his rejection of hypotheses and his advocacy of the 'Method of Analysis'. They interpreted him as concerned only to observe, measure, and determine the laws according to which the objects of our experience behave. The physicists, especially, were embarrassed by Newton's talk about attractions, and tended to avoid discussions about atoms and the intimate structure of matter. This was the opinion that d'Alembert expressed in his *Treatise on dynamics* and elsewhere in his writings. Nature, he wrote:

is a vast machine whose inner springs are hidden from us: we see this machine only through a veil which hides the workings of its more delicate parts from our view . . . Doomed as we are to be ignorant of the essence and inner contexture of bodies, the only recourse remaining for our sagacity is to try at least to grasp the analogy of phenomena, and to reduce them all to a small number of primitive and fundamental facts. Thus Newton, without assigning the cause of universal gravitation, nevertheless demonstrated that the system of the world is uniquely grounded on the laws of this gravitation.[14]

Just as Newton had advocated in discussing gravity, d'Alembert insisted that we can learn something about the hidden causes in nature, only if the laws and relationships by which they operate can be discovered:

The knowledge or the discovery of these relationships [d'Alembert wrote in another place] is almost always the only goal we are allowed to reach, and consequently the only one we should have in view.[15]

Such a positivistic approach to Newtonian science, while not universal, was widespread among the more influential French thinkers. It was set forth by the Abbé de Condillac in his philosophical writings, and popularized for a still wider audience by Voltaire. For example, in discussing ever so briefly Newton's speculations about an all-pervading, elastic aether, Voltaire concluded that even an hypothesis that can explain nearly everything, as he admitted Newton's aether might do, ought not to be admitted. We should build nothing on conjectures, he wrote, not even on those of Newton himself.[16]

Neither school—neither the British nor the French —fully grasped, I think, the essentially disjunctive character of Newton's view of natural knowledge: his cautious separation of demonstrative science from suggestive conjecture. Nor did they quite understand Newton's attitude towards his own atomistic theories: that, for the moment at least, they could not be firmly incorporated into the structure of Experimental Philosophy, but that eventually this might be done, if the proper route could be discovered, the key experiments performed and rightly interpreted.

The procedure of the mechanical philosophers had been, we saw, to derive the qualities and behaviour of visible or macroscopic objects from the properties and behaviour assigned to hypothetical corpuscles. They sought to travel, as it were, from the inside of nature outward. But how, with any assurance or rigour, could this be done? This question sums up what some recent American philosophers have termed, somewhat barbarously, the 'problem of transdiction'.[17] Just as one *pre*-dicts when one makes inferences forward in time; just as geologists and astronomers (and I suppose historians) who argue from present evidence to the past can be said to *retro*dict; so *trans*diction is the term some philosophers have applied to the process of inference from the phenomenal world to that deeper level of reality that the senses cannot perceive. Could this be done by some credible process of inference? If not, the limits of truly scientific inquiry must be severely restricted. Both Descartes and Newton were sensitive to this problem. Descartes, for example, wrote in his *Principles of philosophy*:

Someone could ask how I have learned what are the shapes, sizes and motions of the tiny particles of each body, several of which I have determined just as if I had seen them, although it is certain that I could not observe them with the aid of the senses, since I have admitted that they are imperceptible.

And he explains that he has done so through an intellectual analysis of common experience:

> I have considered in general all the clear and distinct notions we may have in our minds concerning material things, and having found no others except those ideas we have of shapes, sizes and motions. . . . I judged that it must necessarily follow that all the knowledge that men can have of nature must be drawn from them alone.[18]

As to the hidden mechanism of nature, Descartes goes on to explain that having examined *in thought* the possible shapes, sizes and motions of these tiny bodies, and the 'perceptible effects that could be produced by the different ways in which they mingle together' he was pleased to encounter similar effects in those vastly larger bodies our senses can perceive:

> Then I believed that they must infallibly have been so, when it seemed to me impossible to find, in the whole extent of nature, any other cause capable of producing them.[19]

Infallibly? Well, not quite. Descartes is well aware that, as he says, 'God has an infinity of different means' by which He could make things in the world appear as they do. Perhaps it is enough if the causes that are postulated can reasonably produce the observed effects; yet Descartes is quite explicit that the mechanisms he has imagined convey what he calls a 'moral certainty', a certainty short of demonstration, to be sure, but with what we would call a high degree of probability.

Newton's other mentor, Robert Boyle—influenced as he was by both Descartes and Gassendi—little doubted that some version of the corpuscular hypothesis would best explain the divergent properties of particular substances. His wide range of experiments—on the elasticity of air, the colours of bodies, on chemistry—seem designed to show how plausibly the corpuscular model can account for the diverse 'forms and qualities' of things. By broadening the experimental evidence he hoped to increase—extensively, rather than intensively, if I may put it that way—the 'moral certainty' of such corpuscular explanations.

Such reasoning did not satisfy Isaac Newton. The 'moral certainty' of Descartes was delusive, as Newton clearly demonstrated in refuting the Cartesian vortices in the second Book of the *Principia*. Something better, too, was needed than the illustrative empiricism, the multitude of suggestive experiments and the cautious hints of Robert Boyle. And Newton believed he had hit upon it—'the best method of arguing which the Nature of Things admits of'—in his dual method of 'Analysis and Synthesis', or of 'Resolution and Composition', a method of ancient lineage, to which he gave a very special twist. He describes it compactly towards the end of Query 31, but presents it more freely, and less schematically, in a manuscript draft only recently discovered:

> The method of Resolution consists in trying experiments & considering all the Phaenomena of nature relating to the subject in hand & drawing conclusions from them, & examining the truth of these conclusions by new experiments & . . . so proceeding alternately from experiments to conclusions & from conclusions to experiments untill you come to the general properties of things. Then assuming these properties as Principles of Philosophy you may by them explain the causes of such Phaenomena as follow from them: which is the method of Composition.[20]

Analysis through observation and experiment then—not, as with Descartes, a mere *conceptual* analysis—is the path that must be followed if one is to build up a persuasive and valid science: an analysis, too, that whenever possible should be cast in quantitative, in mathematical, language. It is the Method of the *Principia* and the *Opticks*. But can this method reach down into the realm of the non-perceptible? Is there a kind of experiential or experimental evidence that can supply a key to the invisible world? Newton was confident that such evidence might be found; two areas of investigation particularly impressed him as offering alluring possibilities: the study of light and colour; and, more pertinent to our present discussion, chemistry.

In one of his earliest papers Newton described his observations on the colours produced when light passes through thin transparent bodies, the phenomenon of Newton's rings.[21] The brilliant feature of these experiments was his precise measurement of the varying thickness of thin films that yielded the different spectral colours and the different 'orders' of colours. Now Newton was very early convinced, as he wrote to

Robert Boyle, that 'the colours of all natural bodies whatever seem to depend on nothing but the various sizes and densities of their particles'.[22] Colours, then, might provide an indication of particle size. And since his measurements of the rings supplied him with a correlation of film thickness with colour, it was possible, if one could accept the 'analogy' between spectral colours and those produced by reflection or transmission through translucent media, to infer from the colours of natural bodies (and the 'order' to which their colours belonged) the dimensions, or rather the relative dimensions, of their particles. Newton was sufficiently persuaded by his argument to retain his faith in this early paper and include it in his *Opticks*, where, slightly modified, it comprises the Second Book.

But it was chemistry that offered a more likely way of penetrating—by inference from experiment—into the invisible realm. At least by the '70s Newton had begun to devote a considerable part of his energy to chemical experimentation and wide reading in the chemical and alchemical literature. These interests are clearly expressed in the famous letter he wrote to Robert Boyle in February of 1679, a letter often cited for Newton's speculations about the mechanical rôle of a subtle aether. Here Newton frankly indulges in some 'fancying' of his own. He invokes the aether as a hypothetical agent to explain such phenomena as surface tension, capillary rise, and the refraction and reflection of light: that is, to explain *physical* processes. But he invokes something very like his later notions of 'attraction' and 'repulsion' when he discusses *chemical* phenomena:

> When any metal is put into common water [he writes], the water cannot enter into its pores, to act on it and dissolve it. Not that water consists of too gross parts for this purpose, but because it is unsociable to metal. For there is a *certain secret principle* in nature, by which liquors are sociable to some things, and unsociable to others.[23]

By the time Newton composed the *Principia*, in 1686–7, his opinions in one important respect had profoundly altered. The aether has been virtually discarded and attractive *forces* have taken its place, not only for explaining the motions of large bodies, but also (though he is cautious about such speculations in print) to account for phenomena, both chemical and physical, explicable in molecular terms. The 'certain secret principle' in nature that accounts for sociableness and unsociableness has been transformed into forces of attraction and repulsion.

> I am induced by many reasons [his Preface to the *Principia* continues] to suspect that [the rest of the phaenomena of nature] may all depend upon certain forces by which the particles of bodies, by some causes hitherto unknown, are either mutually impelled towards one another, and cohere in regular figures, or are repelled and recede from one another. These forces being unknown, philosophers have hitherto attempted the search of nature in vain . . .[24]

This is all, for a time, that he said in print. But Rupert and Marie Hall brought to light a few years ago an extended draft of this same preface, as well as a suppressed 'Conclusio' to the *Principia*, in both of which Newton spells out his ideas in considerable detail.[25] In each of these precious documents we discover pretty much the same argument, and many of the same bits of supporting chemical evidence, that we find in the *De natura acidorum* of 1692 and in Query 31 of the *Opticks*. Clearly, by 1687 the main features of Newton's theory of matter had been sketched out; already he foresaw the area of investigation—chemistry and those phenomena we treat under physical chemistry—which eventually would lead with some assurance into the molecular and atomic realm. In the Queries of the *Opticks* he indicates at least the general direction scientists would have to follow if they were to come to grips with the 'problem of transdiction' and turn their plausible conjectures about the atomic structure of matter into a true science. But the special route that he appears to be advocating in Query 31 was less fortunate, though by a circuitous route it may be said, at the very least, to have contributed to the achievement of Dalton. But before we see what Newton's English followers made of his suggestions, I must return, for a brief moment, to the transdictive problem in general.

We should remind ourselves of what was involved when scientists of the nineteenth century presumed to speak about atoms and molecules, when they invented mathematically conceived molecular and atomic theories to which they imputed a degree of credibility. For this is what Newton was searching for. These theories, it seems to me, embody a definable procedure. Certain properties are assigned in thought to the hypothetical particles, properties which are in principle quantifiable. Then certain precise configurations or interactions are imagined which are in turn susceptible to mathematical description. But these properties, configurations and so on must possess a further characteristic. They must be such as to yield a statistical or aggregate behaviour that manifests itself in some observable and measurable *molar* properties: the behaviour of these aggregates must be predictable from the assumed characteristics of the particles that compose them. Perhaps you will agree that, at least in a general way, this is what was involved in such varied nineteenth-century achievements as the kinetic theory of gases, electrochemistry, chemical solution theory, and van't Hoff's work on stereoisomerism.

Professor Hall in his paper has already mentioned two recognizable examples of this sort of procedure in the *Principia*: Newton's derivation of Boyle's law (though Newton does not mention Boyle) on the assumption of a fluid composed of mutually repellent particles; and his derivation of a proposition that bore, as he contented himself with saying, 'a great resemblance' to the Snel-Descartes law of refraction. But Newton is oddly diffident about these results, taking refuge in his claim that his inquiry is mathematical not physical: in the first case he remarks: 'But whether elastic fluids do really consist of particles so repelling each other, is a physical question.'[26] The power of this sort of method seems to have eluded him or perhaps he distrusted it.

In retrospect, a more compelling example—and a striking foreshadowing of nineteenth-century procedures—was published by Daniel Bernoulli in 1738. Bernoulli imagines a fluid composed of 'very tiny corpuscles moving in every direction' and confined in a cylindrical vessel closed by a piston-like lid held down by a variable weight. If the force balancing this weight be thought of as caused by the impacts of the innumerable particles on the lid, then as the weight is decreased the volume must increase, and conversely. In effect, Bernoulli shows that the product of pressure and volume is constant (PV = c), as Newton had shown starting from different assumptions. Bernoulli, however, admitted only impacts. The elasticity of air can only result from what we call the translational kinetic energy of the particles. Accepting the mechanical theory of heat—as indeed did Newton—he was therefore led on to inquire into the effects of a change of temperature on the elasticity of air; he came to the remarkable conclusion that the increased pressure when a vessel of air is heated at constant volume must be proportional to the square of the velocity of the particles. This, in essence, was the theoretical derivation, on molecular assumptions, of the law of Charles and Gay-Lussac, which had been anticipated very early in the eighteenth century by the experiments of Amontons.

Bernoulli's achievement is a rare example of this sort of inquiry until late, very late, in the eighteenth century.[27] Not until the last years of the eighteenth century and the opening years of the nineteenth, did the molecular and atomic realm open some of its secrets to men like Coulomb, Laplace, Avogadro and—of course—John Dalton. Only then do we discern the opening of a Second Scientific Revolution, a Molecular Revolution that, at least dimly, Newton had foreseen.

The line of attack that Newton envisaged as a solution of the transdictive problem was, as I have suggested, derived from his chemical investigations. Though more esoteric motives may have encouraged him in his dogged perusal of the alchemical literature, it is at least clear that he was confident that chemistry could supply empirical evidence, not only for confirming the existence of atoms and of corpuscles of higher complexity formed from them, but also for providing some insight into the 'secret motions of things', and the forces producing them. Here, as well as when exploring the larger universe, the chief task of the scientist, as Newton described it, was 'to investigate the forces of nature, and then from these forces to demonstrate the other phenomena'. Chemistry—taken widely enough to embrace a number of physical phenomena—was to provide the key. One of his disciples, Peter Shaw, wrote shortly before Newton's death that when the great man discusses the laws, actions, and the powers of bodies, he always produces chymical experiments for his vouchers; and when, to solve other phenomena, he makes use of these powers, his refuge is to chemistry; whence he manifestly shows, that without the assistance of this art, even he could hardly have explained the peculiar nature and properties of particular bodies.[28]

Shaw, of course, has especially in mind the Queries of the *Opticks*, where, as Priestley put it later, Newton 'indulged bold and excentric thoughts', but he could equally as well have pointed to the little tract *De natura acidorum* printed by John Harris in his scientific dictionary, the *Lexicon technicum*, in 1710.[29] The main burden of both works is to present his corpuscular theory and—as in the preface of the *Principia* he announced he hoped to do—to offer evidence that there must exist short-range forces of attraction and repulsion, analogous to, yet different from, the gravitational force between bodies. In a rather vague, and largely qualitative, fashion Newton suggested in Query 31 how attractions and repulsions could explain such physical effects as cohesion, surface tension and capillarity, and a multitude of chemical phenomena; he speaks not only of solution and precipitation, but of a wide range of different chemical reactions.[30] The extent of Newton's chemical information, and its precision, is remarkable; most of the reactions he describes can be readily interpreted in modern terms. None of them, I suspect, was original with him, though he may have followed nearly all of them with his own eyes. Most are described in the writings of such seventeenth-century authorities, as Robert Boyle, Nicolas Lémery, Angelus Sala, John Mayow and Thomas Willis. It is how Newton interprets this information—in corpuscular and attractionist terms—that is significant. For example when 'salt of tartar' (potassium carbonate) deliquesces in moist air, this is because the particles of the salt *attract* particles of water from the air. This attraction for water, which occurs also in the case of 'oil of vitriol', but not in common salt or saltpetre, has a definite limit or saturation value, an observation of central significance.

Attraction too, seems capable of explaining in a qualitative way common displacement reactions: the release of spirit of salt (HCl) when common salt is treated with sulphuric acid; or the precipitation of in-soluble salts from solution when salt of tartar is added.

The most interesting passage—for it most strikingly illustrates the preferential attraction of certain substances for each other—describes the elementary experiment of showing that iron displaces copper from acid solution, copper displaces silver, and so on for a number of metals, in an order that corresponds to our electromotive series. 'Does not this argue', Newton asks, 'that the acid Particles of the *Aqua fortis* are attracted more strongly . . . by Iron than by Copper, and more strongly by Copper than by Silver, and more strongly by Iron, Copper, Tin, and Lead, than by Mercury?'[31] Clearly, Newton thought, the attractive forces, acting at minute distances between the particles, must vary in strength from one chemical individual to another. In this striking passage, together with others in Query 31, Newton set forth, in attractionist terms, what came to be called in the eighteenth century the doctrine of *elective affinities*. That eventually this famous Query exerted a profound effect, cannot be denied, but whether it was the immediate stimulus to, and the pre-ponderant influence upon, the century's pre-occupation with affinities is not so certain.

In 1718, not long after Newton's *Opticks* appeared, a leading chemist of the French Academy of Sciences, Etienne-François Geoffroy, presented a now classic memoir entitled *Sur les rapports des différentes substances en chimie*.[32] In it Geoffroy published the first table of chemical affinities. Each of a series of parallel columns, headed by the conventional symbol for a familiar substance, displays one above another the symbols of those reactants with which the substance was known to combine. These follow one another in such an order that each reactant displaces all others lower in the column from union with the substance at the head of the column.

Nowhere in his paper does Geoffroy speculate about the cause of these phenomena; he says nothing about atoms or attractions, and speaks only of 'rapports' or relationships; he seems to have the purely practical objective of summarizing in tidy and convenient fashion a body of chemical fact. Had he read Newton's *Opticks* and been stimulated by it? We cannot be sure, and indeed it is not necessary to assume that this is the case. Much, if not most, of the information in the table he could have drawn from the seventeenth-century chemical tradition, as indeed Newton himself had done in accumulating the chemical facts that he set forth in Query 31.

Chemists had long been aware of the property of specific reactivity; they well knew that some substances react together with ease and often with violence, others more quietly or with difficulty; still others were found to be almost or totally inert with respect to common reagents. And it was early observed that certain pairs of substances are particularly disposed to combine together and, once combined, to resist separation. Replacement reactions, too, were described by a number of different chemists. Glauber, for example, explained that when zinc oxide is heated with sal ammoniac, the zinc displaces the ammonia from combination with the acid setting it free.[33] Otto Tachenius (1666) knew not only that acids differed in strength, but also that a stronger acid could displace a weaker one from its salt.[34] Indeed both Glauber and Robert Boyle had described, well before Newton published his *Opticks*, the displacement series for the common metals which we cited above.[35]

Yet Newton's was the first text—one is tempted to call it the first short monograph—in which the well-known instances of chemical affinity were described in one place and in brief compass: the earliest general treatment of a subject to which earlier writers had referred only in passing and in widely separated places. Geoffroy could well have read the important passages of Query 31. He had close contacts with British science; in 1698, on a visit to England, he had been elected, along with other Europeans, a Fellow of the Royal Society, and he kept in close touch with the Society as a faithful correspondent of Sir Hans Sloane. He was sent a complimentary copy of Newton's *Opticks* (1704) which is now in the library of my university, and it is hard to believe that he did not also receive, or at least consult, the Latin *Optice* of 1706 in which the famous Query first appeared.[36] Of this, however, we cannot be certain. At all events, Geoffroy's paper makes no mention of Newton, and he says nothing of those attractions between particles in terms of which Newton sought to explain the selective reactivities of chemical substances. Geoffroy's unwillingness to indulge in speculations earned the approval of Fontenelle who wrote, in his account of the year's activity at the Academy:

> C'est ici que les sympathies & les attractions viendroient bien à propos, si elles étoient quelque chose. Mais enfin en laissant pour inconnu ce qui l'est, & en se tenant aux faits certains, toutes les expériences de la chimie prouvent qu'un même corps a plus de dispositions à s'unir à l'un qu'à l'autre... Ce sont ces dispositions, quelqu'en soit le principe, & leurs degrés que M. Geoffroy appelle *Rapports*, & une plus grande disposition est un plus grand rapport.[37]

Geoffroy's table elicited some criticism but more interest and approval; one writer, for example, remarked in 1723 that by his table alone Geoffroy 'a rendu plus de service à la Chymie qu'une infinité d'Auteurs par des volumes de raisonnemens physiques'.[38] There were, of course, doubters, and it was several years before attempts were made to devise improved tables: among the earliest of these revisions and elaborations were those of Grosse (1730), Gellert (1750), and Rudiger (1756).[39] In France, after about 1740, G.-F. Rouelle, Lavoisier's teacher—and the teacher of a whole generation of French chemists—gave special attention in his lectures to Geoffroy's table, and may have been chiefly responsible for the interest a number of his pupils—among them J.-F. Demachy and G.-F. Venel—later displayed in this aspect of chemistry.[40] None of these men, it should be emphasized, indulged in what Rouelle deplored as 'vains raisonnemens' about the cause of the relationships disclosed in the tables; all, indeed, had practical considerations chiefly in mind, and they avoided, not only the unpopular idea of 'attraction', but for the most part also the sort of explanations that had been current in the previous century.

At this point we should recall that early chemists had various expressions to describe, and hopefully to elucidate, the mystery of selective reactivity. A few used the analogy of magnetic attraction; but the majority appealed to an 'animate model' and readily used metaphorical images derived from human relationships. The tendency is well illustrated by Francis Bacon, who wrote:

It is certain that all bodies whatsoever, though they have no sense, yet have perception: for when one body is applied to another, there is a kind of election to embrace that which is agreeable, and to exclude or expel that which is ingrate: and whether the body be alterant or altered, evermore a perception precedeth operation; for else all bodies would be alike one to another.[41]

In the same spirit Joachim Jungius, a generation later, spoke of a 'power' or 'appetite' in natural bodies by which they are mutually drawn together and combine. Glauber, the greatest practical chemist of the seventeenth century, remarked in his *Furni novi philosophici* (1648) that 'sand and its like have a great community [Gemeinschaft] with the salt of tartar and they love each other very much, so that neither of them willingly parts from the other'.[42] Newton himself, we saw, spoke in 1679 of chemical substances as being 'sociable' or 'unsociable'.

The word 'affinity' (*adfinitas* or *affinitas*) was often used, and had animistic overtones we are inclined to forget. Originally, in classical Latin, it denoted a human relationship by marriage, as distinguished from consanguinity, and the Catholic Church later extended it to such spiritual and sacramental relationships as that between god-parents and god-children. The metaphor came easily to be broadened to imply any kinship or close resemblance.

In chemistry, 'affinity' made an early appearance in the writings of Albertus Magnus in the thirteenth century; we find the term used by the Latin Geber; by Bernard Palissy in the sixteenth century; and in Newton's day by Sylvius de le Boë (1659), Hooke (1665), Mayow (1674) and Barchusen (1698).[43] The 'animate model' is everywhere evident, and the word carried with it the notion of a fundamental similarity, a close kinship, even an identity of natures, between chemical substances that react together. John Mayow made the marriage metaphor quite explicit (as Barchusen did the image of friendship or kinship) when he wrote:

Salt has as great affinity and relationship with nitro-aërial spirit and also with sulphur; for these very active elements

75

are by turns married to salt as to a fitting bride, and are fixed in its embrace.[44]

The early makers of affinity tables doubtless were as unwilling to become entangled in such outmoded conceptions, as they were sceptical about invoking Newton's short-range attractive forces. Just as they avoided the word 'attraction', so at first they were even reluctant to speak of 'affinity'.

Two chemists of outstanding repute in the eighteenth century can be said to have restored respectability to the term: Hermann Boerhaave, author of the widely-read *Elementa chemiae* (1732); and with considerably greater enthusiasm, P.-J. Macquer, the acknowledged leader of chemical thought in France in the generation before Lavoisier.

Let us first consider Boerhaave, for he has been credited with having 'impressed on the term *affinity* the meaning which it has retained since his time', that of the force which brings and holds together chemically *dissimilar* substances.[45] Boerhaave may well have resuscitated the word, but he certainly did not envision affinity in this way. Like his Dutch contemporaries, he was more or less under the Newtonian spell, and in his early inaugural discourses praised Newton's experimental method in science and spoke favourably of the evidence Newton supplied for the rôle of attractive forces in chemistry. Nevertheless the older views had left their mark, for when he discusses in his famous textbook the action of solvents (*menstrua*), in the passages to which scholars are wont to refer, he invokes *both* Newtonian attractions *and* the older notion of affinity, distinguishing sharply between them. Attractions, which he calls in one place an 'appetite of union', account for the coming together of *unlike* substances, in particular for the dissolving action of solvents upon solutes. Affinity, however, he uses in the traditional sense: it is that mysterious power which acts between *identical* or *like* substances, which brings together particles of the same nature into homogeneous masses, as when particles of a solute come together during precipitation and crystallization.[46]

If, as most historians of chemistry would agree, the theory of affinity, or of elective attractions, was the boldest attempt made in the eighteenth century to give unity to the newly emerging science of chemistry, much credit must be accorded P.-J. Macquer. In his *Elémens de chymie théorique* (1749) he was the first to place a discussion of affinities at the very centre of an exposition of chemical theory, and his views were later set forth in the article 'Affinité' of his great *Dictionnaire de chimie* (1766). Macquer adopts a theory of the constitution of chemical substances which in some degree resembles Newton's. The underlying entities are of two kinds: constituent particles (*parties constituantes*) and molecules or integral particles (*parties intégrantes*); constituent particles combine and separate according to the laws of chemical affinity. Affinity, Macquer insists, is not a word devoid of sense 'but a truly physical, very real, very general' property of bodies.[47] It is responsible for all chemical combination, not merely the combination of 'like' substances, and is subject to invariable laws. In an elaborate discussion, he distinguishes affinities of several kinds ('les affinités simples, les composées, les réciproques, les doubles', etc.) and gives examples of each. Yet that diffidence towards unsupported conjecture, that positivistic tendency among French scientists, is evident in Macquer: he declines to speculate about the cause of these affinities. In his early work he mentions attraction only once, and in a deprecatory way.[48] In the *Dictionnaire* he wrote:

On ne cherche point ici la cause de ce grand effet, qui est si général qu'il peut être regardé lui-même comme cause de toutes les combinaisons, & servir à en rendre raison. Il est peut être une propriété aussi essentielle de la matière que son étendue & son impénétrabilité, & dont on ne peut dire autre chose, sinon, qu'elle est ainsi.[49]

And the reader, he goes on, may satisfy his curiosity by consulting the works of Newton, Freind, Keill and the Abbé Marcuzzi 'qui ont essayé de porter la lumière du calcul sur ces objets obscurs'. One senses perhaps a cautious change in Macquer's views between 1749 and 1766, and indeed this may point to a growing inclination in France to give a greater credence to Newton's chemical speculations, or at least to a hope that a physical explanation for the phenomenon of chemical affinity could be discovered.

Maupertuis noted this change of attitude among the chemists. In his *Dissertation physique à l'occasion du*

Negre Blanc (1744), the short preliminary version of his *Venus physique*, he devotes a paragraph to Geoffroy and his 'rapports'. A few years later he added a new paragraph to the *Venus physique*, identifying the 'rapports' with attractions, and remarking that, though the astronomers were the first to employ attractions, 'La Chymie en a depuis reconnu la nécessité; & les chymistes les plus fameux aujourd'hui, admettent l'Attraction, & l'étendent plus loin que n'ont fait les astronomes' (*Œuvres de Mr de Maupertuis*, Dresden, 1752, 247).

It was to this end, and perhaps stimulated by the works of Macquer, that the Academy of Rouen proposed as a prize essay subject for 1758 to: 'Déterminer les Affinités qui se trouvent entre les principaux Mixtes, ainsi que l'a commencé Mr Geoffroy; et trouver un Système Physico-méchanique de ces Affinités.' The prize was divided between George Louis Le Sage, the Genevan physicist and mathematician who died the following year, and Jean Philippe de Limbourg, a physician from the neighbourhood of Liège. Le Sage, who produced an elaborate mechanistic theory to account for attractions, was deemed to have treated in superior fashion the second part of the proposed question, whereas Limbourg, a pupil of Rouelle, devoted special attention to the chemical evidence. The second chapter of Limbourg's *Dissertation*, entitled 'De la nature & des causes des affinités', is especially relevant to our discussion. Affinity cannot be explained, he insists, by an 'identité de principes' in the substances that combine, nor by the action of some mechanical instrumentality. The principal cause is the force of attraction, and similitude enters in only insofar as a 'similitude de parties'—some correspondence, we are to suppose, in corpuscular size or shape, or in disposition of parts—permits bodies to approach near enough together for the short-range forces of attraction to be exerted. These forces are identical with the attraction that physicists speak of, and differ only in degree. In any case, the cause of these chemical attractions or affinities is as obscure as that of the physicists' gravitational attraction; to attempt to explain either kind is to indulge in purely imaginary suppositions.[50]

The influence of Limbourg's *Dissertation* is hard to assess; there was little in it to induce chemists to dis-

card the conveniently vague term 'affinity' and speak
instead of Newtonian 'attractions'. Not long after its
publication, two of Rouelle's other pupils made this
point clear. Demachy commented in 1765:

Tirons néanmoins avec les Chymistes tout le parti qu'ils
ont raisonnablement tiré des affinités & de leur application
aux travaux chymiques, & ne regardons ce mot affinité que
comme une acception, un terme qui désigne un effet, mais
qui rarement explique la cause.[51]

The same attitude is expressed in the same year by
Venel in his article 'Rapport ou Affinité' in Diderot's
Encyclopédie. Chemists understand by these *words*
(Venel italicizes the word 'mots') only the aptitude of
certain substances to unite chemically with certain other
substances, whatever may be the cause. 'Les Chymistes
sagement circonspects', he writes, 'se gardent bien de
théoriser sur le formel, le mécanisme, les causes de
l'affinité chymique.'[52]

In the spirit of their master, Rouelle, both Demachy
and Venel are defending the autonomy of chemistry;
chemistry is not physics, as Venel, in particular, had
strongly and picturesquely argued.[53] The times however were changing; in physics, of course, Newton had
triumphed in France; but even chemistry was not quite
what it had been: men with a different background and
training, whose formation was not derived from medicine and pharmacy, were becoming interested in it:
men who knew, or thought they knew, something about
physics.[54] Buffon was one of these, and so too was the
Dijon lawyer, Guyton de Morveau, whom Buffon came
to know in 1762, and with whom he corresponded and,
for a brief period, collaborated in experiments destined
for the *Histoire des minéraux*. In the same year 1765 in
which Demachy and Venel published the opinions we
have just cited, Buffon defended the opposing view:

Les lois d'affinité par lesquelles les parties constituantes de
ces différentes substances se séparent des autres pour se
réunir entre elles, et former des matières homogènes, sont
les mêmes que la loi générale par laquelle tous les corps
célestes agissent les uns sur les autres; elles s'exercent
également et dans les mêmes rapports des masses et des
distances; un globule d'eau, de sable ou de métal, agit sur
un autre globule comme le globe de la terre agit sur celui de
la lune; et si jusqu'à ce jour l'on a regardé ces lois d'affinité
comme différentes de la pesanteur, c'est faute de les avoir bien

conçues, bien saisies, c'est faute d'avoir embrassé cet objet dans toute son étendue.[55]

To Guyton, Buffon is the 'Newton of France'; he has seen farther than Newton into what lies behind chemical affinity; he has restored unity in nature; and his insight into the universality of the law of attraction 'will henceforth be the compass for chemical theory'.[56] In 1772 Guyton published his remarkable *Digressions académiques,* in which he applied Buffon's attractionist theory to problems of solution, crystallization and other chemical matters.[57] For French chemistry, a turning point had been reached; and the publication three years later of Torbern Bergman's *Disquisitio de attractionibus electivis* confirmed it. Guyton became the correspondent and translator of Bergman, and soon emerged as the acknowledged expert on affinity theory in France.[58]

Yet before Bergman, and before the French chemists, the British had taken the important step of interpreting the affinity tables of the Continental writers in attractionist, and Newtonian, terms. They were the earliest to do so. The first man in England to call attention to Geoffroy's table was the largely forgotten physician and chemist, William Lewis. He reproduced the table in a pharmaceutical work, his *New dispensatory* of 1753, but confined himself to calling attention to its practical importance for 'officinal processes', that is, for the preparations of the pharmacist.[59]

The chief innovators were men of the Scottish school—the chemists of Glasgow and Edinburgh—who deserve to be remembered for this as for so much else. The first published reference to 'elective attractions', appeared in Joseph Black's *Experiments upon magnesia alba* (1756). Black, in interpreting his results, makes frequent use of the concept of differing forces of attraction between substances, and at one point remarks that 'a few alterations may be made in the column of acids in Mr Geoffroy's table of elective attractions'.[60] Black's use of the phrase 'elective attractions', a phrase that Bergman later made popular, is at least suggestive. Perhaps it was from Scotland that Bergman received his inspiration.

The doctrine of elective attractions, and the phrase, were almost certainly derived by Black from his teacher at Glasgow, Dr William Cullen. Cullen launched his course of chemistry at Glasgow in 1747, and according to his biographer began at once to discuss chemical affinities with his students.[61] This is hardly surprising, for he was aware of Geoffroy's table as presented by Lewis, and recommended Boerhaave to his students 'or Macquer to those that understand French'.[62] Indeed it is not too much to say that Cullen's doctrine is Newtonian atomism and attractionism combined with Macquer's elaborate picture of the several kinds of affinity. Of attraction, Cullen remarked:

> The combination of bodies depends on that inclination or tendency which they have to approach one another and in certain circumstances to remain coherent. To this general fact the English philosophers have given the name of *Attraction*, a word which has given rise to endless cavils among foreigners, because it seems to imply a power in bodies by which they can run together. If this were really what were meant by it, if it were intended to express an original primary principle, such cavils would not be groundless, as such a supposition would stop any farther researches into the vast chain of causes and effects. . . . But the great NEWTON who first brought this term into general use, has often put us on our guard against this by telling us that it was merely intended to express a general fact, and it is in this sense that we use it. The foreigners who have not embraced this term have been under the necessity of using others in the same acceptation.[63]

Cullen, then, would seem to have been the earliest to develop a full-blown chemical theory that combined Newton's attractionist atomism with those chemical facts of affinity assembled and sifted by chemists on the Continent. Cullen's doctrine was picked up by his pupil, Joseph Black, who employed it, not only in his famous doctoral dissertation, but in his teaching. Both men taught that chemical combination takes place between atoms, forming the larger aggregates we call (as indeed, on occasion, did Macquer) 'molecules'. And both men used diagrams to illustrate what they believed to take place in reactions of double decomposition.[64] These diagrams may have been, first and foremost, a pedagogical device, a 'visual aid'. But they disclose crude attempts to quantify the doctrine of 'elective attractions', and to determine—as Newton had long ago hoped would prove possible—the relative strength of these forces. As an example, Cullen used the following diagram to show what happens when silver nitrate reacts with mercuric chloride, using letters to indicate the relative strength of attractions:

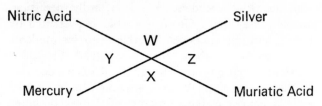

From the table of affinities $y > x$ and $z > w$, therefore $y + z > x + w$. Thus when silver nitrate and mercuric chloride (corrosive sublimate) are mixed together, the partners will be exchanged and silver chloride and mercuric nitrate will result. Joseph Black, in his turn, actually assigned numbers, instead of letters, to these relative affinities. They are arbitrary, if you will, but were intended to reflect the information derived from the tables of affinity.

This sort of thing was soon carried to great lengths, for example by William Higgins in his *Comparative view of the phlogistic and antiphlogistic hypotheses* (1789). A thoroughgoing atomist, Higgins later claimed to have anticipated John Dalton; but except for having perhaps recognized the important fact of multiple proportions, though not its full significance, his pretensions are surely unjustified. Yet he is interesting for his exhaustive efforts to assign numbers (after the manner of Cullen and Black) to indicate the relative strength of interparticulate attractions. 'Chemical philosophy', he wrote in words that Newton would doubtless have approved, 'will never reach its meridian splendour except by means of such principles'.[65]

Newtonian atomism—with its attendant doctrine of attractions—was, it should be apparent, a wide-spread chemical doctrine when John Dalton entered upon his scientific career. In the last decades of the eighteenth century it flourished not only in Britain, but—through the influence of Buffon, Guyton de Morveau and especially Torbern Bergman—on the Continent, where its popularity is attested by the title that Goethe gave to a famous novel: *Elective affinities*.

But this specific path to a solution of the transdictive problem—this key to finding the underlying forces of corpuscular nature—was far from leading chemistry to its 'meridian splendour'. Indeed, for reasons which were becoming increasingly evident, it was destined to prove illusory. Yet it may have contributed, though indirectly and almost accidentally, to Dalton's very special answer of the problem of transdiction. At least, as an intruder into Daltonian scholarship, I argued that this possibility, once widely held, deserves re-examination.[66]

At this point an important question merits brief consideration. It may be protested that the new habit of speaking of 'attractions' instead of 'rapports' or 'affinities' was merely a matter of words, and that it can hardly have had any real significance for the work of chemists of the late eighteenth century. This, I believe, was not the case: men were led, as a result, to think of interparticulate *forces*, and therefore of entities that, in principle, could be measured. We noted this tendency in the case of Cullen, Black and Higgins. It was characteristic, too, of Bergman, about whom Guyton wrote in 1786: 'il a prévu tout l'avantage que la Chymie pouvoit retirer de l'expression des affinités en nombre & de la détermination des figures des molécules qui s'unissent'.[67] And Bergman's example undoubtedly stimulated Wenzel and Kirwan. Wenzel sought to obtain numerical values for affinity from the speed of reactions; Kirwan, for his part, in a careful quantitative study of the solution of various metals in mineral acids, wrote:

> The advantages resulting from these inquiries are very considerable, not only in promoting chymical science, which, being a physical analysis of bodies, essentially requires an exact determination, as well of the quantity and proportion, as of the quality of the constituent parts of bodies.

And farther on:

> But the end which of late I had principally in view, was to ascertain and measure the degrees of affinity or attraction that subsist betwixt mineral acids, and the various bases with which they may be combined, a subject of the greatest importance, as it is upon this foundation that Chymistry, considered as a science, must finally rest.[68]

Even more elaborately and somewhat later a similar investigation was undertaken by the German chemist, J. B. Richter. In search of some sort of mathematical law, he embarked on a long series of experiments on the common acids and bases to discover whether the weights with which they combined to form neutral salts could be some measure of their 'affinities' or 'attractions'. He ascertained the weight of each base (lime, potash, magnesia, etc.) necessary to neutralize a fixed amount of each of the common acids, and conversely the amount of each acid that would neutralize a fixed quantity of a chosen base. His figures were scattered through long, prolix works, filled with extravagant computations. The results only became usable, and more widely known, when another chemist, E. G. Fischer, reduced them to a simple table. This table, which was included by Berthollet in his *Essai de statique chimique* of 1803, revealed the combining weights, or rather the combining weight ratios, of the acids and bases.[69] Now if you were a chemist in the British tradition, for whom the existence of Newtonian atoms admitted of no possible doubt, and who unquestioningly believed that the process of chemical combination is a joining of atom with atom, it might occur to you that these gross combining weights must reflect, in the case of pure substances, the relative weights of the constituent atoms themselves.

This was the interpretation that John Dalton placed on Richter's work when he learned of it, though precisely when is hard to determine.[70] It is now well established that Dalton's great theory was originally inspired by his interest in meteorology and the gases of the atmosphere. In studying the physical behaviour of mixed gases, he adopted Newton's model that air is an elastic fluid constituted of small particles or atoms of matter, which repel each other by a force increasing as their distance diminishes. Yet Dalton's experiments showed that in a mixture of two gases each constituent behaves as if the other were not present: the particles of one species neither attract nor repel the particles of the other kind, and he sought to confirm this by experiments on gaseous diffusion and solubility. Obviously the atoms of different gases must be different. But what property set them apart? It occurred to him that the distinguishing property of the differing atomic species might be, not the shape or volume of the particle, but *its weight*. But how could one be sure? How could one actually determine the relative weights of single *atoms*?

The answer seemed to lie in chemical evidence. So, I have suggested, he combed the chemical literature, in the course of which he encountered Richter's table of equivalents. Here was a method that, if applied to reactions between elementary substances—between gases, or between gases and substances like carbon or the metals—could yield the weights he sought. It was in the course of this reading, or in conducting his experiments, that he hit upon the great confirmation of his speculations: the *Law of Multiple Proportions*, which he announced at the same time as his atomic theory. This 'law' states that if two elements combine to form two or more compounds, the fixed proportions in which two elements combine together are simple integral ratios. Such a 'law' makes sense only if the elements combine as separate discrete units, each unit possessing a characteristic weight. As Berzelius, the great Swedish chemist, later wrote in a letter to Dalton: 'The theory of multiple proportions is a mystery without the atomic theory.'

This attribution of a definite weight to the atoms of each individual kind of chemical element is, we all know, the cardinal feature of Dalton's work. Though Dalton would not have thought of it in this way, it is obvious that it satisfied those transdictive criteria of which I spoke at the beginning of this paper: (1) A quantifiable property—the relative weight of the atoms —is assigned to the ultimate particles of the elements or simple substances; (2) when substances combine, atom with atom, the weight of the resulting molecule will be obtained by simple addition, if the molecule is formed by the elective attraction of atom to atom; (3) and lastly—if only pure substances are involved—the relative weights of molar or aggregate quantities must be as the weights of the atoms of the substances being compared. Dalton's was surely the most important step ever taken in the quantification of chemical theory. And it is the first successful example of the kind of transdictive procedure which Newton was hoping for. There are, of course, other ways of proceeding. But with Dalton's work the atom, long-invoked and much talked about, had at last a claim to enter the inner shrine of science.

Notes

1 Letter to Robert Boyle, 28 February 1678/9, *The Works of the Honourable Robert Boyle* (London, 1744) i, 70.

2 The University Library, Cambridge, MS. Add. 3996. See Richard Westfall's careful study of this notebook in *The British Journal for the History of Science*, i (1962) 171–82.

3 *An Essay concerning human understanding*, Book IV, Ch. 12, Art. 13.

4 *Mathematical principles of natural philosophy* (ed. Florian Cajori, Berkeley, California, 1934), 547. Hereinafter cited as 'Motte-Cajori', the English translation being that of Andrew Motte (1729). In accordance with current pedantry I have altered Motte's 'frame' to 'feign', which is probably a better rendering of *fingere*.

5 'Letter to the Grand Duchess of Tuscany', in Stillman Drake, *Discoveries and opinions of Galileo* (Garden City, New York, 1957) 179.

6 I. Bernard Cohen, *Isaac Newton's papers & letters on natural philosophy* (Cambridge, Massachusetts, 1958) 57. Reply to Hooke.

7 Cohen, op. cit., 119.

8 Newton's famous doctrine of 'Fits of easy Reflexion and easy Transmission' (*Opticks*, Book II, Part III, Propositions xii–xx) may seem to refute this statement, but it is not an hypothesis in Newton's sense of the term; he intends it rather as a non-committal description of the effects he observed in studying refraction phenomena of thin transparent media.

9 The University Library, Cambridge, MS. Add. 3970, fol. 478 v. This was apparently an early version of the section on method near the end of Query 23/31 of the *Opticks*.

10 Motte-Cajori, xviii.

11 In the Latin *Optice* of 1706 this appears as Q. 23. Modern scholars have only recently realized how drastically the Queries of the Latin edition of the *Opticks* differ from the new and altered ones of the second English edition of 1717/18. See Alexandre Koyré, 'Les Queries de l'Optique', *Archives Internationales d'Histoire des Sciences*, xiii (1960) 15–29. But Koyré overlooked the fact that Samuel Horsley, in his *Isaaci Newtoni Opera quae exstant omnia* (1779–85), had indicated all the important changes.

12 Smith was nevertheless selective: he ignored completely those speculations about the aether Newton added to the later Queries of the *Opticks*. See Henry John Steffens, 'The Development of Newtonian Optics in England, 1738–1831', a Thesis presented to the Faculty of the Graduate School of Cornell University for the Degree of Master of Arts (Ithaca, N.Y., 1965).

13 Shaw's most influential contributions to chemical Newtonianism were his notes to Boerhaave in *A new method of chemistry* (2nd edn, 2 vols, London, 1741).

14 *Mélanges de littérature, d'histoire et de philosophie* (4th edn, Amsterdam, 1767) iv, 258–9.

15 *Discours préliminaire de l'encyclopédie* (ed. Louis Ducros, Paris, 1893) 40. For a fuller discussion, see my paper, 'Where the Statue Stood: Divergent Loyalties to Newton in the Eighteenth Century', in Earl R. Wasserman, ed., *Aspects of the eighteenth century* (Baltimore, 1965) 317–34.

16 *Elémens de la philosophie de Neuton* (Amsterdam, 1738) 176.

17 Maurice Mandelbaum, *Philosophy, science and sense perception* (Baltimore, 1964) 61–2.

18 *Les Principes de la philosophie*, Quatriesme Partie, Art. 203.

19 Ibid.

20 The University Library, Cambridge, MS. Add. 3970, fol. 478 v.

21 What has been called Newton's 'Second Paper on Light and Colours', the results of which long remained unpublished, was sent to the Royal Society as a letter to Henry Oldenburg, dated 7 December 1675. See Cohen, op. cit., 177–200, and *The correspondence of Isaac Newton* (ed. R. W. Turnbull, Cambridge, 1956) i, 362–86.

22 *Works of the Honourable Robert Boyle*, i, 71.

23 Ibid. My italics. For Newton's chemical researches see Douglas McKie, 'Some Notes on Newton's Chemical Philosophy', *Philosophical Magazine*, Ser. 7, xxxiii (1942), 847–70; also Marie Boas and A. Rupert Hall, 'Newton's Chemical Experiments', *Archives Internationales d'Histoire des Sciences*, xi (1958) 113–52.

24 Motte-Cajori, xviii.

25 A. Rupert Hall and Marie Boas Hall, *Unpublished scientific papers of Isaac Newton* (Cambridge, 1962) 302–8 and 320–47.

26 Motte-Cajori, 302. Cf. Halley's comment in his review of the *Principia*: 'Next the density and compression of fluids is considered . . . and here 'tis proposed . . . whether the surprizing *Phenomena* of the Elasticity of the Air and some other Fluids may not arise from their being composed of Particles which flie each other; which being rather a Physical than Mathematical Inquiry, our Author forbears to Discuss.' Cohen, op. cit., 409.

27 Historians of science have been puzzled to account for the long oblivion which fell upon Bernoulli's work, but I think it can be readily explained. Bernoulli was pretty much of a Cartesian, and his work appeared at precisely the moment when French physicists were becoming adherents of the attractionist physics of Newton; and attractions had no place in Bernoulli's scheme of things. But more important, perhaps, is a fact to which I have already alluded: that the scientists in France, the physicists who were mathematically equipped to cope with such matters, had a persistent doubt that anything meaningful or demonstrable could be asserted about the invisible world of atoms and molecules.

28 *The philosophical works of the Honourable Robert Boyle . . . by Peter Shaw, M.D.* (3 vols, London, 1725) i, 260. Compare Boerhaave's similar comments in his *Sermo academicus de chemia* (Leiden, 1718) 39–40.

29 John Harris, *Lexicon technicum: or, an universal English dictionary of arts and sciences* (Vol. II, London, 1710). Newton's paper is printed in the Introduction, and is reproduced in facsimile in Cohen, op. cit., 256–8.

30 *Opticks: or a treatise of the reflections, refractions, inflections and colours of light by Sir Isaac Newton* (reprinted from the 4th edn, London, 1931) 375–406.

31 Ibid., 381.

32 *Mém. Acad. Sci.* (Année 1718; Paris 1719) 202–12. Geoffroy's paper is mentioned in every history of chemistry covering the period. For recent treatments see J. R. Partington, *A History of chemistry* (Vol. III, London, 1962) 49–55; also Maurice Crosland, 'The Development of chemistry in the eighteenth century', *Studies on Voltaire and the eighteenth century* (Geneva, 1963) 382–390, a most useful summary.

33 Partington, op. cit., ii, 355.

34 Ibid., 293.

35 Glauber, in his *Furni novi philosophici* (Amsterdam, 1648), described the relative facility with which the several metals amalgamate with mercury. Boyle in his *Mechanical qualities* (1675) explained the order in which metals replace one another from acid solutions of their salts. *Works of the Honourable Robert Boyle* (London, 1744) iii, 640. Before either man, Sylvius de le Boë explained the replacement of one metal in acid solution by another as the result of the varying 'affinities' of the different metals for the acid. See Partington, op. cit., ii, 288.

36 This volume is described in my note, 'Newton in France— Two Minor Episodes', *Isis*, 53 (1962) 219–21. Geoffroy did not receive the book until late in 1705 or early 1706, for he wrote to Sloane from Paris on 20 January 1706: 'J'ay reçu tout ce que vous m'avés envoyé depuis le commencement de la guerre, sçavoir les volumes des transactions philosophiques des annés 1702 et 1703 avec L'excellent traitté d'Optique de Mr Newton que le pere de Fontenays ma remis entre les mains de votre part' (British Museum, Sloane MSS. 4040, fol. 114).

37 *Hist. Acad. Sci.* (Année 1718; Paris, 1719) 36. In his *éloge* of Geoffroy, Fontenelle wrote later in 1731: 'Il donna en 1718 un système singulier et une table des affinités ou rapports des différentes substances en chimie. Ces affinités firent de la peine à quelques-uns, qui craignirent que ce ne fussent des attractions déguisées, d'autant plus dangereuses que d'habiles gens ont déjà su leur donner des formes séduisantes: mais enfin, on reconnut qu'on pouvait passer par-dessus ce scrupule et admettre la table de Geoffroy, qui, bien entendue et amenée à toute la précision nécessaire, pouvait devenir une loi fondamentale des operations de chimie et guider avec succès ceux qui travaillent.' *Œuvres de Fontenelle* (nouv. edn, Paris, 1792) vii, 400; *Hist. Acad. Sci.* (Année 1731; Paris, 1733) 99–100.

38 *Nouveau cours de chymie suivant les principes de Newton & de Sthall* (Paris, 1723) lxvii. Sénac, author of this anonymous book, was familiar with Newton's *Opticks*, and discusses the work of Keill and Freind; far from avoiding 'raisonnemens physiques' this is what his book is about; instead of 'attractions' in the Newtonian fashion, he speaks of the 'magnétisme des corps'. His speculations were virtually without influence; they are ignored by Baron who cites Sénac frequently in his edition of Lémery's *Cours de Chimie* (Paris, 1756).

39 The earliest discussion of these affinity tables is Demachy's *Recueil de dissertations physico-chymiques* (Amsterdam, 1774); a later, and more valuable, source is Guyton de Morveau's article 'Affinité' in the Dictionary of Chemistry of the *Encyclopédie méthodique* (Paris, 1786) tome I, 535–613. As Guyton points out, Demachy was responsible for resurrecting the table of Grosse, a chemist about whom almost nothing is known except what he tells us, and assigning it the date 1730. In 1737 Voltaire sought chemical information from Grosse whom he describes as an associate of Boulduc. See *Voltaire's Correspondence*, ed. Besterman (Vol. VI, Geneva, 1954) Nos. 1207 and 1289.

40 For Rouelle see Rhoda Rappaport, 'G.-F. Rouelle: An eighteenth-century chemist and teacher', *Chymia* (Vol. 6, Philadelphia, 1960) 68–101. Pierre Duhem (*Le Mixte*. Paris, 1902, 43) found the school of Rouelle opposed to theories in chemistry, and stresses their 'empirisme chimique'.

41 *The Works of Francis Bacon* (ed. Spedding, Ellis and Heath, Cambridge, 1863) v, 63.

42 For Jungius, see Partington, op. cit., 420. The citation from Glauber is given, without page reference, by John Maxson Still-

man, *The Story of early chemistry* (New York and London, 1924)
499.

43 For the early history of affinity theory, see Hermann Kopp, *Geschichte der chemie* (Zweiter Theil, Braunschweig, 1844) 285–290. The work of Albertus Magnus, *De rebus metallicis et mineralibus libri V*, is analysed by Ferdinand Hoefer, *Histoire de la chimie* (Paris, 1866) i, 384–5; Albert wrote that sulphur darkens silver and generally burns metals by its affinity to these bodies (*propter affinitatem naturae metalla adurit*). The relevant work of Geber is the *Summa perfectionis*, which may be consulted in the translation of Richard Russell (London, 1678). For Palissy, see Partington, op. cit., ii, 75; for Barchusen, see Kopp, op. cit., 287–8, and Raoul Jagnaux, *Histoire de la chimie* (Paris, 1891) i, 300–1. For the later history of affinity consult Jagnaux, op. cit., 301–60, and M. M. Pattison Muir, *A history of chemical theories and laws* (New York and London, 1907) 379–430. Short accounts are given by Maurice Daumas in: *Histoire générale des sciences*, ed. René Taton (tome II, *La Science moderne*, Paris, 1958) 559–69; by Daumas in *Histoire de la science* (Encyclopédie de la Pléiade, Paris, 1957) 934–44 and by Maurice Crosland, loc. cit., 382–90.

44, John Mayow, *Medico-physical works* (Alembic Club Reprints, No. 17, Edinburgh and Chicago, 1908) 35. Robert Boyle objected to this sort of explanation: 'I look upon amity and enmity as affections of intelligent beings, and I have not yet found it explained by any, how those appetites can be placed in bodies inanimate and devoid of knowledge or of so much as sense.' Cited by Pattison Muir, op. cit., 380. Nicolas Lémery (who, like Boyle, explained differential reactivity in terms of the *shapes* of the particles) had no patience with the 'animate model'. In his *Cours de chimie* (ed. Baron, Paris, 1759, 49) he uses the word 'affinité' only once, and pejoratively, in referring to the astrologer's doctrine of the correspondence of the seven planets and the seven metals.

45 Pattison Muir, op. cit., 381. The error originated with Jagnaux, who only says, however, that Boerhaave 'redonna au mot affinité le sens qu'il a maintenant en chimie'. Pattison Muir's elaboration of this statement is echoed by Stillman and by Daumas.

46 Peter Shaw, *A new method of chemistry* (2nd edn, 2 vols, London, 1741) i, 492–3. Boerhaave's use of attraction in the case of *dissimilar* substances may have been only a way-station, but it was immensely significant. The rival theory of Stahl and his disciples still involved affinities in the older sense: all substances react because of a fundamental resemblance, or a sharing of common qualities. See Hélène Metzger, *Newton, Stahl, Boerhaave et la doctrine chimique* (Paris, 1930) 139–48. Stahl's pecular system of *latus*, an application of this principle, is discussed by Demachy, op. cit., 100–5.

47 *Plan d'un cours de chymie expérimentale et raisonnée, avec un discours sur la chymie. Par M. Macquer . . . et M. Baumé* (Paris, 1757).

48 Between different bodies, Macquer wrote, there is 'une convenance, rapport, affinité, ou attraction si l'on veut, qui fait que certains corps sont disposés à s'unir ensemble . . . C'est cet effet, quelle qu'en soit la cause qui nous servira à rendre de tous les phénomènes que fournit la Chymie, & à les lier ensemble', *Elémens de chymie théorique* (Paris, 1749) 20. Macquer has completely discarded the notion of identity or similarity as a cause of combination, and unlike Boerhaave discerns a single effect, his 'affinité', in all chemical reactions.

49 *Dictionnaire de chymie* (2 vols, Paris, 1766) i, 48.

50 *Dissertation de Jean Philippe de Limbourg, Docteur en Médecine, sur les affinités chimiques, qui a remporté le prix de physique de l'an 1758, quant à la partie chymique* (Liège, 1761). Cf. Fortunato Felice, *De Newtoniana attractione unica cohaerentiae naturalis causa* (Berne, 1757) passim; and Jacob Reinbold Spielmann, *Instituts de Chymie* (trans. Cadet. 2 vols, Paris, 1770) i, 22–4.

51 *Instituts de chymie*, i, 96–7.

52 *Encyclopédie, ou dictionnaire raisonné des sciences, des arts et des métiers* (35 vols, Paris, 1751–80) xiii, 1765.

53 Ibid., Art. 'Chymie', iii, 1753. Cf. Charles Coulston Gillispie, *The edge of objectivity* (Princeton, 1960) 184–7.

54 This subject is taken up in my paper, 'Some French Antecedents of the Chemical Revolution', *Chymia*, v (1959) 73–112.

55 *Histoire naturelle*, xiii (1765) Seconde Vue; *Œuvres Complètes de Buffon*, ed. Flourens (nouv. edn, 12 vols, Paris, n.d.) iii, 414–24. Buffon argued that whereas the shape of celestial bodies has no effect on the law of gravitation because the distances are so vast, when the distances are small the effect of differing shape may be very great. Accordingly, he believed it possible to calculate the shape of 'parties élémentaires' or 'parties constituantes' of homogeneous bodies if the law of attraction for a particular substance could be determined by experiment.

56 *Elémens de chymie, théorique et pratique* (Dijon, 1777) i, 57. For the influence of Buffon on Guyton de Morveau see Crosland, loc. cit., 385–7.

57 *Digressions académiques, ou essais sur quelques sujets de physique, de chymie & d'histoire naturelle* (Dijon, 1762). The book was actually published in 1772, but the incorrect date appears on the majority of surviving copies. See W. A. Smeaton, 'L. B. Guyton de Morveau (1737–1816)', *Ambix*, vi (1957) 18–34. The *Digressions* has two principal parts, a 'Dissertation sur le Phlogistique', the influence of which I have discussed in my *Lavoisier the crucial year* (Ithaca, New York, 1961), and an 'Essai physico-chymique sur la Dissolution et la Crystallization, Pour parvenir à l'explication des affinités par la figure des parties constituantes des Corps'.

58 In 1780–85 Guyton translated the first two volumes of Bergman's *Opuscula physica et chemica* (Moström Nos. 150 and 165). These did not include the important 'Disquisitio de attractionibus electivis' (*Nova Acta Regiae Societatis Scientarum*, ii, 1775, 161–250; Moström No. 97); Guyton does not refer to Bergman in the section on affinity in his *Elémens de chymie* (1777), but discusses his work at length in the *Encyclopédie méthodique*. See above, note 39. Guyton surely had a hand in the French translation of Bergman's 'Disquisitio' (*Traité des affinités chymiques ou attractions électives*, Paris, 1788).

59 Nathan Sivin, 'William Lewis (1708–1781) as a Chemist', *Chymia*, viii (1962) 67–73. Sivin discusses the modifications Lewis made in Geoffroy's table.

60 *Experiments upon magnesia alba, quick-lime and other alcaline substances* (Alembic Club Reprints, No. 1, Edinburgh, 1893) 46.

61 J. Thomson, *An account of the life, lectures, and writings of William Cullen, M.D.* (2 vols, Edinburgh and London, 1859) i, 23–31 and 44–5. This may not be exact. W. P. D. Wightman has tried to reconstruct from surviving fragments Cullen's Glasgow lectures of 1748–9, the first year in which he took sole responsibility for the new course in chemistry. ('William Cullen and the Teaching of Chemistry—II', *Annals of Science*, xii, 1956, 192–205). Wightman's identification of the phrase 'habits of mixts' with 'elective attractions' is not convincing; Cullen's chemical theories at this time were evidently primitive and confused, derived partly from Boerhaave and Stahl. See Cullen's 'Reflections on the Study of Chemistry' in Leonard Dobbin, 'A Cullen Chemical Manuscript of 1753', *Annals of Science*, i (1936) 138–56.

62 'Notes of Dr Cullen's Lectures on Chemistry made by Dr John White of Paisley.' I am indebted to Catherine R. McEwan, Librarian of the Corporation of Paisley, for providing me with a microfilm of this manuscript. It bears the date 1754, but the lectures were probably delivered at Edinburgh in 1757–8, and certainly before Cullen could recommend Andrew Reid's translation of Macquer (*Elements of the theory and practice of chemistry*, 2 vols, London, 1758).

63 'Lectures on Chymistry by Dr Willm Cullen'. Clifton College Falconer MS., fols 13–14. This dates from the 1760's, for Cullen refers to 'the late Dr Alston' (Charles Alston, the physician and botanist, who died in November 1760) and mentions 'some late experiments at Petersburgh' on the freezing of mercury, a clear reference to the experiments of Braun and Lomonosov which were carried out in December 1759.

64 M. P. Crosland, 'The Use of Diagrams as Chemical "Equations" in the Lecture Notes of William Cullen and Joseph Black', *Annals of Science*, xv (1959) 75–90. This paper was not published until 1961; earlier I called attention to Black's use of what Crosland calls the 'double-circle' diagrams, and emphasized that Cullen and Black had preceded Bergman in discussing double elective attractions. See Marshall Clagett, ed., *Critical problems in the history of science* (Madison, Wisconsin, 1959) 517–18.

65 For a careful evaluation of Higgins see Partington, op. cit., iii, 736–54. In the same year (in the 'Discours Préliminaire' of his *Traité élémentaire de chimie*) Lavoisier spoke with some diffidence of chemical affinities and elective attractions. He called them the part of chemistry 'la plus susceptible, peut-être, de devenir un jour une science exacte', but added that 'les données principales manquant, ou du moins celles que nous avons ne sont encore ni assez precises ni assez certaines pour devenir la base fondamentale sur laquelle doit reposer une partie aussi importante de la chimie', *Œuvres de Lavoisier* (6 vols, Paris, 1864–93) i, 5–6. For the subsequent history of affinities, notably the work of Berthollet, see Frederic L. Holmes, 'From Elective Affinities to Chemical Equilibria: Berthollet's Law of Mass Action', *Chymia*, viii (1962) 105–45.

66 'Some Daltonian Doubts', *Isis*, lii (1961) 544–54. A re-examination seems indeed to be under way, my critics still favouring the view that Dalton's achievement was independent of Richter. See the generous but sceptical remarks of Frank Greenaway (*John Dalton and the atom*, London, 1966, 234–5) and Arnold Thackray's recent paper, optimistically entitled 'The Origin of Dalton's Chemical Atomic Theory: Daltonian Doubts Resolved' (*Isis*, lvii, 1966, 35–55).

67 *Encyclopédie méthodique—Chymie*, i, 539. Guyton describes in his *Elémens de chymie* (i, 60–7) experiments to measure affinities by determining the attractive forces between mercury and various metals. See Crosland (1963) 387.

68 *Conclusion of the experiments and observations concerning the attractive powers of the mineral acids* (London, 1783) 20–2.

69 See my 'Quantification in Chemistry', *Isis*, lii (1961) 205–6.

70 'Some Daltonian Doubts', loc. cit., 548.

J D—H

6

Arnold Thackray

Quantified Chemistry—the Newtonian Dream

One widely accepted view of the history of chemistry attributes crucial importance to the 'chemical revolution' that Lavoisier began in the later eighteenth century. He initiated 'the postponed scientific revolution in chemistry', to use Butterfield's phrase.[1] And, to quote Gillispie, 'Dalton completed the chemical revolution'.[2] Ergo, praise Dalton.

I too want to praise Dalton but, more urgently, I want to argue for a re-interpretation of eighteenth-century chemical history. In particular I want to suggest that the conceptual importance of Newtonianism has been underestimated. The controversy which took place over the chemical reactions involved in combustion and calcination, and Lavoisier's brilliant resolution of that controversy, have naturally aided such a false estimate. But if we are to gain a true appreciation of the ideas that increasingly underlay chemical theory as the eighteenth century progressed, it is to Newtonianism we must look.

The three Newtonian beliefs of particular relevance concern imponderable fluids, the internal structure of matter, and short-range forces. Not one of these beliefs was abandoned because of Lavoisier's work. Indeed chemistry came to possess two imponderable fluids, caloric and light, in place of one, phlogiston. Again, belief in an internal structure to matter was hardly upset by Lavoisier's acceptance of the prevailing view that chemical elements are merely 'the last products of analysis'. And his admission that one day the precision of the data might be brought to such perfection that the mathematician in his study would be able to calculate any phenomenon of chemical combination in the same way . . . as he calculates the movement of the heavenly bodies[3]

was scarcely likely to disturb the Newtonian dream of a quantified science of short-range forces.

It thus seems to me that though Lavoisier's work of reclassifying, ordering and administering chemistry was of the greatest importance, he had little effect upon its fundamental concepts. Instead it was the peculiar task of John Dalton, the self-educated provincial worthy, to provide an effective alternative to Newtonian ideas. This he did by flatly denying an internal structure to matter, while successfully quantifying not the force mechanism but the units of chemistry. Chemists awoke from their Newtonian dream to find themselves confronted with an aesthetically unpleasing but operationally powerful *New system of chemical philosophy*.[4]

In the present paper I can only trace out one particular and limited aspect of the Newtonian tradition.[5] That aspect is the attempt to quantify chemical mechanism. Of course Newtonianism in chemistry was initially a rival of Cartesian, chymical and empiric schemes. But as Newtonian astronomy grew in prestige, so the associated chemical beliefs gained in acceptability. In particular the dream of chemistry as the quantified science of short-range forces, the microcosmic counterpart of Newton's own dazzling quantification of the macrocosm, this dream was to entrance the major chemists of the later-eighteenth century. Only against the background of their hopes, aspirations and vain endeavours, and the century-long tradition from which their efforts sprang, can Dalton's successful quantification be appreciated in all its naïve revolutionary power.

A belief in the explanatory capacity of short-range attractive and repulsive forces runs all through Newton's work. As far back as 1687, in the preface to the first edition of the *Principia*, he had declared that

I . . . suspect that [the rest of the phaenomena of nature] may all depend upon certain forces by which the particles of bodies . . . are . . . impelled . . . or . . . repelled . . .

However for my purpose it is sufficient to consider the group of publications he gave to the world in the first two decades of the eighteenth century, following his move to London and, more significantly, the death of Robert Hooke.

In 1704 the *Opticks*, a work with enormous chemical implications, first appeared. The additional queries added to the 1706 Latin edition included a discussion of the relative attractive forces between different chemicals. This discussion led on to the general conclusion that the particles of bodies 'are moved by certain active principles, such as is that of gravity, and that which causes fermentation, and the cohesion of bodies . . .'[6] The 1710 *De natura acidorum* went further, asserting of acids that 'they are endued with a great attractive force, in which force their activity consists',[7] while the 1713 general scholium to the *Principia* added mysterious hints about 'a certain most subtle spirit . . . by the force and action of which . . . the particles of bodies attract one another at near distances'.[8] Finally, the revised version of Query 31 in the 1717 *Opticks* concluded that

there are therefore agents in nature able to make the particles of bodies stick together by very strong attractions. And it is the business of experimental philosophy to find them out.[9]

In the space of thirteen years the Newtonian chemical programme was thus displayed to the world. And much of eighteenth-century science can be seen as an attempt to complete 'the business of experimental philosophy' that Newton had begun. As early as 1734 J. T. Desaguliers was confidently saying that

[Newton's] Opticks . . . contain a vast fund of philosophy; which (tho' he has modestly delivered under the name of queries, as if they were only conjectures) daily experiments and observations confirm . . .[10]

Not surprisingly, this confirmation of Newton's view of nature was pursued most enthusiastically by members of his own immediate circle. So it is to that circle I now turn.

The formation of a British group of Newtonian natural philosophers can perhaps be traced back to Newton's friendship with David Gregory. Certainly it was Gregory's Newtonian lectures in Edinburgh which first excited the interest and enthusiasm of Archibald Pitcairne. Through Pitcairne we can trace the important link with Leyden and Herman Boerhaave (a student of Pitcairne's), as well as the addition to the Newtonian circle of such men as Richard Mead and George Cheyne. The real establishment of a southern-based Newtonian group followed Gregory's move to Oxford in 1691. Of particular value in the formation of this group were the lectures given by his pupil John Keill, lectures which deeply influenced such men as Desaguliers and John Freind.[11]

Typical of the earlier works of the circle was Cheyne's 1705 *Philosophical principles of natural religion*, a book which well illustrates how Newtonian works could casually assume, yet fail to develop, ingredients of the Daltonian position. Cheyne mentions that

the particles of natural fluids must be similar, of equal diameters, of equal solidity, and consequently of equal specifick gravities . . . and of the same uniform nature. . . . Water seems to consist of . . . particles of equal diameters, and equal specifick gravities.[12]

These observations led no further, for to Cheyne, as to all true Newtonians, weights were of importance only if they could help towards an investigation into attractive forces.

Of particular interest is the effect of the 1706 Latin *Opticks* on the by then well-established group. Whereas their earlier publications had been Newtonian in a restrained, corpuscular way, their post-1706 work places the greatest possible stress on short-range attractive forces. There is plenty of evidence that well before 1706 the group was aware of Newton's belief in the importance of these forces. Yet only following his publication of the Latin *Opticks* did they also commit their ideas to print, with fulsome references to the Latin queries.

For instance John Keill, in some 1708 theorems on attraction, showed how an attractive force diminishing more rapidly than the square of the distance could be used to explain solution, fermentation, effervescence, crystallization and precipitation.[13] His ideas were taken further by his brother James. James showed that

the attractive force varies, according as the particles are cones, cylinders, cubes, or spheres, and *caeteris paribus* a spherical particle, has the strongest attractive power.

He thus first stated an idea that was to be subtly altered and powerfully exploited in the hands of Buffon, with important effects on French attempts to realize the Newtonian dream. James also went on to remark how

a few different sorts of particles, variously combined, will produce great variety of fluids. . . . If we suppose only five different sorts of particles . . . and call them a, b, c, d, e, their several combinations, without varying the proportions, in which they are mixt will be these following[14]

ab	ac	ad	ae
bc	bd	be	cd
ce	de	abc	adc
bdc	bde	bce	dec
abcd	abce	acde	abde
bcde	abcde		

Like the later statements of Bryan and William Higgins, this passage shows how the ideas Dalton was to develop were available throughout the century, at any rate within the Newtonian tradition. The writings of the Keills show equally that attractive forces, not weights and combining ratios, were the matters of real concern. This is also evident in the work of their close friend, John Freind. His 1709 *Praelectiones chymicae* made a sustained attempt to explain the whole of chemistry by the use of short-range forces, but could only lamely conclude its sophisticated algebraic discussion with the statement that

at present, 'tis enough for our purpose, if from numbers and calculations, we can point out the way, which leads us to a solution of this phenomenon.[15]

However other members of the Newtonian circle, notably Francis Hauksbee and Brook Taylor, were actively embarked on experiments designed to provide just that necessary factual information which Freind lacked.

It was as a result of Hauksbee's experimental work that Newton was to modify the 1717 *Opticks*, and further stress the importance of short-range attractive forces.[16] Hauksbee was assisted by Taylor in some of his experiments, and in July 1712 Taylor himself read his first paper to the Royal Society. This paper begins:

The following experiments seeming to be of use in discussing the proportions of the attractions of fluids, I shall not forbear giving an account of it. . . .[17]

The experiments described were similar to Hauksbee's and concerned the ascent of liquids between glass planes. The practical importance of such experiments was that 'by these schemes the proportions of the power of attraction are in some measure evident to the eye'. The final portion of Taylor's paper, belatedly published in 1721, describes how

I took several thin pieces of fir-board, and having hung them successively in a convenient manner to a nice pair of scales, I tried what weight was necessary . . . to separate them at once from the surface of stagnating water . . . the weight in every trial being exactly proportional to the surface, I was encouraged to think the experiment well made. . . .[18]

Like so much of the work of the early Newtonians, this experiment is often seen as an isolated and uninteresting event. To view it in this way would be a mistake. It was rather part of an enthusiastically begun and far-reaching inquiry into all the forces operative in nature—an inquiry which involved much work in magnetism and electricity as well as chemistry, and on which many of the investigations carried out later in the century were to be based.

One further publication that demands some reference is Stephen Hales' *Vegetable staticks*. Though it only appeared in 1727, it resulted from work begun 'about 20 years since'[19]—i.e. at just that period when the early Newtonians were most active. Indeed Hales' references to the writings of James Keill, Francis Hauksbee and John Freind ('[who] has from [Newton's] principles given a very ingenious rationale of the chief operations in chymistry'[20]) make plain his sympathies with this group, and must have helped direct the attention of later readers to their work. And, like them, Hales is full of admiring references to the queries in *Opticks*.

While it was this British group who most actively pursued Newton's ideas, there is evidence that his post-1700 publications quickly attracted attention in France. Crucial here was E. F. Geoffroy's 1698 visit to London, his election as an F.R.S. and his subsequent official correspondence with Hans Sloane.[21] A further channel for the communication of Newtonian ideas was Taylor's correspondence with Remond de Montmort, and their mutual visits. We may also notice that though the *Principia* and the 1706 *Opticks*, being in Latin, needed no translation, a French abstract of the 1704 *Opticks* was quickly prepared, and two rival translations of the 1717 edition were soon available.[22]

Finally it is worth remark that the *Nouveau cours de chimie*, published anonymously in 1723, was in large part a word-for-word translation of Freind's Newtonian chemistry. If, as Baron stated in 1756,[23] this work was produced from students' notes on Geoffroy's lecture course, it provides strong additional evidence of the latter's Newtonian inclinations. It thus seems possible that Geoffroy's 1718 table of affinities, though dressed in language of studied neutrality, was a work of consciously Newtonian origin, and that Fontenelle's somewhat barbed comments on it in the Academie's *Histoire* were written with this fact in mind.[24]

The work of the early Newtonians in England, and the resulting controversy in France, represent a phase of activity that soon passed away. The Keills and Freind did not publish further work of chemical significance after 1710. Hauksbee died in 1713, and Taylor was plagued with ill-health. Though Stephen Hales continued to experiment, Newton's own involvement seems, not surprisingly, to have declined with age. In France Geoffroy's work and the published translation of the *Opticks* appear to have provoked reaction. For a time Cartesian orthodoxy was dominant.[25] The interest of the 1720's and 30's thus lies not with chemical speculation and experimental investigation, but with the developing tradition of Newtonian textbooks of natural philosophy.

In England this tradition had its beginnings in those two laudatory works, Cheyne's *Philosophical principles* and Hauksbee's *Physico-mechanical experiments*. The pirated 1717 edition of Desaguliers' lectures, and the 1720 translation of 'sGravesande's Latin text served as reinforcements, but the really important books were Pemberton's *View of Sir Isaac Newton's philosophy* and Desaguliers' own edition of his *Experimental philosophy*. The Latin texts of such Dutch writers as 'sGravesande and Musschenbroek made Newtonian ideas widely available on the Continent, while Boerhaave's *Elementa chemiae* provided a standard chemistry susceptible to Newtonian interpretation.[26] Indeed in its English translation, with copious notes by Peter Shaw, it became a sort of Newtonian chemical Bible, enjoying unique popularity through the rest of the eighteenth century.[27]

The importance of the popularizing textbooks is that they assisted the general acceptance of the idea that short-range forces are at the basis of chemical phenomena. For instance 'sGravesande, having asserted the existence of an attractive force which declines very rapidly with distance, and then becomes a repelling force, goes on to say that 'this attractive and repelling force is prov'd by innumerable chymical experiments'.[28] Or again, Benjamin Martin was to claim in his 1751 *Plain and familiar introduction to the Newtonian experimental philosophy* that 'all the more considerable operations of chemistry are explicable upon this most simple principle . . . [that] there is between different kinds of bodies a different power of attraction between their constituent particles'.[29]

While British and Dutch texts of natural philosophy were creating that climate of thought in which Newtonian presuppositions would appear as self-evident truths, it was in France that the next development of chemical significance took place. In 1745 Clairaut endeavoured to show that further terms of the form $1/r^n$ needed adding to Newton's $1/r^2$ gravitational law in order to reconcile theory and observation. Buffon, already the translator of *Vegetable staticks* and other Newtonian works, counter-attacked. He asserted the primacy of the $1/r^2$ law for the whole of nature, insisting that

metaphysical, mathematical and physical reasons therefore all accord to prove that the law of attraction can only be expressed by a single term, and never by two or more terms.

The resulting series of papers[30] was necessarily inconclusive for Clairaut could only reply that

the metaphysical, mathematical and physical reasons that M. Buffon has employed are . . . of no effect against the law that I have proposed to reconcile astronomical phenomena with those which happen every day before our eyes. . . .

Buffon's extended attempt to show how even chemistry could be explained on a $1/r^2$ gravitational law finally appeared in 1765, in volume 13 of his *Histoire naturelle*. It is worth quotation at length as it so well illustrates those mid-century Newtonian aspirations which were to find echo in the chemical texts right down to Fourcroy and Thomas Thomson. Also it shows Buffon, as a good Newtonian, accepting but not dwelling on that uniformity of all the particles of a chemical species, which uninformed commentators have often hailed as the particular achievement of Dalton. To quote:

> we are ignorant of the figure of the constituent particles of bodies. Water, air, earth, metals and all homogeneous substances, are unquestionably composed of elementary particles, which are similar among themselves, but whose figure is unknown. Posterity, by the aid of calculation, may disclose this new field of knowledge, and ascertain, with considerable precision, the figure of the elements of bodies. They will take the principle we have established as the basis of their reasoning: *All matter is attracted in the inverse ratio of the square of the distance . . . [variation only arising] from the figure of the constituent particles of each substance; because this figure enters as an element or principle into the distance.* Hence, when they discover, by reiterated experiments, the law of attraction in any particular substance, they may find, by calculation, the figure of its constituent particles.[31]

Buffon's hope of calculating particle shape was based upon the assumption of one simple, uniform attractive law in nature. In this desire to simplify the Newtonian world picture he was typical of the mid-century, which produced a host of such schemes. The systems devised by such men as Gowin Knight and Bryan Robinson are important mainly for their influence on the theory of imponderable fluids, and thus lie outside the scope of this paper. However the work of Buffon, and also that of R. J. Boscovich, was to influence deeply future attempts to quantify chemical mechanism. Unlike Buffon, Boscovich chose to simplify the Newtonian world-view by positing only one primary particle. Associated with this particle was a distance-variant force law, in marked contrast to the unvarying law and different particles of Buffon's scheme. Like Buffon, Boscovich too was convinced that it was within his own system that 'the general theory for all chemical operations'[32] lay.

Buffon's vision profoundly affected Guyton de Morveau, Lavoisier, Fourcroy and the whole school of French chemists. The quasi-mathematical exposition of Boscovich's *Theoria* was to prove more fascinating to British chemists such as Priestley, Thomson and Davy. But while the channels of transmission and the forms of the vision were different, the necessary programme of chemical research was the same in both cases. And the inspiration was that same Newtonian dream of a chemistry quantified like astronomy, which had so excited the early British group. Only this time the task of quantification was to be taken on not by physicians, physicists and speculative visionaries, but by the major chemists of the day.

Geoffroy's 1718 table of affinities had quickly excited comment and correction. After all, a table printed without any supporting philosophy was equally acceptable to all sorts and conditions of chemist. To tabular-minded pharmacists and metallurgists Geoffroy's work would seem eminently sensible, while Stahlian theorists could welcome it in the same way as Newtonians. Even the staunchest Cartesian had little ground for complaint in a 'table of the different relationships observed in chemistry'. Yet only two further tables were produced by 1750. In contrast the 50's themselves saw three new tables, the 60's four and the 70's five.[33]

This awakening interest in affinity tables towards the middle of the eighteenth century cannot be divorced from the growing acceptance of Newtonianism by chemists. As early as 1749 the influential French chemist P. J. Macquer had combined an exposition and reproduction of Geoffroy's table with a cautiously Newtonian text. Macquer's *Élémens de chymie* was to set the pattern in textbooks for the rest of the century. Its first chapter is devoted to the discussion of chemical units. The second chapter, entitled 'Of the relations or affinities between bodies', treats of chemical mechanism. It says that:

different bodies, whether principles or compounds, have such a mutual conformity, relation, affinity or attraction, if you will call it so, as disposes some of them to join and unite together. . . . This effect, whatever be its cause, will enable us to account for, and connect together, all the phenomena that chymistry produces.[34]

To find Macquer more openly advocating a Newtonian position it is necessary to turn to the *Dictionnaire
de chimie* that he published anonymously in 1766, the
year of Dalton's birth. Possibly because the *Dictionnaire*
was anonymous Macquer did not hesitate to favour the
system Buffon had put forward, saying

if . . . universal gravitation . . . be an essential property of
matter in general . . . its effects . . . must necessarily act . . .
in chemical combinations and solutions.

The resulting exposition concluded with a statement
typical of those many chemists from Freind to Davy
who were entranced by the Newtonian dream. In a
passage that Fourcroy was to repeat word for word
more than forty years later, in the very year that Dalton's *New system* appeared, Macquer speculated that

perhaps time, experience, the encrease of chemical knowledge, lastly, the zeal of persons skilled in mathematics and
chemistry, will hereafter throw much more light upon these
subjects, of which now we have but confused notions. However, I cannot but consider them as the true key of the most
hidden phenomena of chemistry, and consequently of all
natural philosophy.[35]

Macquer's influence was considerable. His col-
laborators and pupils included Baumé, Lavoisier,
Berthollet and Fourcroy. And Guyton was to learn his
chemistry from Macquer and Baumé's texts. It is thus
not surprising that the last third of the eighteenth century saw a sustained French endeavour to quantify
chemical mechanism.

Guyton was early prominent in this endeavour.[36] His
wholehearted adoption of the position outlined by
Buffon is already clear in his 1772 *Digressions académiques*, and he was soon adapting Brook Taylor's
method of separating solids from the surface of a liquid
to obtain a measure of their relative attractive force.
His 1776 contribution to the *Encyclopédie* supplement
further indicates his Newtonian inspiration. It vigorously praises Keill and Freind 'whose efforts have not
been completely unfruitful'. Macquer and Buffon are
given the central place, especially Buffon, whose work
'opens a vast scope of new knowledge'. By 1777 Guyton,
now praising Buffon as 'the Newton of France', was
able to present a quantified list of relative adhesions.

What is the order that these adhesions follow? It is precisely the order of the chemical affinities. . . . What satisfying consequences the application of this hypothesis to new observations promises. There are already some affinities determined by numerical relationships: we are able to say . . . that the affinity of mercury with gold is to the affinity of mercury with zinc as 446 : 204; and one perceives what exactitude these mathematical expressions will bring into chemistry . . . some day one will attain to the rigorous demonstration of the figures which the elements of bodies must necessarily have.[37]

With the Newtonian dream apparently beginning to be realized through his work, it is little wonder that Guyton felt excited. This excitement is again evident in the eighty-nine closely-packed pages on affinity which he wrote for the first volume of the chemical section of the *Encyclopédie méthodique*. In the light of such industry and enthusiasm, we can perhaps understand Lavoisier's admission that 'a sentiment of self-love' was one reason for his own decision 'to decline entering upon a work in which [Guyton] is employed'.[38]

This admission of Lavoisier's is important, as the comparative paucity of his own work on affinities has led many later commentators, in concentrating on Lavoisier, to underestimate the significance to chemical theory of affinity studies. However Lavoisier in that same preface to the *Traité élémentaire* did admit that

[the study of affinities] is perhaps the best calculated of any part of chemistry for being reduced into a completely systematic body . . .

and that

this science of affinities . . . holds the same place with regard to the other branches of chemistry, as the higher or transcendental geometry does with respect to the simpler and elementary part . . .

Even his own earlier cautious and positivistic paper on the affinities of oxygen[39] displays that same hope of a quantified chemistry which so excited French scientists from Buffon to Berthollet.

In the remaining space at my disposal I can barely mention those many attempts to quantify chemical mechanism which took place in Scandinavia, Britain and Germany. As early as 1758 Torbern Bergman was embarking on his momentous researches into attractive forces, with appropriate references to Keill and Clairaut.[40] In Britain William Cullen was somewhat more cautious. Notes of his 1762 lectures, still preserved in Manchester University Library, show him saying of elective attractions that though 'nothing would be of more importance to the art of chemistry than to establish some just theory on this subject . . . this has never yet been done'.[41] Similar caution was displayed by his pupil Joseph Black. Concentration on particular aspects of these two figures has again served to disguise from many commentators the importance of the Newtonian dream to the chemical community at large.

However even Cullen was using affinity diagrams with appropriate algebraic symbols, and speaking highly of Macquer's textbook, before 1760. Further evidence of the importance he attached to a quantified affinity theory is seen in a 1762 letter from his pupil William Fordyce about 'two tables which I propose, provided you give me leave, to prefix to my tables of chemical attraction'.[42] These tables of Fordyce are the earliest known numerical tables of affinities. Their production is indicative of the growing desire to quantify affinities. This desire was soon to find expression in the use of numbers by Elliott, Fourcroy, William Higgins, and all those others in whom the wish for quantified chemical mechanisms overleapt the need for results deriving from experiment. Higgins' *Comparative view* especially, is best seen not as some pale precursor of Dalton's work —that claim could be carried back at least to George Cheyne—but as a full-blooded attempt to exploit the Newtonian tradition of quantified force mechanisms for a particular anti-phlogistic purpose.[43]

The laborious experimental attempts to quantify affinity undertaken by such chemists as Richard Kirwan, Carl Wenzel and J. B. Richter can only be hinted at. Their painstaking work on a host of subsidiary problems, their variety of methods—from Guyton's adhesion techniques, through Wenzel's rate of solution investigations to Richter and Kirwan's neutralization studies—all these must be passed over. So too must the growing awareness that affinities were not as simple as had been hoped, being influenced by such factors as temperature and state of solution. Yet the grand objective of a quantified, predictive science of chemical mechanism remained, and its importance can scarcely be overemphasized. Nor can the amount of emotional and intellectual capital committed to the corresponding research programme be easily exaggerated. It is perhaps sufficient to observe that the famous reproduction of Richter's table in Berthollet's 1803 *Essai de statique chimique* was accompanied by no Daltonian stress on reacting weights, but simply by the comment that

all these numbers can . . . be regarded as representing the force of affinity . . . Richter's work contains excellent things for the theory of affinities.[44]

The textbooks of the close of the century, from Nicholson's *Chemical dictionary* and Thomson's *System* to Chaptal's *Élémens* and Fourcroy's *Philosophie chimique*, remained convinced that the key to chemical understanding lay in a quantified science of affinities. Yet the Newtonian dream was already fading. Actual experimental results remained discordant and progress was obstinately slow. Berthollet's ruthless critique of existing techniques and assumptions only served to highlight the problem.

His 1801 *Récherches sur les lois de l'affinité* and the *Essai de statique chimique* painfully exposed the half-thought-out nature of much previous work. But, though critical, Berthollet was thoroughly committed to the Buffonian version of the Newtonian dream, if I may call it so. His *Essai* begins:

The forces which produce chemical phenomena are all derived from the mutual attraction of the molecules of bodies, to which the name of affinity has been given, to distinguish it from the attraction of astronomy. It is probable that both are only the same property. . . .[45]

The *Essai* made plain the magnitude of the problems involved in quantification. To Berthollet, if not to other less dedicated workers, it also made plain the need for renewed zeal and fresh efforts.

However in the very year the *Essai* appeared Dalton was already observing, with quiet surprise, that

an enquiry into the relative weights of the ultimate particles of bodies is a subject as far as I know entirely new . . .[46]

And it was Dalton's inquiry, not Berthollet's, which was to transform chemistry. Indeed so successful was

Dalton's advocacy of a *New system of chemical philosophy*, that the Newtonian tenets which underlay so much eighteenth-century hope and work in the science have long since been forgotten. Dalton may or may not have 'completed the chemical revolution', but he certainly ended the Newtonian dream. Only as we now recapture that dream can we begin to understand the motives and the aspirations of eighteenth-century chemists, and the power and originality of Dalton's work.

Notes

1 H. Butterfield, *The origins of modern science* (2nd edn, London, 1957) heading to chapter XI.

2 C. C. Gillispie, *The edge of objectivity* (Princeton and London, 1960) 258.

3 A. L. Lavoisier, 'Mémoire sur l'affinité du principe oxygine', *Mémoires de l'Académie Royale des Sciences*, 1782 (publ. 1785) 534.

4 The title Dalton chose for his never completed book (London; Part 1, 1808; Part 2, 1810; Vol. 2, Part 1, 1827; no more published).

5 The whole Newtonian tradition is dealt with at much greater length, and more exhaustive documentation is included in 'The Newtonian tradition and eighteenth-century chemistry' (University Library, Cambridge, Ph.D. dissertation no. 5848).

6 I. Newton, *Optice* (London, 1706) 344. The quotation is reproduced as it later appeared in the 1717 English edition.

7 J. Harris, *Lexicon technicum* (Vol. 2, London, 1710); printed in the introduction.

8 I. Newton, *Philosophiae naturalis principia mathematica* (2nd edn, London, 1713) 484. The quotation is reproduced as it later appeared in the 1729 English edition.

9 I. Newton, *Opticks* (2nd English edn, London, 1717) 369.

10 J. T. Desaguliers, *A course of experimental philosophy* (London, 1734–44) i, preface.

11 For further information on all this group see the Ph.D. thesis (op. cit. (5)) and such standard reference works as the *Dictionary of national biography*.

12 G. Cheyne, *Philosophical principles of natural religion* (1st edn, London, 1705) 61.

13 See *Philosophical Transactions*, xxvi (1708–9) 97–110. Contrast this with Keill's earlier *Introductio ad veram physicam* (Oxford, 1702).

14 James Keill, *An account of animal secretion* (London, 1708) 19 and 61–2.

15 The quotation is taken from the English edition: J. Freind, *Chymical lectures* (London, 1712) 102.

16 See the important study of H. Guerlac, 'Francis Hauksbee: expérimentateur au profit de Newton', *Archives Internationales*, xvi (1963) 113–28.

17 *Phil. Trans.*, xxvii (1712) 538.

18 *Phil. Trans.*, xxxi (1721) 204–8.

19 S. Hales, *Vegetable staticks* (London, reprinted 1961), preface xxvi.

20 Ibid., xxvii.

21 See I. B. Cohen's important study of 'Isaac Newton, Hans

Sloane and the Académie Royale des Sciences' in *Mélanges Alexandre Koyré* (Paris, 1964) i, 61–116.

22 Ibid., 106–7, and bibliography.

23 T. Baron (ed.), *Cours de chymie* (Paris, 1756) preface iii. Further research suggests that Baron's statement is incorrect.

24 E. F. Geoffroy, 'Table des differents rapports observés en chimie entre differentes substances', *Mémoires de l'Académie Royale des Sciences*, 1718 (publ. 1719) 202–12. For Fontenelle, see the corresponding *Histoire*, 35–7.

25 See P. Brunet, *L'introduction des théories de Newton en France au XVIIIe siècle* (Paris, 1931) chs. 2 and 3.

26 For bibliographical details of all these works see the Ph.D. thesis (op. cit. (5)) or the bibliography in I. B. Cohen, *Franklin and Newton* (Philadelphia, 1956).

27 It was among the earliest chemical works read by Dalton, some time before 1790. See A. W. Thackray, 'The emergence of Dalton's chemical atomic theory', *British Journal for the History of Science*, iii (1966) 4.

28 W. J. 'sGravesande, *Mathematical elements of physicks* (trans. John Keill, London, 1720) 16.

29 B. Martin, *Plain and familiar introduction to the Newtonian experimental philosophy* (London, 1751) 7 and 10. I have reversed the order of the two passages quoted.

30 *Mémoires de l'Académie Royale des Sciences*, 1745 (published 1749) 329–64, etc.

31 Buffon, *Histoire naturelle* (Paris, 1765) xiii, p. xiii. The quotation is reproduced as it later appeared in the 1785 English edition.

32 R. J. Boscovich, *Theoria philosophiae naturalis* (Venice, 1763). Quotation from p. 160 of the English edition (Chicago and London, 1922).

33 See the list in A. Duncan, 'Some theoretical aspects of eighteenth-century tables of affinity—I', *Annals of Science*, xviii (1962) 177–94.

34 P. J. Macquer, *Élémens de chymie théorique* (Paris, 1749) 20. The quotation is reproduced as it later appeared in the 1758 English edition.

35 *Dictionnaire de chymie* (Paris, 1766) ii, 194 and 201. The quotations are reproduced as they later appeared in the 1771 English edition. For Fourcroy's use of this passage see *Encyclopédie méthodique, Chimie*, Vol. 5 (Paris 1808) 422.

36 See W. A. Smeaton's valuable series of studies on Guyton, especially 'Guyton de Morveau and chemical affinity', *Ambix*, xi (1963) 55–64.

37 Guyton de Morveau, *Élemens de chymie* (Dijon, 1777–8) i, 65–6.

38 A. L. Lavoisier, *Traité élémentaire de chimie* (Paris, 1789). Quotations from pp. xxi–xxii of the 1790 English translation.

39 Op. cit. (3).

40 See the article 'De attractione universale' in T. Bergman, *Opuscula physica et chemica* (Leipzig, 1788–90) vi, 38–64.

41 Manchester University Library, catalogue no. CH C 121 1–4. 4 vols. Quotation from Vol. 4, page 317.

42 See M. P. Crosland on 'The use of diagrams . . . in the lecture notes of William Cullen . . .', *Annals of Science*, xv (1959) 75–90; and see J. Thomson's *Life of Cullen* (Edinburgh, 1832) i, 570–71.

43 For the 'precursor' view see J. R. Partington and T. S. Wheeler, *The life and work of William Higgins* (London, 1960) Part 3.

44 C. L. Berthollet, *Essai de statique chimique* (Paris, 1803) i, 137.

45 Ibid., 1.

Notes   **46** J. Dalton, 'On the absorption of gases by water and other liquids', *Manchester Memoirs*, 2nd Series, i (1805) 286.

C A Russell   I wish to comment on Mr Thackray's remarks that the unity-of-matter ideal in the nineteenth century owed much to the Newtonian dream. Without denying some debt here, would it not be more likely that this ideal springs mainly from the influence of Romanticism on chemistry? In Germany the *Naturphilosophen* are widely believed to have played an important part in moulding chemical thought. They laid upon their adherents the necessity for looking for connections between phenomena that were once regarded separately, and doubtless stimulated much of the early German organic chemistry. Is it not therefore probable that the nineteenth-century search for a unified view of all matter owed at least something to them?

Sir Humphry Davy was certainly addicted to the unity-of-matter ideal, and, more than other English chemists, was influenced by the Romantic tradition. On the other hand, there is room for much doubt that he was deeply in debt to Boscovich. If this is true, Davy at least would not seem to be an obvious disciple of Newton.

Arnold Thackray   I am not qualified to judge developments later in the nineteenth century, but there seems to me to be no doubt of the prime influence of Newtonianism on earlier workers. Davy himself refers to the idea of the unity of matter as 'This sublime chemical speculation sanctioned by the authority of Hooke, Newton and Boscovich.[1] Similarly Thomas Thomson says 'it has been the opinion of many distinguished philosophers in all ages, that there is only one kind of matter. . . . This opinion was adopted by Newton; and Boscovitch has built upon it an exceedingly ingenious and instructive theory.[2]

Thus, until it has been shown otherwise, I think it reasonable to maintain that Newtonianism was the dominant influence on chemists such as Thomson and Davy, though I do not deny the existence of other influences, including Naturphilosophie. Obviously it is not possible to apportion 'influence' in a quantitative way. My concern was rather to delineate a major and too-often neglected tradition in *eighteenth-century* chemistry, without in any way claiming 'exclusive rights' for it.

A M Duncan   Mr Thackray has drawn attention to the long gap in the production of affinity tables between 1718 and the groups of tables produced in the 1750's, 1760's and 1770's. Could he suggest any explanation for this gap?

Arnold Thackray   One partial explanation of the revived interest in affinity tables from the 1750's onward would seem to be the growing acceptance of Newtonianism by chemists, to which I drew attention in the paper. Another important factor, I am sure, was the steadily growing volume of chemical research undertaken in the later eighteenth century, a growth itself related to the onset of the industrial revolution. However, much further research would be necessary to provide a satisfactory answer to Mr Duncan's question.

1 H. Davy, *Elements of chemical philosophy* (London, 1812) i, 489.

2 T. Thomson, *A system of chemistry* (Edinburgh, 1802) i, 386.

7

B B Kelham

Atomic Speculation in the Late Eighteenth Century

Chemical atomic theories were known and used before Dalton's time. One of the first theorists was an Irishman named Bryan Higgins, who conducted a school of chemistry in London. George Fordyce was another who put forward atomic ideas. He was a Scot, and also conducted a school of chemistry and medicine in London. Both Higgins and Fordyce were qualified in medicine, which was not surprising as most universities only taught chemistry as part of a medical course at that time. Another exponent of chemical atomism was William Higgins, the nephew of Bryan Higgins, whose claim to importance in respect of atomic theory rests on one publication, the *Comparative view of the phlogistic and antiphlogistic theories*, which was printed in 1789 shortly after William left Oxford.

Bryan Higgins

Bryan Higgins came from a Catholic family in Ireland and, as the penal laws were in force, he probably received his education abroad. In 1765 he entered the University of Leyden and about one month later graduated and obtained the degree of M.D. He did not study at Leyden but went there purely to qualify. In 1770 he married and settled in London, and in 1774 he opened his school of chemistry in Greek Street, Soho. He seems to have had a high reputation for he immediately attracted a number of important people to his lectures. One such was Joseph Priestley, but the outcome was not altogether happy for he took offence at Higgins' reference to his gases as 'conceits of air' and in the following year he published an attack on his former lecturer.[1] Bryan Higgins also sold purified chemicals to many eminent chemists of the time. Richard Kirwan, the famous Irish chemist, was one of his customers. It was while he was at a gathering at Kirwan's house in Newman Street that he met Empress Catherine the Second, and received an invitation to visit Russia. Whether or not he went is uncertain. He was not, however, averse to travel and in 1797, when he was fifty-six years old, he went to Jamaica to advise on the manufacture of rum.[2] He stayed there, at Spanish Town, for several years before returning to England.

Bryan Higgins must have arrived at his atomic theory sometime prior to 1775, for most of his ideas are included in his *Syllabus of the discourses and experiments with which the meetings of the subscribers are to be opened, after the course of chemistry is concluded*, which was published in 1775. It was reprinted in a slightly modified and incomplete form in his *Philosophical essay concerning light*, which was published in 1776.

This latter publication is in many ways reminiscent of Newton's *Opticks*, and, in fact, it contains many quotations from Newton[3] to whom Higgins openly acknowledges his indebtedness. However, Newton did not effectively apply his theory to the explanation of chemical phenomena, and it was this that Bryan Higgins attempted to do from 1775 onwards.

Bryan was considerably hindered by the state of chemistry at that time. Robert Boyle's definition of element:

I mean by elements . . . certain primitive and simple, or perfectly unmingled bodies, which not being made of any other bodies, or of one another, are the ingredients of which all those called perfectly mixt bodies are immediately compounded and into which they are ultimately resolved.

had been published in 1661[4] and was still accepted. Substances which could not be synthesized or analysed were elements. Unfortunately, Boyle had never named an element and seemed to consider them to be intangible substances. Confusion persisted until 1789 when Lavoisier produced his list of elements. In the meantime, chemists were compiling their own lists.

Bryan Higgins wrote: 'By the word element, I express the whole natural quantity of any sort of Matter whose several parts possess the same properties.'[5] By this he meant that an element was any substance which could not be decomposed. His views were generally oversimplified and he postulated seven elements: earth, water, acid, alkali, air, phlogiston, and light.[6] Acids were considered to be substances which contained acid fluid, and their differences were considered to be the results of the presence of other substances. The different alkalis were explained in a similar manner.[7] He admitted the possible existence of other elements and wrote:

Another, or perhaps many other elements, may be hereafter added to this list; but in the present state of our knowledge, it seems more advisable to rest on these only, than to reckon as many elements as there are portions of matter which have hitherto eluded the Art of Analysis.[8]

In this way he felt that even if the range of his chemical inquiry was restricted it would be profound.[9]

Bryan Higgins believed in the phlogiston theory. This theory explained combustion in terms of the release of an inflammable element called phlogiston. Consequently all inflammable bodies were believed to contain phlogiston as one of their constituents, and could not, therefore, be elements. In fact, the residue after combustion—after the removal of the phlogiston—was considered to be the element. It is this which accounts for the inclusion of acid and alkali as elements, and the rejection of metals and non-metals. As far as Bryan Higgins was concerned, a metal was a compound of alkali and phlogiston. Consequently, he did not consider that transmutation was impossible, and, although he himself never dabbled in this field, he did not reject, out of hand, the claims of others. He reported favourably on a sample of gold supposedly produced from mercury, by Dr James Price of Guildford.[10]

Bryan's seven elements proved inadequate to explain most chemical reactions, and he had to resort to a more comprehensive list of secondary elements or 'a classical arrangement . . . of bodies, composed of two or three primary elements; which bodies in various chemical processes, not being decomposed, we call chemical elements or the elements of the chemists'.[11]

He warned against the mathematicians and their ideas of infinite divisibility[12] and went on to write:

I consider the smallest parts, into which any mass of matter is ever divided in the processes of nature or art, as the ultimate parts of that mass, and as small bodies which are incapable of actual division or diminution.[13]

He called these ultimate parts atoms and believed that they were what really existed.

He considered that the atoms of all elements were of the same shape, and wrote:

that the atoms of each element are globular or nearly so; and that the spiral, spicular and other figures ascribed to these atoms, are fictious, unnecessary ,and are inconsistent with the uniformity of nature, and are repugnant to experience.[14]

In this statement he was rejecting earlier atomic ideas put forward by such men as Boyle, Mariotte, and Swedenborg. It was necessary that the atoms of different elements should differ in some respect, but Bryan Higgins was not very explicit on this point. Newton[15] had suggested that all matter was built up from one primary substance, but Bryan Higgins rejected this,[16] so that it appeared that atoms of his elements were not differentiated by either size or shape. This only left the material of composition as a point of difference. He considered that they would have different weights and wrote 'that (specific) gravity depends as much on the species of the gravitating bodies as on the quantity of them'.[17] He continued, 'it is reasonably inferred that each atom of an heavy homogeneous body, doth gravitate according to the same law which regulates the gravitation of the mass',[18] so that he recognized that the weight of a molecule was the sum of the weights of its atoms. He was, in fact, asserting the universal application of Newton's ideas on gravitation. There was attraction between the atoms which was dependant on their distance apart and also on polarity, so that attraction was 'more forcible in one direction or axis of each atom, than in any other direction'.[19]

Bryan Higgins was now faced with the problem of explaining the compressibility of gases. Simple attractive forces would bring the hard atoms into contact, and hence, compression would be impossible. What was required was a repulsive force. Like all chemists who considered fire to be a chemical substance, Bryan Higgins studied it thoroughly. He recognized that fire caused a body to expand and therefore counteracted the attractive forces.[20] He, therefore, postulated that all bodies were pervaded by fire, and that the resultant force between atoms was the sum of the attractive and repulsive forces. In other words, he thought that a small atmosphere of fire would result in a weakened attraction, while a large atmosphere of fire would result in repulsion. Thus, the atoms of air were considered to be surrounded by large atmospheres of fire, and the atoms of earth with small atmospheres of fire. He considered fire to be a compound of the two 'elements' phlogiston and light.[21] In consequence, the smallest particle of fire was the molecule, and the repulsive forces could only increase in fixed units associated with this molecule. He wrote 'that fire produces effects on bodies diametrically opposed to the effects of attraction: that it counteracts and in effect weakens, balances or overthrows the force of attraction'.[22]

This presented a problem with regard to the combination of gases. He suggested that the atmospheres of fire had to be broken or blended, and that this could be affected by heating or by means of an electric spark, which would replenish 'the minute spaces, in which the atmospheres extend, with a denser fiery fluid'. This was a satisfactory explanation for the combination of such gases as hydrogen and oxygen, which occurred only with the aid of a spark, but did not really explain the combination of ammonia and hydrogen chloride, which occurred spontaneously.

The idea of explaining repulsive forces by atmospheres of fire seems to have been originated and worked out by Bryan Higgins, although similar ideas were put forward in the same year, 1775, by Bergman,[23] and two years later by Lavoisier.[24] In 1779, William Cleghorn in his thesis[25] put forward a theory of fire which accorded with the views expressed by Bryan Higgins. He considered fire to consist of mutually repelling particles, which were attracted in varying degrees by the particles of other substances. Repulsive forces were explained in a similar way by William Higgins and by John Dalton.[26]

One of Bryan Higgins' experiments was the combination of an acid and an alkali—hydrogen chloride and ammonia.[27] He considered that one atom combined with one atom, and that at this point saturation occurred. In this sense he was putting forward a law of definite proportions. He did not, however, extend his theory to the combination of one atom with two or more atoms. This was left to George Fordyce and William Higgins.

George Fordyce

George Fordyce was born in Aberdeen and studied under Cullen in Edinburgh, obtaining the degree of M.D. in 1758. He completed his education by travelling to Leyden to study anatomy. It is interesting to note that Bryan Higgins' education may have been very similar. Priestley ascribes Bryan's view of fixed air to Cullen[28] and thereby suggests that Bryan Higgins may have been a pupil of Cullen. In 1759, Fordyce opened a school of chemistry in London and later in 1764 extended it to cover medicine and materia medica.

Fordyce kept to a strict routine. He lectured from 7.00 a.m. to 10.00 a.m. for six days a week, giving three lectures on chemistry, medicine, and materia medica one after another. He was fond of company and social life, and is reported to have frequently returned, after a convivial evening, just in time to begin the next morning's lectures.

At what stage he developed his atomic theory is unknown,[29] but he was teaching it in 1784, and may well have been for many years before.

He had a very simple view of the elements, believing in two only, air and water.[30] However, he found it necessary to use a list of simple compounds or 'chemical elements' to explain chemical reactions. His list contained about sixty substances including the metals. sulphur, respirable air, inflammable air and phlogisticated air as well as the various acids and alkalis, and earths. He believed that 'A compound may become an element'.[31] By this he meant that if any compound could act as an whole to combine with another substance, then he would consider that compound to be an element. He wrote:

Thus a particle of volatile alkali, may unite with a particle of an acid, forming sal ammoniac, in which they have one common sphere of chemical attraction, at which they may unite with copper, and when so combined, the three particles acquire one sphere of mechanical action.[32]

He explained this by means of a diagram;

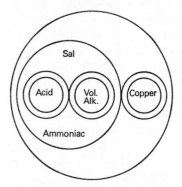

He believed in the phlogiston theory[33] and explained the increase in weight on calcination by supposing that phlogiston had a negative weight, and that the metal only had its full weight when separated from the phlogiston. In 1785, he carried out an experiment which indicated 'that water gains weight on being frozen'[34] or that water gained weight on losing phlogiston.

Fordyce considered atoms to be the mechanical limit to which matter could be divided, and he called them the 'smallest integral parts of matter'. He made an important extension to Bryan Higgins' theory when he considered that one of the smallest integral parts of an element could unite with one or two of the smallest integral parts of another element. In this respect, he appears to have been the first to have a concept of combination in more than one proportion.

It was William Higgins, who extended this idea to produce a more acceptable theory.

William Higgins

William Higgins was born in Ireland in 1762/3, but in his early teens was sent to live with his uncle in London, to obtain an education. He assisted with most of Bryan's experiments as well as attending his lectures, and thereby became proficient in the practical techniques of chemical experimentation and in the theory of chemical reaction. He obtained an education in chemistry which was not closely linked with medicine, and there is no doubt that his early training in atomic theory did much to form his later ideas.

From 1777 onwards, the London houses of Sir Joseph Banks[35] in Soho Square and Richard Kirwan in Newman Street became regular meeting-places for scientists of the time. Fordyce and Bryan and William Higgins met on these occasions[36] and it seems probable that the uncommitted William Higgins had the opportunity of studying both atomic theories. Certainly William did not accept his uncle's ideas without question for in 1784 he had accepted Lavoisier's theory of combustion,[37] and was therefore one of the first British chemists to reject the phlogiston theory. This freed him from the encumbrance of phlogiston, and enabled him to have an unrestricted view of the elements. It will be shown later that he failed to take full advantage of this.

In 1786, William left Bryan and went to Magdalen Hall, Oxford[38] and later in 1787 migrated to Pembroke College. It was while he was at Pembroke College that he wrote his *Comparative view of the phlogistic and antiphlogistic theories* which was published in 1789. It was intended as a refutation of Kirwan's *Essay on phlogiston*[39] but its present importance is that its ideas were put forward using the atomic theory.

When William first went to Oxford, the Professor of Chemistry was Dr Austin,[40] and his work is frequently quoted in the *Comparative view*.[41] Austin also had some ideas on atomism. He assumed that the atoms of gases had equal weights, and explained their different specific gravities by supposing that the distances between the atoms were different.[42] This latter idea is one which William Higgins also used,[43] although with less mathematical precision.

William's views on atoms and the attractive and repulsive forces between them were very similar to his uncle's. He did not give a straightforward list of his elements, but made it clear that a substance which could not be decomposed was an element. He wrote:

Though we have not hitherto been able to decompose pure calcareous, argillaceous, siliceous, barytic and magnesian earths, or fixed vegetable and mineral alkalis, yet we suspect them to be compounds . . . but until we resolve these into their constituent principles, we must consider them as simple substances, and not attribute their different properties to one common principle. I think I may presume to say that sulphur, phosphorus, phlogisticated air and metals are as simple bodies as the earths and that we know as little of their origin constituent principles.[44]

In other words, William Higgins did not accept sulphur, phosphorus, phlogisticated air or the metals as ultimate elements, yet he was prepared provisionally to write of their ultimate parts or atoms. This view is substantiated when he writes:

Although, I do not think sulphur contains phlogiston, or the solid matter of light inflammable air, I by no means suppose it to be a simple body, but to be relatively to our knowledge of chemistry as simple as the earths, or the two fixed alkalies; all of which I make no doubt will be analysed at some future period, when the science of chemistry will be more cultivated than at present, by men of genius, fortune and leisure.[45]

William considered fire to be a definite chemical substance, and wrote:

fire unites chemically to bodies, and of course must gravitate towards them. Can we therefore doubt but that fire is a substance, and not a quality as some philosophers are pleased to suppose?[46]

It is uncertain whether he considered it to be an element. William's list of true elements was probably small like his uncle's.

The most notable feature of William Higgins' book is his use of symbols and formulae to represent molecules of compounds. Thus, he writes S—d as the formula of volatile vitriolic acid (sulphur dioxide) where S represents an atom of sulphur and d represents an atom of dephlogisticated air or oxygen. This representation indicates an advanced appreciation of the atomic theory, and the use of the initial letter of the element as a symbol representing one atom of the element is the system now in use, and was superior to the system later used by Dalton.[47] Higgins' symbols have been criticized on the grounds that they were not uniquely related to a particular element. 'I' sometimes represented an atom of iron and sometimes an atom of inflammable air. However, in the context in which they were used there was little possibility of confusion. Another cause of criticism is his use of symbols to represent atoms of substances which he does not believe to be elements. Even further doubt is cast on his symbols by the use of V to represent a molecule of volatile vitriolic acid, although this may well be a forerunner of the shorthand notation sometimes used nowadays to represent common groups in organic chemistry.

William extended his theory to include the combination of a second atom of dephlogisticated air or oxygen to sulphur to form a molecule of perfect vitriolic acid or sulphur trioxide. Its formula he wrote:[48]

where S represented an atom of sulphur and d and D represented atoms of dephlogisticated air or oxygen. He wrote:

We may conclude, that, in volatile vitriolic acid, a single ultimate particle of sulphur is intimately united only to a single particle of dephlogisticated air; and that, in perfect vitriolic acid, every single particle of sulphur is united to two of dephlogisticated air, being the quantity necessary to saturation.[49]

He also produced formulae for the various oxides of nitrogen, although they were based on very little experimental evidence. He wrote:[50]

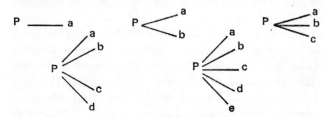

where P represented an atom of phlogisticated air or nitrogen and a, b, c, d, e represented atoms of dephlogisticated air or oxygen.

In these examples there can be little doubt that William Higgins in many ways anticipated the law of multiple proportions.

William retained his uncle's ideas on the simplicity of nature, and assumed that the simplest compound was formed by the union of one atom of each element. A similar assumption was later made by Dalton. This led to errors in the above formulae, but did not invalidate the subsequent reasoning.

In his formulae, William Higgins also introduced the valency bond. The representation, by means of a line, of the bond between two atoms, was a concept which was not again used until 1858, when it was revived by Couper.

The *Comparative view* contains several examples of gases combining in simple proportions by volume. Higgins wrote, '2 cubic inches of light inflammable air require but 1 of dephlogisticated air to condense them'[51] and 'Two measures of volatile vitriolic acid contain two measures of dephlogisticated air'.[52] Such examples seem to indicate that William had a vague understanding of the law of gaseous volumes before it was enunciated by Gay-Lussac.[53] However, his views were very rudimentary, and were based on few experimental results and there is no evidence that he generalized his findings.

As shown earlier, Bryan Higgins rejected the idea that atoms were composed of different quantities of a primary substance. William, however, seems to have accepted this view. Nowhere in the *Comparative view* is there a clear statement on the matter, but he later wrote, 'the specific weight of the ultimate divisions of all kinds of ponderable matter is the same—their size or diameter only constitutes the difference'.[54]

William considered that the formula of volatile vitriolic acid (sulphur dioxide) was SO and wrote:

100 grains of sulphur . . . require 100 or 102 of the real gravitating matter of dephlogisticated air to form volatile vitriolic acid, and as volatile vitriolic acid is very little short of double the specific gravity of dephlogisticated air, we may conclude, that the ultimate particles of sulphur and dephlogisticated air contain equal quantities of solid matter.[55]

According to his theory of atomic constitution, atoms having the same weight would contain equal quantities of the primary matter, and would therefore be of equal size and, of course, identical. That this was not so with the atoms of sulphur and oxygen must have caused William Higgins some difficulty, but he ignored the problem in his writings.[56] Bryan Higgins' idea of atoms, being composed of different materials, would have been competent to explain this.

On the formation of water, William Higgins wrote:

As 2 cubic inches of light inflammable air (hydrogen) require 1 of dephlogisticated air (oxygen) to condense them, we must suppose that they contain equal number of divisions, and that the difference of their specific gravity depends chiefly on the size of their ultimate particles.[57]

He had no doubt at all that the formula of water was HO and wrote:

water is composed of molicules (*sic*) formed by the union of a single particle of dephlogisticated air to an ultimate particle of light inflammable air, and that they are incapable of uniting to a third particle of either of their constituent principles.[58]

He considered the experimental evidence available and came to the conclusion that water was composed of oxygen and hydrogen in the proportion of 6 to 1 by weight.[59] He later wrote:

According to Mr Lavoisier, the proportion of dephlogisticated air in water, is to the inflammable air as 7 to 1; and indeed, agreeable to all experience, it is at least 6 to 1.[60]

It has been suggested[61] that William Higgins did not recognize the atomic weights of hydrogen and oxygen from this information. I cannot agree with this. His information—the proportions by weight of the elements and the molecular formula—was virtually the same as that used to find the weights of the sulphur and oxygen atoms in the previous example.

William Higgins did not see the importance of atomic weights; he was much more concerned with inter-atomic forces; he gave an arbitrary numerical value to the attractive force of each atom and was by mathematical means able to explain the limited number of compounds between any two elements, and to arrive at some theoretical justification for the law of multiple proportions. Such considerations were common at this time; both Cullen and Black attempted to explain the forces between atoms and used diagrams which were not so very different from those of William Higgins. The work on combining proportions of such chemists as Kirwan and Richter was probably prompted by a similar desire. Atomic weights were of no immediate concern for Higgins and he did not rationalize them on a numerical basis by selecting a unit, such as the weight of a hydrogen atom. When he did write of atomic weights he used the term 'quantities of solid matter'.[62]

William's atomic theory had in the case of water to explain how an atom of oxygen weighing six times as much as an atom of hydrogen, and, therefore, being six

times its size, could occupy half its volume. He overcame this difficulty by assuming different sized atmospheres of fire, so that the small hydrogen atoms had
large atmospheres and were widely spaced, while the
large oxygen atoms had small atmospheres and were
comparatively close.[63] When he wrote 'the difference in
their specific gravity depends chiefly on the size of their
ultimate particles',[64] we must assume that he meant by
ultimate particles, the atoms plus their atmospheres of
fire. This does not seem very satisfactory, but Higgins
was seldom rigorous in his wording.

Summary of William Higgins' theory

William Higgins' theory was in many ways unsatisfactory. It was founded on a limited and incomplete
list of elements, and was mostly applied to substances
which were considered to be compounds. Important
ideas were often based on limited experimental evidence
and no attempt was made to explain the equal atomic
weights of sulphur and oxygen. Atomic weights were
not important to Higgins, and, although there is
evidence that he determined several, he made no
attempt to give them numerical values by selecting a
unit for them.

On the other hand, Higgins put forward some very
advanced ideas. He used atomic symbols and valency
bonds, deduced molecular formulae, partly anticipated
the law of multiple proportions, and had an intuition
regarding the law of gaseous volumes.

William Higgins' failure to persevere with the atomic theory

William Higgins was a young man of about twenty-
seven years when the *Comparative view* was published,
and historians of science have been puzzled by the fact
that he published nothing more on atomic theory for
twenty-five years.[65] There is no evidence to explain this
and we can only speculate.

In the second half of the eighteenth century, chemical atomic theories were well known in London. Bryan
Higgins and Fordyce had instructed several hundred
pupils in their schools. William Higgins himself received all his scientific education in terms of the atomic
theory, and it therefore seems reasonable to assume that

he did not consider it to be a novel idea. This view is supported by the fact that he made no attempt to explain his theory to his readers, presumably expecting them to be familiar with it. If he had been uncertain about this, he must have felt it confirmed by the unenthusiastic reception accorded to his book.[66] Its atomic ideas went unnoticed while the chemical world was involved in the phlogiston controversy.

In 1792, William Higgins returned to Dublin to take up the position of chemist to the Apothecaries' Hall, and later in 1795, he moved to the Dublin Society. In both positions he was concerned with the application of chemistry to practical problems[67] and his atomic theory was forgotten until after the publication of Dalton's work. A consideration of his angry claims for priority is beyond the scope of this paper.

Conclusion

Several brave attempts to explain chemical phenomena in terms of an atomic theory were made in London in the second half of the eighteenth century. Bryan Higgins and George Fordyce were joined in 1786 by Dr Austin, who left the Professorship of Chemistry at Oxford to become Physician at St Bartholomew's Hospital. Their teaching created a sizeable body of chemists, who believed and thought in terms of atoms, and it certainly influenced William Higgins. There was no comparable school in England, and certainly not one in Manchester, which could have influenced Dalton. Dalton's ideas were almost certainly derived independently of this group, which only assisted him by paving the way for his ideas and making them readily acceptable in the metropolis.

A complete atomic theory was not possible until the phlogiston theory had been overthrown, and this was the work of Lavoisier in 1783. This left chemistry in a state of chaos, and the French chemists began the process of renaming and rationalization which culminated in the *Traité élémentaire de chimie* of 1789. In this book a list of about thirty elements was given, and for the first time a clear and unambiguous concept of element was put forward. It was on this as his foundation that Dalton, in the first few years of the nineteenth century, built his atomic theory.

Acknowledgment: my thanks are due to Dr W. V. Farrar for his help and advice.

1 J. Priestley, *Philosophical empiricism* (London, 1775).

2 B. Higgins, *Observations and advice for the manufacture of muscovado sugar and rum* (St Jago de la Vega, in several parts 1797–1803).

3 Newton's atomic theory is probably derived from the classical theories via Gassendi and Boyle.

4 R. Boyle, *The Sceptical Chymist* (London, 1661).

5 B. Higgins, *Philosophical essay concerning light* (London, 1776).

6 B. Higgins, *Syllabus of the discourses and experiments with which the meetings of the subscribers are to be opened after the course of chemistry is concluded* (London, 1776) 9.

7 Ibid., 20, 25–6.

8 B. Higgins, op. cit., (5) 10.

9 Ibid., 13.

10 J. Price, *An account of some experiments on mercury made at Guildford in May 1782 in the laboratory of J. Price, M.D., F.R.S.* (2nd edn, Oxford, Clarendon Press, 1783).

11 B. Higgins, op. cit., (6) 10–11.

12 B. Higgins, op. cit., (5) 10.

13 Ibid., 2.

14 B. Higgins, op. cit., (6) 9–10.

15 Newton, *Opticks* (London, 1704), Query 31.

16 B. Higgins, op. cit., (5) 24–5.

17 Ibid., xxxix, and B. Higgins, op. cit., (6) 49.

18 B. Higgins, op. cit., (5) 14.

19 B. Higgins, op. cit., (6) 12.

20 He also recognized that the 'adiabatic' expansion of a gas resulted in cooling. See B. Higgins, op. cit., (6) 61.

21 Ibid., 50.

22 Ibid., 13.

23 T. Bergman, *De attractionibus electivis* (1775).

24 A. L. Lavoisier, *Mémoires de l'Académie des Sciences*, 1777, 420.

25 W. Cleghorn, *Disputatio inauguralis theoriam ignis complectens* (Edinburgh, 1779).

26 Dalton's ideas were almost certainly derived from Lavoisier.

27 These were considered to be as near to the pure acid and alkali fluids as it was possible to get.

28 J. Priestley, op. cit., (1) 43.

29 His *Syllabus of Lectures in Chemistry* is undated. He was certainly teaching it in 1784, for a manuscript copy of his notes, dated August 1784–December 1785, is extant.

30 This idea is derived from Van Helmont (1577–1644) who showed that vegetable matter could apparently grow from water only. Van Helmont's experiments were repeated by Boyle and others. Bryan Higgins rejected them. See B. Higgins, op. cit., (5) 26.

The idea was supported by the repeated distillation of pure water in a glass apparatus, which left a residue of earth. This was due to the glass being dissolved, but was thought to indicate the conversion of water to earth. Bryan Higgins also rejected this, ibid., 26.

31 G. Fordyce, *Elements of agriculture and vegetation* (London, 1789) 7.

32 Ibid., 104.

33 Fordyce's chemical views are given in J. R. Partington, *A history of chemistry* (London, 1962) III, 692.

J D—K

Notes

34 'Experiments on the loss of weight in bodies on being melted or heated', *Phil. Trans. Roy. Soc.*, lxxv, 13.

35 President of the Royal Society from 1778 until his death in 1820.

36 P. McLaughlin, *Studies*, 1939, 600–1.

37 W. Higgins, *A comparative view of the phlogistic and antiphlogistic theories* (London, 1789) xi.

38 As a Catholic, William had been unable to obtain an education in Ireland, yet, in England, he managed to enter the University of Oxford, a stronghold of the Protestant faith. How he managed this is unknown; the Bursar of Pembroke College, Mr G. R. F. Bredin, was unable to find any record of an exceptional admission; perhaps William apostatized.

39 R. Kirwan, *Essay on phlogiston* (London, 1787).

40 Austin was Professor of Chemistry from 1785–6.

41 Pp. 62, 71–2, 74, 80, 250.

42 Austin, *Phil. Trans. Roy. Soc.*, lxxviii (1788) 13.

43 W. Higgins, op. cit., (35) 15.

44 Ibid., 32.

45 Ibid., 120.

46 Ibid., 175.

47 In 1814, Higgins allowed superiority to Dalton's symbols. W. Higgins, *Experiments and discourses on the atomic theory and electrical phenomena* (London, 1814) 10–11.

48 W. Higgins, op. cit., (35) 39.

49 Ibid., 36–7.

50 Ibid., 133–4.

51 Ibid., 37.

52 Ibid., 37–8.

53 Thomas Thomson in 1813 conceded Higgins priority in this respect. *Annals of Philosophy*, ii (1813) 445.

54 W. Higgins, *Phil. Mag.*, xlix (1817) 245 footnote.

55 W. Higgins, op. cit., (35) 36.

56 Dalton also had, and ignored, the name difficulty, which arises from the incorrect formula for sulphur dioxide.

57 W. Higgins, op. cit., (35) 37.

58 Ibid., 37–8.

59 Ibid., 2–3.

60 Ibid., 148–9.

61 T. S. Wheeler and J. R. Partington, *Life and work of William Higgins* (London, 1960) 131.

62 W. Higgins, op. cit., (35) 36.

63 See ibid., 37, for an example of this juggling with atmospheres of fire to obtain the correct specific gravity.

64 Ibid., 37.

65 W. Higgins, op. cit., (45).

66 It ran to a second edition, and sold about a thousand copies.

67 The minutes of the Dublin Society of 18 June 1795 contain the resolution appointing Higgins on the recommendation of Richard Kirwan, and state that 'he be directed . . . to make such experiments on dying (*sic*) materials and other articles, wherein Chymistry may assist the Arts'.

*The Industrial
Background to
John Dalton*

On an engraving published by S. and N. Buch, in 1728, Manchester is described thus:

A spacious, rich and populous inland town in the Hundred of Salford. This town is adorned with many noted buildings . . . and with handsome broad streets both new and old: and a large bridge over the River Irwell which joyneth Salford, a populous beautiful town giving the name to the Hundred, and seemeth a suburb thereto.[1]

But by the time John Dalton died there in 1844 profound and far-reaching changes had taken place both in the English scene and its economy. Instead of speaking of beautiful towns with broad streets and handsome buildings, Edward Baines Jr. was writing:

I admit that the manufacturing districts have a repulsive exterior. The smoke that hangs over them—their noisy, bustling, and dirty streets—the large proportion of the working classes seen there, many of whom have their persons and clothes blackened with their occupations—the hum and buzz of machinery in the factories—the flaming of furnaces—the rude earnestness of the 'unwashed artificiers'—and their provincial dialect—are little calculated to gratify 'polite ears' or to please the age accustomed to parks and green fields.[2]

It is against a background of such changes that we must examine the life and activities of John Dalton in Manchester.

While one must treat population statistics in the eighteenth century with reserve, it is obvious that in the hundred-odd years separating the above quotations what is tantamount to a population explosion took place in Lancashire. At the time that Buch's engraving was published, Manchester probably contained some 13,000 people, while by the time Baines was writing there were 300,000 in the built-up area alone, with anything up to 1·5 million if we include adjacent districts. The technical background to this phenomenal expansion was the progressive mechanization of the textile industry, which changed a domestic economy, based on a combination of farming with spinning and weaving, into the factory system. The change was made possible through a series of mechanical inventions: Kay's shuttle (1733), Hargreave's jenny (1767), Arkwright's water-frame (1768), and Crompton's mule (1774), supplemented by the introduction of steam power which freed the factories from their dependence on rapidly flowing streams, and concentrated much of the industry in the growing towns. The first Manchester cotton-spinning mill was built by Richard Arkwright in the 1780's; it was powered by a Newcomen-type engine. The first Boulton and Watt engine in Lancashire, at Peter Drinkwater's mill near Piccadilly, dates from the end of the same decade. Unlike spinning, mechanical processes of weaving took longer to influence domestic production (Edmund Cartwright's loom dates from 1787), but the transformation of domestic weaving into a factory-based industry was complete by the end of Dalton's life. Then Lancashire supported nearly a tenth of the entire British population and produced one half of its exports—piece goods to the value of £17·5M.

To further the movement of the goods produced, roads were improved. The end of the period between the two quotations also covers the formation of the main railway pattern of the region. In 1830 Manchester was connected with Liverpool by rail; in 1840 with Leeds, and in 1842 with London, while that notable early civil engineering feat, the Woodhead tunnel, giving connection with Sheffield, was completed the year after Dalton died.

But to attribute these changes in the Manchester region of Lancashire solely to the outcome of mechanical invention, as seen in the rise of the cotton industry, would be to misrepresent the total situation. A. E. Musson and E. Robinson make the point that:

It would appear, from our investigations in Manchester, that there was a closer association between science and industry in the early Industrial Revolution than has hitherto been thought.[3]

Similarly, Frank Greenaway, in a notable paper to the Manchester Literary and Philosophical Society in 1958 recorded that:

A few mechanical inventions in the textile industry have monopolized the attention of some social and economic historians, but it should be realized that chemical innovation was both an accompaniment of mechanical invention (e.g. bleaching by improved methods for the increased quantity of cloth) and a source of new substances and new wealth.[4]

So, on closer scrutiny we find that in addition to the finishing trades that were the obvious adjuncts to the cotton industry (bleaching, dyeing, and calico printing, which 'exhibited a most interesting combination of chemical skill with mechanical ingenuity'), there were in the Manchester region also iron works at Gorton, steelworks at Newton Heath, metal trades, including tin plate workers, braziers who cast 'motion-work', and clock-makers who deployed their skill in cutting gear wheels for the new machines, at Oldham, Rochdale, Bury, Bolton and Dukinfield, paper works, where the making of paper was 'brought to great perfection' at Bolton, Farnworth, and Bury, in addition to the coal mines that were scattered throughout the area and even penetrated the town itself. This then, very briefly, was Dalton's Manchester, his home for half a century at a time of unprecedented change and growth. But when one studies the earlier standard biographies of Dalton one finds it difficult to believe that such as this was the background at least to his physical existence; and in his own writings there is little to augment the paucity of reference to industrial developments by his biographers.

I think that it can be argued, however, that contemporary industrial development was nevertheless an important formative factor in Dalton's career, since the new manufactures needed new educational institutions to service the new society.

In 1783, i.e. ten years before Dalton came to Manchester, a short-lived College of Arts and Sciences had been formed. Dr Thomas Percival was President, and of the lecturers, Dr Thomas Henry dealt with chemistry, Henry Clarke with natural philosophy, and Thomas

Barnes with the history and progress of Arts and Manufactures. The history of the College is obscure but it only survived for a few years and a New College, or Manchester Academy, followed in 1786. Barnes became Principal of the new foundation, Percival was a member, and it was to this institution that John Dalton was invited to come in 1793 at the age of twenty-seven, to teach mathematics and natural philosophy. Although during the next half century he established himself as the greatest chemical thinker of his time, Greenaway suggests that, when appointed, his knowledge of chemistry probably did not extend beyond some reading of the writings of Robert Boyle, the *Elementa chemiae* of Hermann Boerhaave and the *Chemical essays* of Richard Watson.[5]

By all accounts Dalton quickly established himself in his new environment. It has been pointed out by W. H. Chaloner[6] that the core of the intellectual life of Manchester was a small coterie based on the Literary and Philosophical Society, so, since Dalton became a member of this society within a year of going to Manchester, and was successively its Secretary, a Vice-president, and President for twenty-five years, it might be profitable to look at the constitution of this élite. Who were they? What was their background? What were their relations with other centres of intellectual and industrial development in Great Britain and Europe, and which of them became especial friends of Dalton? Before going on to answer these questions, however, it is valuable to remind ourselves of one significant fact about the evolution of technology in these islands. Elsewhere I have pointed out that, while mechanical technology was largely an English product, it was to a very large extent Scottish personnel or Scottish trained personnel that made the vital contributions to the development of the correlative non-mechanical technology, in other words particularly to the founding and development of the chemical industry. And the background to the application of chemistry was frequently the Medical Faculties of the Universities of Edinburgh and Glasgow, with Leyden as a continental extension. The English universities, Oxford and Cambridge, made few or no contributions to applied science in the eighteenth century. They were, to quote Greenaway, 'in a state of comfortable indolence'.[7] They 'contributed little enough to the life of the country as a whole, and virtually nothing in a direct way to those physical sciences with which we are concerned'.[8]

Why this was so was suggested even during Dalton's lifetime. W. Cooke Taylor who toured Lancashire shortly before Dalton's death wrote that:

The factory system is a modern creation; history throws no light on its nature, for it has scarcely begun to recognize its existence; the philosophy of the schools supplies very imperfect help for estimating its results because an innovating power of such immense force could never have been anticipated.[9]

But this innovating power had been released by an instrument-maker in the University of Glasgow who appreciated the commercial significance of the principle of latent heat.

Furthermore, Scotland was fortunate in its early learned societies. There was a philosophical society in Edinburgh in 1737, subsequently the Philosophical Society of Edinburgh of which Dr Joseph Black was a member, and finally in 1783 the Royal Society of Edinburgh. There were also several chemical societies.[10]

With this signal difference in the activities of the universities of England and Scotland in mind, let us, therefore, go on to study the background and activities of those of the Manchester élite who are most likely to have influenced Dalton.

As was said above, John Dalton joined the Literary and Philosophical Society within a year of going to Manchester. The Society was then twelve years old (founded in 1781). It had been founded in the home of Dr Thomas Percival, an Edinburgh and Leyden trained practitioner. The opening manifesto sets out its objectives. They were 'to collect and publish important communications . . . and so save from oblivion many valuable discoveries or improvements in arts, and much useful information in various branches of science'. Percival had been one of the first students of the Warrington Academy among whose subscribers were Dr John Roebuck, again of Edinburgh and Leyden, the pioneer vitriol manufacturer and co-founder of Carron Iron-Works in Scotland; Thomas Bentley of Liverpool who became the business partner of Josiah Wedgwood and James Percival, then of Manchester.[11]

Percival's uncle had been a student of Boerhaave at Leyden and he himself after a period at Edinburgh also went there (M.D. 1765). As a student in Edinburgh he lodged with one of Principal William Robertson's married sisters and constitutes an important link with Edinburgh, where he studied, with Birmingham and the Lunar Society through Joseph Priestley, and with the Royal Society in London. To begin with in the Literary and Philosophical Society there was not much of a dividing line between those in the professions and those who were engaged in manufactures. This is seen if we look at the activities of a few of the prominent early members. These included Thomas Henry, F.R.S., a native of Wrexham, who in addition to practising medicine, engaged in chemical manufacture, particularly of *Magnesia Alba*. He was a friend of Joseph Priestley and Benjamin Franklin, and numbered among his European correspondents P. J. Macquer, J. Hellot, C. L. Berthollet, and many others. In the early days of the Literary and Philosophical Society he read an important paper on Chemistry and Arts in which he emphasized the need for a closer union between science and technics. Then there was Charles Taylor the dyer and fustian manufacturer who claimed to know all the eminent chemists of Europe. It was to Taylor's firm, Messrs. Maxwell and Taylor, that James Watt sent his son, James Junior. The introduction came through Thomas Henry with whom Watt was in correspondence concerning chlorine bleaching.[12]

Young Watt did not remain in Manchester for long but seems to have made friends quickly. He numbered among them, Thomas Henry's sons, of whom William Henry was an intimate of Dalton, Joseph Priestley Jr., and one of Dr Percival's assistants, John Ferriar, a native of Jedburgh and Edinburgh medical graduate with whom Watt became co-secretary of the Society in 1790. Apart from his apprenticeship to Maxwell and Taylor, James Watt Jr. appears to have acted as representative for the Boulton and Watt concern in Lancashire, and during his stay there (1788–92) was one of the main contacts between Manchester scientists and European science, though by no means the only one.

Henry Clarke, the mathematician who lived in Manchester till 1799, was an international figure, and Adam Walker, self-taught mathematician and friend of Priestley, also had European contacts.

Musson and Robertson go so far as to say that 'the majority of the members of the Society were either engaged in or at least interested in, the extension of science and art to the manufacturing process',[13] and they mention among others, John Wilson of Ainsworth who experimented on bleaching and dyeing, particularly the Turkey Red process.[14]

So far as friendship with Dalton is concerned, to those already mentioned might be added Peter Ewart a pupil of John Rennie and former employee of Boulton and Watt, who established himself as an engineer and cotton manufacturer in Manchester and enjoyed Dalton's friendship for half a century; Peter Clare, a clockmaker, who was Dalton's closest companion and latterly secretary; John Kennedy, a Scots engineer from Kirkcudbright, and pioneer in the field of steam-powered spinning, whose daughter married the sanitary reformer Edwin Chadwick; or Thomas Hoyle, the calico printer, famed for Hoyle's purples. The resident staff of New College was small, and to help them out visiting lecturers came to supplement the courses given by the professors. These included John Rotheram, John Warltire, and Henry Moyes, all of whom had been educated in Scotland, as well as Thomas Garnett of the Andersonian Institute in Glasgow, who lectured on the applications of chemistry to the common purposes of life, as well as to the useful arts of bleaching, dyeing, agriculture, etc.[15,16]

One could go on, but I think that sufficient has been said to demonstrate that there is ample evidence to show that Dalton's Manchester associates and contacts were displaying considerable interest in the application of chemistry to the industrial arts. Dalton, unlike his Scottish contemporaries or the members of the Lunar Society, does not appear to have shared these interests. He made no technical discovery and engaged in no commercial activities. We do not even know whether he entered into discussions of the application of chemistry to practical affairs. During his long association with the Literary and Philosophical Society he read no less than 116 papers of which, however, only 26 have survived in the Memoirs. Of these one or two have a slightly industrial flavour, for example, his lecture of 6 October 1820 'On Oil, and the gases obtained from it by heat',[17] and this, I would remind you, was just at the time that public gas companies were being established, some of which experimented with the production of gas by the cracking of oil rather than the destructive distillation of coal.[18] But, by and large, Greenaway is correct when he writes that 'Great events took place in his England, even in his Manchester, but he seems to have been untouched by them, or to have done nothing to touch them'.[19]

While, traditionally, Henry Cavendish has been represented as the prime chemical misanthrope, Dalton in many ways runs him a close second. 'He was not visited much,' says R. Angus Smith, 'because his house was incapable of hospitality, and he himself lived too much in himself to be capable of entertaining others.'[20]

Little of Dalton's correspondence that I have been able to examine throws much light on his relations with his contemporaries. In 1805, for example, on his way to London he visited Birmingham and dined with James Watt, but all that Dalton records of the meeting is that he 'spent some hours most agreeably' with the veteran engineer.[21] Henry Roscoe also quotes letters from Thomas Charles Hope of Edinburgh, and Thomas Thomson of Glasgow which emphasize the interest of the Scottish professors in the application of their subject, but in general all the evidence is against Dalton having any real contact with practical affairs.

Thus, in contrast to many of his contemporaries, and one might instance from widely different spheres, Humphry Davy, Bryan Higgins, W. H. Wollaston, or Thomas Young, Dalton, although he travelled and lectured in London, Birmingham, Edinburgh, and Glasgow, did not to any great extent keep in touch with other scientists. Thus Manchester, while it had a formal scientific academy in the Literary and Philosophical Society never became a focal point as did the Lunar Society in Birmingham whose world-wide connections are revealed through the Bolton and Watt correspondence still preserved particularly in the Assay Office in

Birmingham. Greenaway goes so far as to say of Dalton that 'he was actually miserably isolated'.

While I believe that by and large Greenaway is correct about Dalton, I have certain reservations. Dalton was certainly not a practical chemist in the sense that Joseph Black, or Humphry Davy, or Antoine Lavoisier were chemists. Their chemistry was the chemistry of the properties of substances and their interactions. Dalton became one of the founding fathers of chemistry because his atomic hypothesis gave a theoretical basis to the increasingly quantified observation of Black, Lavoisier, and others. But one should not see him as living totally isolated, a mere theoretician. The Industrial Revolution was not solely a material revolution: it was also a thermodynamic revolution. Watt's separate condenser engine (1769) was born in the University of Glasgow where Watt enjoyed the friendship of Dr Joseph Black. The subvention of Watt by Black and Dr John Roebuck of Carron has been dealt with elsewhere. The point I want to make is that the practice of power production is associated with late eighteenth and early nineteenth-century theoretical interest in the properties of gases, particularly their thermal expansion and specific heats. In this field John Dalton made contributions that established him as one of the leading thinkers in Europe.[23] He also worked on the absorption of gases by water and it may be significant that his friend Dr William Henry is credited with invention of aerated water. But that is by the way. Further consideration of this point would almost certainly remove some of the impression that John Dalton lived and thought in a state of total isolation from the stirring developments that were going on virtually on his own doorstep.

Writing in 1929, W. H. Brindley pointed out that prior to the time of Dalton we have little knowledge of the chemical manufactures of the Manchester area, and so far as I know this is still substantially true—no comprehensive compilation having come my way.[24] It might therefore be useful as a lead to others more appropriately placed than I to conclude by bringing together briefly such records as we have.

A useful starting point to a history of the chemical industry is the founding of vitriol works at Birmingham in 1746, and at Prestonpans on the Forth in 1749, by Roebuck and Garbett. Roebuck was a native of Sheffield, and had studied medicine at Edinburgh and Leyden, but elected to pursue an industrial career. He was a subscriber to the Warrington Academy and had many associations with the Lunar Society. So far as I know the first vitriol works in the Manchester area was that of Walker, Baker, and Singleton at Pitsworth Moor founded in 1783 by a nephew of the Walker of Kingscote and Walker, a London company. Diligent search might reveal others founded before this. Certainly, the local availability of sulphuric acid was important since there must have been a considerable demand for it from the finishing trades particularly after the introduction of chemical bleaching with chlorine in 1787, a development with which James Watt and Dr Thomas Henry were associated,[25] among others. Dr Thomas Cooper probably learned of the useful properties of chlorine through young Watt and following experiments with Charles Taylor, and a Mr Baker (possibly of Walker, Baker, and Singleton) established a chemical bleaching works at Raikes near Bolton, the traditional bleaching centre. To an expanding industry the advantages of a rapid chemical process were obvious and it spread rapidly. Ridgeways of Horwich, also near Bolton, built Wallsuches to operate it.[26] Dalton acted as consultant to other bleachers, the Sykes of Edgely, and analysed water for them.[27]

As already mentioned, Manchester was also the scene of experiments in the improvement of dyeing under the aegis of John Wilson of Ainsworth. These, however, were not so successful as those of George Macintosh of Dalmarnock on the Clyde. About the same time, i.e. 1785, the above Charles Taylor set up works in Manchester for Turkey Red dyeing.

It was the son of George Macintosh of Dalmarnock, namely Charles Macintosh, who established a new industry in Manchester. To develop his patent (1822 No. 4804) for making a waterproof textile by cementing together two layers of fabric with a solution of rubber in naphtha, Charles Macintosh established a manufactory in partnership with R. W. Barton and J. & H. H. Birley, under the name of Charles Macintosh & Co., first in Glasgow and in 1824 in Manchester. The

naptha used was a by-product of the recently established coal-gas production with which H. H. Birley, in
addition to being a cotton spinner and manufacturer,
was connected. Another rubber manufacturing firm,
David Moseley and Sons, was founded in 1833.

Manchester was in fact the scene of one of the first
two large-scale industrial lighting schemes in Great
Britain. The initial idea of coal-gas illumination came
from the Scottish engineer, William Murdoch who was
then employed by Boulton and Watt of Birmingham.
In 1805 Boulton and Watt undertook the installation of
a thousand separate burners in the cotton mill of
Phillips and Lee. George A. Lee has been described as
one of the most scientific men of his time. He included
William Murdoch and Dalton's life-long friend, Peter
Ewart, in his circle, and in addition to introducing gas-
lighting in his mills, was a pioneer in the development
of cast-iron beams in mills, and heating them with
steam. His gas plant was used for large-scale experiments not only by Boulton and Watt, but by Dr
William Henry.[28]

Figures obtained from the plant form the basis of
Murdoch's paper to the Royal Society in 1808.[29] The
offices of the Manchester Police Commissioners were
lit with gas in 1807, and Burleigh and Kennedy had it
installed in 1808. These were of course smallish individual plants but one of Dalton's students, Samuel
Clegg the elder (1781–1861) was a pioneer in the development of a municipal supply. In Manchester, unlike
most other towns, the public supply was not provided
by a private company. W. H. Chaloner tells us:

In the home of *laissez-faire* the Police Commissioners created
an early example of municipal socialism by starting to manufacture the new illuminant, gas, at first for the purpose of
lighting their own offices (1807) and later for the lighting of
the streets and the supply of private consumers (1816). The
large gasworks which they erected in 1817 proved a financial
success from the start, and the Commissioners used the gas
profits to defray other municipal expenses such as those in-
curred for paving and refuse disposal.[30]

But it took more than the profits of the manufacture
of coal-gas to right the ills that the Industrial Revolution had wrought on the 'handsome broad streets' por-
trayed by S. and N. Buch. In the 1830–40 period it is

reported that half of them were beset with stagnant pools, heaps of refuse, and ordure. Such was the mushroom growth of the new industrial region that in some districts there was only one privy to each 200-250 inhabitants, and we are hardly surprised to learn that only 40 per cent of the children born to these conditions reached the age of five.[31] But there were plenty of 'amenities' of another kind. W. C. Taylor reports in his *Notes of a tour in the manufacturing districts of Lancashire* published in 1842 that the Borough of Manchester contained 769 beerhouses, 498 public houses, 309 brothels, 163 brothels where prostitutes were kept, and 223 houses of ill fame to which they resorted.

I am straying from the strictly industrial background to John Dalton, but we should not forget that it has been claimed that the introduction of gas lighting in the streets made a significant contribution to the suppression of vice.

Old Murdoch alone, has suppressed more vice than the Suppression Society; and has been a greater police officer into the bargain than old Colquhoun and Sir Richard Birnie united. It is not only that men are afraid to be wicked when its light is looking at them, but they are ashamed also: the reformation is applied to the right place. . . . Why was not this new light preached to them long ago: twenty bushels of it would have been of more value than as many chauldrons of sermons.[32]

Finally, let us take a look at the hard core of early nineteenth-century chemical industry, the alkali industry. We have seen that Dalton contributed next to nothing to industrial progress in Manchester, although by his theorizing in time he obviously influenced the whole of it profoundly. To quote yet again from Greenaway:

Already before Dalton's day the control of chemical industry was demanding measurement of increasing precision. The most important branch of chemical industry was that centred on the textile industry, with its need for cleansing and bleaching. . . . The alkali industry, with its steadily increasing factory system was acutely conscious of economic factors, which entailed an understanding of quantities of substances entering into reactions which were believed to be fundamentally simple but which were confused in practice. The efficacy of bleaching processes meant a good deal to the solvency of any textile manufacturer, as Berthollet had been well aware. The volumetric methods which were to be so closely associated with the practice of routine analytical chemistry were born in the textile industry but spread everywhere, when the system of proportions to which Dalton had given a rational basis made an interlocking system of analysis possible.[33]

Manchester, however, did not play any outstanding part in the evolution of the British alkali industry, although at one time Leblanc soda was produced on the north side of the city. After James Muspratt's (1793–1885) initial venture in Liverpool in 1829, Widnes, Warrington, Runcorn, and St Helens became the great centres of the heavy chemical industry in England, although in fact at one time the greatest chemical works in Europe was that of Charles Tennant at St Rollox, Glasgow, whose founder was himself a bleacher. An offshoot of the parent firm, Messrs Tennant, Clow and Co. of Liverpool, appeared on the Manchester scene in 1837 when they purchased Thomson's Chemical Works. This firm had been founded in 1813 at Ardwick Bridge by Edward P. Thomson for the manufacture of heavy acids, sodium hydroxide, and sulphate. Dr James Young (Paraffin Young) was their works manager till 1852, assisted by William Gossage, another well-known name in the early heavy chemical industry. Tennant, Clow and Co. was only one of a number of works established for the production of sulphuric and other acids within a short distance of the centre of Manchester but details of the others still elude me.

To sum up: during Dalton's life in Manchester, although economic affairs took pride of place, there was a by no means insignificant undercurrent of intellectual life. To many entrepreneurs economic success came relatively easily, and perhaps few manufacturers appreciated the potential value of fundamental science for the continuity and progressive growth of the industrial arts. There nevertheless was a substantial majority who did. A fresh and more detailed examination of the developments of the late eighteenth century would almost certainly uncover a perhaps hitherto unsuspected interest in science among industrialists and an economic interest among scientists, particularly chemists. But it now seems unlikely that we shall have to include John Dalton among the latter.

Notes **1** Quoted in W. H. Chaloner, 'Manchester in the latter half of the eighteenth century', *Bulletin of the John Rylands Library*, xlii (1959/60) 40.

2 Quoted in Donald Read, *Press and people—1790–1850* (London, 1961) 1.

3 A. E. Musson and E. Robinson, 'Science and Industry in the late Eighteenth Century', *Economic History Review*, 2nd Series, xiii (1960) 238.

4 F. Greenaway, 'The Biographical Approach to John Dalton', *Manchester Memoirs*, c. (1958/9) 47.

5 Ibid., 60.

6 Chaloner, op. cit., 40.

7 Greenaway, op. cit., 47.

8 Greenaway, *John Dalton and the atom* (London, 1966) 36.

9 W. Cooke Taylor, *Notes of a tour in the manufacturing districts of Lancashire* (London, 1842) 3.

10 A. and N. L. Clow, *The chemical revolution* (London, 1952) 582.

11 F. W. Gibbs, *Joseph Priestley* (London, 1965) 11.

12 Clow, op. cit., 186.

13 Musson and Robinson, op. cit., 244.

14 Clow, op. cit., 216.

15 Musson and Robinson, op. cit., 234 ff.

16 It might be noted in passing that we know that Dalton too had contemplated a career in medicine and had considered going to Edinburgh. It is interesting to speculate how different might have been the course of history had he fallen in with the more application-conscious chemists of the Scottish universities. See, however, Thomas Thomson, *A history of chemistry* (London) 286.

17 *Manchester Memoirs*, ix (1824), 64. Another paper is 'On the Nature and Properties of Indigo, with Directions for the Valuation of Different Samples', ibid., 427. He also looked into the chemical properties of rocks in Manchester and its vicinity (ibid., x (1831) 148). And towards the end of his life he became interested in the destructive distillation of caoutchouc (*Philosophical Magazine*, ix (1836) 479). His *Journals* (destroyed in 1940) showed that he had also spoken to the Lit. and Phil. Soc. on sulphuric acid, bleaching powder and alum, all important industrial chemicals.

18 Clow, op. cit., 436.

19 Greenaway, *John Dalton and the atom*, 3.

20 R. Angus Smith, 'A centenary of science in Manchester', *Manchester Memoirs*, 3rd Series, ix (1883) 230.

21 William Henry, *Memoirs of the life and scientific writings of John Dalton* (London, 1854) 63.

22 Clow, op. cit., 94.

23 John Dalton, 'Experimental Essays on the Constitution of Mixed Gases; on the Force of Steam or Vapour from Water and other liquids. both in a Torricellian Vacuum and in Air; on Evaporation; and on the Expansion of Gases by Heat', *Manchester Memoirs*, v (1802) 535. And elsewhere.

24 W. H. Brindley, *The soul of Manchester* (Manchester, 1929) 194.

25 Clow, op. cit., 186.

26 S. H. Higgins, *A history of bleaching* (London, 1924) 80.

27 Ibid., 116.

28 Andrew Ure, *A dictionary of chemistry*, article: *coal gas*.

29 *Philosophical Transactions of the Royal Society*, xcviii (1808) 124.

30 Chaloner, in *Manchester and its region* (Manchester, 1962) 133.

31 Donald Read, op. cit., 9.

32 *Westminster Review*, xi (1829) 290.

J R Ravetz

Dr Clow's paper prompts me to propose what is not so much a question as a riddle. We have seen that in Manchester as in the other centres of the early industrial revolution, there was an élite of natural philosophers and manufacturers who were convinced of the applicability of the results of the sciences to industrial production, and who also believed in the necessity of institutions for educating a section of the youth along these lines. Yet their conviction produced hardly any viable results; and the effects of that historic failure are with us to this day.

In attempting to explain that failure, we must keep in mind, not only the higher technological schools of the late eighteenth century, on the Continent, of which the greatest was the École Polytechnique; but also the movement for establishing the Technische Hochschulen in Germany, which began in the 1820's, when there was as yet hardly any heavy industry for these schools to serve.

Had the industrial revolution really been brought about by a sequence of simple mechanical inventions made by self-taught artisans, the failure in education might have been more natural; but the presence of philosophically minded men among the industrial élite does leave us with a most perplexing riddle.

G R Talbot

I was very interested in a number of minor points which were made in Dr Clow's paper. I think that it is perhaps worth clarifying one in particular. The discovery of latent heat by Dr Black does not seem to have been in any way influential on Watt's work. Indeed, there is a good case for Watt as an independent discoverer of both specific and latent heats. The legend that Watt was applying scientific ideas established by Dr Black has, of course, long since been refuted, but the most careful examination is needed fully to document that this is so.

Dr Clow mentioned Dalton's contribution to the study of specific heat and other related matters. Dalton was indeed very interested in heat, but his views were largely derivative, probably coming originally from Black via William Henry and Thomas Thomson. He was also very interested in and approved of the ideas of Professor Leslie. Except in a limited sense, namely his experimetal work, Dalton's views on heat were entirely uninfluential. He almost always based his ideas on wrong assumptions from what were generally considered, even at that time, to be discredited secondary sources. His determination of absolute zero on Irvine's principle is a particularly gross example. Dalton was entirely uncritical of many previous authors, particularly Scotsmen, though it has been suggested that he was the first to realize that Newton's Law of Cooling could be used to define a scale of temperature as an alternative to the established scale. I wonder if Dr Clow knows of any concrete examples of the importance of Dalton's work on heat?

A Clow

I was merely throwing out suggestions. I hope historians will explore the question of Dalton's studies on gases and vapours and the industrial and technological significance of this work.

J D—L

9

Gordon Manley

*Dalton's
Accomplishment in
Meteorology*

Since the days when, early last century, Dalton could
enjoy the sight of the hawthorn hedges on his morning
stroll to see his raingauge at Mayfield, close to where
the Institute of Science and Technology now stands,
Manchester has emerged as the capital of northern
England. Manchester is justly proud of Dalton, for he
was a home-bred product of that north-western sea-
board that has always tended to maintain an outlook
independent of London. In a place where the weather
is always with us, it is appropriate to review what
Dalton did towards its understanding. Michael Polanyi
has drawn our attention to those forward steps in
science that are taken, from time to time, with the
highest powers of the mind. Dalton took such steps: he
has been described by Sir Napier Shaw, in the *Manual
of meteorology*,[1] as the true founder of the physics of
a mixture of air and water-vapour, who crossed the
threshhold of the physical explanation of countless
phenomena of the atmosphere.

In that same *Manual*, Shaw declared the science of
meteorology to be essentially the combination of the
knowledge which is obtained from the laboratory and
the weather map. Before 1820, the year in which the
first synoptic charts were constructed by Brandes, for
two centuries almost every physicist paid some attention to the phenomena presented by the atmosphere
within his field of view. But there could be no conception of the laws governing the motions of the atmosphere in a general circulation, until it became possible

to map the distribution of pressure and temperature, and to ascertain the variations of temperature with height. It was not until 1851 that, in Britain, observations were assembled with the aid of the electric telegraph into the first daily weather map.

It has been said that meteorology stands among the most difficult of the sciences, on account of the complex nature, the vast extent and the eternal mobility of the substance under discussion. To this must be added our own physical limitations, and our subjection to the vicissitudes of that ocean of air at the bottom of which we live. Progress in the understanding of the behaviour of the atmosphere depends on the existence of organized cooperative effort to an exceptional degree. The immediate assemblage, transmission and exchange of stupendous volumes of observational data now goes on through every hour of the day. Yet it is still true, as Shaw said, that for the effective study of meteorology there must be coordination between the physical side and the geographical side.

My object here will be to show that Dalton attacked the atmosphere by both methods, within the limitations of his time and temperament. He did much to show to his contemporaries where other steps to understanding could be taken; although he was hampered in many ways from making the advances himself, not least by facets of his own personality whose effects we can now perceive.

In endeavouring to assess his true achievement we must try to imagine the world of 1800. We must never forget that Dalton did his work in that age of Watt, when steam was in the air; when Constable painted the clouds and Luke Howard named them; when de Saussure had attained, in 1787, the summit of Mont Blanc; when the first balloon ascents were being made, and the elastic fluids, or gases, were first isolated and named; when illumination by gas was beginning. Yet it was the age of the coach, long before the spread of railways and the telegraph, long before the Bunsen burner; Volta's electric battery was still to appear. We must not overlook the difficulties of the laboratory, the necessary patience, the imperfection of many instruments, the delays in procurement.

It was perforce a time when, in the words of his

friend Gough writing in 1809, 'meteorology is in its infancy, and the cultivators of the science have little to do but collect facts for the use of their successors'. But it is proper to recall that Dalton was bred into an environment which would be hard to surpass, as a stimulus to the observant mind. He was, as we know, a poor country boy; throughout his life he could make do on little. Like the Herdwick sheep of his Cumbrian fellside, he could thrive where others failed. His instruments were often home-made, his methods were simple; but he applied a very vigorous mind to what lay in front of him. He was brought up in an eighteenth-century farming community, in a land where he who would climb must be ready to take bold strides from footholds already tested; in a part of the world where water in every form abounds; where keen observation and rumination on the atmosphere and what it might bring could not but be built in. A hundred years earlier, another home-bred Cumberland scientist, the Reverend Thomas Robinson of Ousby beneath Crossfell, had acquired instruments; and he was observing what he called the falling of the vapours, and comparing the level of the cloud-base against the several groups of hills that can be seen from his upland rectory.[2]

Dalton's schooling ended when he was twelve; but at the age of eleven his master, John Fletcher, had given him instruction in surveying and mensuration, a matter of which modern educationists might take note. One might speculate whether John Fletcher had come under the influence of a rather remarkable Cumbrian worthy called George Smith, who between 1740 and 1760 emerged not only as an archaeologist, but also as a capable surveyor and mathematician, as his contributions to the *Gentleman's Magazine* show.[3] He, according to Hutchinson, is said to have done much to disseminate a regard for scientific pursuits in his county. We may be sure that his knowledge fell on fertile soil, and we note that he kept a very good meteorological journal. Then there were men such as Dr Brownrigg of Keswick, whose early work on gases was stimulated by the ever-present dangers of the nearby Cumberland coalfield. Books may have been few, but ideas were in the air.

In whatever larger setting we have to place Dalton's

meteorological achievement, we must recognize that until he went to Kendal to join his brother, at the age of fifteen, he would have been almost wholly dependent on his remote country environment for his ideas. But, remote though it was, there were thoughtful minds at work. Keenness of observation, a basic regard for quantitative measurement, and tough endurance and persistence are the natural endowment of many a North-countryman today. In Dalton we can see them flowering in adolescence through an unusual circumstance; his friendship for John Gough of Kendal. It was Gough who taught him to systematize his daily readings; we should therefore look into the ideas and the contemporary knowledge that Gough could acquire.

Gordon Manley

*Dalton's
Accomplishment in
Meteorology*

From the very earliest days of the Royal Society it had been recognized that systematic synchronized observations were needed, but there was no means of disseminating them in such a way as to integrate the behaviour of the atmosphere over a wide area, other than at long intervals and in the very simplest terms. Derham published his thrice-daily observations in tabular form in the *Philosophical Transactions* for 1697–9 and these set a pattern for many later observers. In 1708 Derham was exchanging letters with Scheuchzer in an effort to compare the weather on particular days, but with two months to await a reply from Zürich, little could be learnt. In England the fashion for printing monthly summaries of daily observations began about 1750; and for a hundred years such tables were to be found in all the current journals of scientific intelligence. That they were inadequately standardized was slowly becoming evident in Dalton's time. Abroad, the efforts of the Mannheim Society to collect and study synchronized observations in the 1780's, and President Jefferson's efforts in the newly-born United States, all go to show that men were conscious of the need to acquire knowledge of the larger atmospheric circulation.

Nevertheless, before communications became sufficiently rapid meteorology was perforce almost wholly confined, as Gough saw, to the study of the properties of the atmosphere and its behaviour so far as they could be observed by eye, and locally measured. Pressure and temperature, wind force and direction, the character, frequency and amount of precipitation were being regularly recorded at a number of observatories, and the late eighteenth century saw the beginnings of comparative climatology. Richard Kirwan's *Estimate of the temperature of different latitudes* appeared in 1787, and Dalton used it. Kirwan made much of the 'Height of the line of permanent congelation', for, fifty years earlier, the age of mountain exploration had begun, and was culminating in de Saussure's Alpine studies and his ascent of Mont Blanc. It was in the same year, 1787, that Dalton began to keep, in much the same style as Derham, that meteorological journal which provided the foundation for his work. He maintained his daily observations for fifty-seven years, and in them we can perceive both his strength and his limitations. Why did he begin, and why did he keep his observations in that manner?

Many were alert to the behaviour of the atmosphere in that decade when, after his arrival to teach in Kendal in 1781, he began to learn so much from John Gough. The astonishing haze that spread over Western Europe during the summer of 1783, after the violent eruption of Laki in Iceland, was widely discussed. In 1784 Gilbert White in Hampshire noted the spread of the smoke-haze from London with a north-east wind, and in the winter of that year he appears to have been one of the first to comment on the nocturnal inversions in his valley. Somewhat earlier, Heberden had published in 1766 his comparisons of measurements of rainfall in Pall Mall and on the tower of Westminster Abbey; less rain was caught at the higher level. In an age of agricultural improvement and keen gardening, Daines Barrington had emphasized the need to co-ordinate the keeping of daily meteorological observations with the many country activities in which a true Englishman should take an interest. He produced his *Naturalists calendar* in 1767, for the recording of such observations. Using the forms provided by this calendar, his brother, who became Bishop of Durham, maintained daily readings for fifty years. Bishops and lawyers, squires and doctors and instrument-makers were all busy accumulating daily observations, in the cause of what would now be called nature-study rather than physics. Gough was clearly influenced by this 'naturalist' attitude. He was, although blind, a remarkably accomplished botanist, and when he set up instruments and began to keep his own daily observations in June 1787 his contemporary Gilbert White was similarly engaged.

Indeed, blind John Gough has his own very deserved niche in the world of science. Nine years older than Dalton, he had earlier attended the Friends' School at Kendal, to which Dalton came to teach in 1781. Gough showed astonishing ability, and we know that at the age of fifteen he was absorbing Derham's comments on meteorological observations. In 1778 he went to read mathematics as a private pupil of another Cumberland worthy, John Slee of Mungrisdale; then, relying on his very highly developed senses of touch and smell, he became known as a botanist; and he was also known as a linguist. Dalton became one of Gough's pupils; new worlds of thought opened before him, and we can read with pleasure the very generous acknowledgement that he was always ready to give to the older man. Moreover, Dalton might well have become a botanist, or even a geologist in those earlier years; but the study of the behaviour of the atmosphere proved more attractive, perhaps because of its mathematical and physical content.

Dalton's thoughts turned to the fall of meteors in 1786 and to the aurora in the March of 1787. But he did not begin his systematic daily meteorological observations until September 1787, having made his own instruments which he set up behind the school. Six years later, he published the results in his *Meteorological essays.* He also tabulated for comparison the results of the daily observations kept during the same years by his friend Peter Crosthwaite at Keswick, for whom he had himself made and supplied a thermometer and barometer. It is evident that he appreciated that the averages of temperature for the months at Kendal and Keswick would not be strictly comparable, on account of differences in the manner of exposure of the thermometers and in the hours at which observations were made.

It becomes therefore all the more surprising to find how very little reference Dalton makes to Gough's observations in Kendal, half a mile distant from his own location. It might be surmised that Dalton was loth to compare his instruments with those made by others.

145

Fifteen years elapsed before he published in 1803 his
admission that his early method of constructing a barometer was faulty.

Gough published the results of his own observations
quite independently; they appeared before this Society
in Garnett's lengthy summaries, in the *Memoirs*[4] for
1795, of the results from several northern observers,
from Liverpool to Dumfries. Dalton's contribution is
not mentioned, and this leads me to think that at the
time when he began work in Manchester his *Meteorological essays* of 1793 were but little known. Indeed
Dalton says in his second edition (1834, p. 212) 'the fact
is that this Essay has fallen into the hands of few'.[5]

After he went to Manchester in 1793, the original
Kendal series of observations at the Friends' School
were continued until 1810 by his brother. They are
neatly and rigorously entered, but still there is no
evidence of comparison with Gough, in respect of
either temperature, pressure, or rainfall.

Dalton's Manchester observations

Dalton continued his own observations in Manchester
in the same manner, save that his thermometers were
attached to a board outside his bedroom window and
his morning readings were made at 8h.; whereas in
summer at Kendal he had taken them at 6h. Every few
years he provided the Society with a summary. He
filled the gaps, when he was absent from Manchester,
with the aid of the observations kept by his friend
Thomas Hanson, the surgeon, in Salford, and later he
used those of John Blackwall at Crumpsall. To both
sources he makes pleasant acknowledgement; but it is
very difficult to find how he contrived any adjustment,
although he knew perfectly well that it would be necessary if accuracy was to be his aim. There is a hint that
for some time, about 1802, he had not cast up his
monthly means on account of other activities.[6] Moreover we are never very clear whether he made some
allowance for the changes of exposure when he moved
from the College in 1798 and later, when he went to
live with the Johns at 10 George Street in 1804. When
he moved again to Faulkner Street in 1830, he began to
notice that the results he was getting appeared to indicate that the average temperature was slightly higher as

a result of difference of aspect. He comments on this in his last paper (1840); but he made no effort that we know of to provide such adjustments or corrections as would bring his whole series of fifty years' observations into homogeneity. Moreover, a study of the differences between his annual means and those derived from other contemporary sources, exhibited in Figure 1, gives the impression that his averages had become, relatively, higher some time before his 1830 change of residence, so that this last was not the only reason.

In the same 1840 paper he stated that 'the same Barometer has been used for 37 years . . . it stands nearly 1/10″ higher than other good Barometers do in the same situation, probably from some difference in the mercury'.[7]

Hence it appears that as time went on he became increasingly reluctant to make those comparisons, either of pressure or of temperature, that would have led him to devote thought to the effects of radiation, of air movement, of changes in exposure and the like, quite apart from the characteristics of the instruments he used. For example, his monthly means through the summer of 1815 are decidedly low when compared against others, and we can only surmise that his thermometer was faulty; this is apparent from Figure 1.

It is surprising to find that he never took up the discussion of diurnal range, so vigorously advocated by Gough (in *Nicholson's Journal*, 1809); and indeed he seems to have shown no interest in the use of the contemporary maximum and minimum thermometers, imperfect though they were. How often he noted 'hard frost in the country'; but how little he did to measure it.

It is also remarkable that, although he knew of

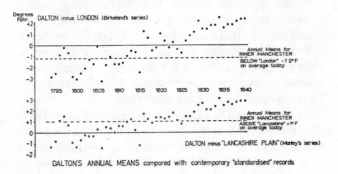

Figure 1

DALTON'S ANNUAL MEANS compared with contemporary "standardised" records

Howard's work he never made use of Howard's newly
devised nomenclature for the types of cloud, and indeed I have found no reference to it in his writings.

That he was critical of the way in which the Royal
Society's observations were kept at Somerset House is
noteworthy (*Memoirs*, 1819 and 1840). But consideration of his 1819 remarks leads me to think that his
strictures were rather on the ground of lack of punc-
tuality, perfunctory reading and arithmetical reduction,
not of the manner in which the instruments were
exposed.

If all his manuscript observations had survived, it
would have been possible to analyse them and make
reasonable adjustments for ourselves, to allow for
change of location and the like; but this we cannot now
do. We are therefore left with undoubted admiration
of Dalton's assiduity; but with equally undoubted
wonderment at the reluctance of such a percipient mind
to compare his instrumental observations with those of
others, or to bring them into homogeneity as a record
of the climate.

His rainfall measurement however remains for us,
and this appears to have been maintained in the same
manner throughout. Dalton's record is valuable; it provides Manchester men with the means to study the fluc-
tuations of rainfall, in considerable detail, since 1786.

The remarkable consistency of his eye observations
of the daily weather can be tested. I have elsewhere
commented,[8] on the effect of the varying alertness, at
different types of station, with regard to the frequency
with which the fall of snowflakes is observed and recorded. At a good airfield, where a constant watch can
be maintained by night and day, annual average fre-
quencies naturally exceed those forthcoming from a
station maintained by a single observer reading instruments once daily. Hence Ringway (248 ft) has averaged,
over the last twenty years, 25 days yearly with snow or
sleet observed to fall; it is reasonable to think that a
normal amateur observer within Manchester would
have averaged 14 over the same period.

From 1804 to 1826 Dalton's average is 16·4; and over
this period there is evidence from other stations that
the frequency of snow was about 20 per cent above that
of the present day. Abraham Shackleton's record at

Braithwaite (750 ft) near Keighley gave an average for
1804–26 of 39·2 days; in the same area, Oakes (760 ft),
near Huddersfield, for 1945–64 gives 32·6 days. Similar
comparisons with other observers make it clear that
Dalton was remarkably consistent, although he, like
many observers today, did not trouble about a few
flakes falling in cold rain, and he could not keep a continuous watch; but at least up to 1827 his alertness did
not diminish.

The assiduity of his instrumental observations is
balanced by indications of a more complex personality
than might at first appear. His gruff retort that 'he never
had time to get married' may hint at a deep-down
struggle within himself to find the time or energy, or
even willingness, to make a more critical examination
of the endless series of readings that he so regularly
undertook. Certainly their maintenance fulfilled that
'nature-study' tradition that had come to him through
Gough; and it was presumably in accord with that sense
of dutiful regularity that went with his upbringing.
Among his Quaker contemporaries Abraham Shackleton kept fifty-eight years of daily observations on his
farm above Keighley, John Gray at York provided
twenty-four years, and near London Luke Howard gave
us thirty-four years. It must remain a matter for conjecture whether Dalton's curious reluctance to compare his instrumental readings with those of others was
in some way related to a distrust arising from his recognition of the defect of colour-blindness and subsequently, of possible defect in his instruments. We do
not subsequently hear of any further interest on his
part in the botany for which Gough was so noted.

Dalton's more fundamental contributions

Dalton's accomplishment lies rather in the manner in
which with part of his personality he began to break
away from the contemporary habit of accumulating
and tabulating observations, and to attack the physics
of the atmosphere he beheld. From the preface to his
second edition of the *Essays* he evidently knew that the
more fundamental contributions to the physics of the
atmosphere, that is to meteorology, for which he is
justly renowned, derived from his early work. After he
had made his first journey to London; after he had

begun to gain so much from the resources of Manchester's Chetham Library, and from the collection that this Society was beginning to acquire; but before the walls of the laboratory, the narrow bedroom, the constant demands of his pupils, the growing city itself had begun to close around him, he produced for the Society, in 1799, an unusually remarkable paper;[9] the first serious attempt to consider a large-scale problem in quantitative and experimental terms. In it he not only assembled the data with regard to rainfall; he attempted to give a quantitative account of the water balance of England as a whole, and for practical purposes settled the question that the origin of springs lay in the rainfall. Moreover he discusses the amount of evaporation, based on his measurements and, imperfect though these were, the whole paper is quite astonishing when it is considered how few and how scattered were the available observations; he was about 100 years ahead of his time even if he generalized too boldly from limited data. And in it we find the first statement of his convictions with regard to water vapour. This gradual recognition of the place of water vapour in the atmosphere and the establishment of the laws of its behaviour has been discussed by many writers. It is quite evident from his original *Meteorological essays* that such ideas were forming in his mind as early as 1793, but several years elapsed before he gave them full expression in the papers before this Society that were published in 1802. We have already heard elsewhere how from the thoughts on mixed gases and on solution he made those bold forward steps in chemistry which we justly acknowledge. But if we read the *Essays,* and the occasional flashes in his later papers, what a remarkable number of contributions to meteorology he might have made if he had had the time to devote more thought to them. His early determination of the height of the aurora, with the aid of simultaneous observations by his friend Peter Crosthwaite at Keswick, was far ahead of its time; his thoughts on the relationship of the aurora with the earth's magnetism, and the height at which meteors become visible, led him to think about the extent and density of the atmosphere. We can read his much later papers on the composition of the atmosphere that he sent to the *Philosophical Transactions* in 1826 and 1837, and note that, old though he had become, if he had promised in an earlier paper to present further work, he did so even after long delay. In the *Essays*, and in his later papers, his thoughts touch on radiation, on the latent heat of evaporation, the development of surface mists, the height of clouds, the variation of rainfall with height, the dynamical cooling of air. He did his best to use his opportunities on his annual holiday in the Lake District, bringing down samples of air from Helvellyn. He saw Sadler's balloon ascent in 1812 so, when Green came to Manchester in 1827, he got him to take samples of the air 9000 feet above Cheshire. He was always conscious of the moisture in the atmosphere and of all forms of precipitation. He discussed Peter Crosthwaite's observations of the height of the cloud base, seen against Skiddaw, and in his article on Meteorology in Rees' *Cyclopaedia* (1819) he gives a tantalizing note to the effect that he had sometimes measured the altitude of the upper clouds and never found it to exceed four or five miles; later, he says: small white streaks are sometimes seen at three, four, five miles or more, but in these high regions any condensation is probably insufficient to produce a cloud of great density or opacity. All this remained tantalizing because he never took this matter further. And although he corresponded with Howard, he never uses Howard's terms for the clouds. But in the same publication he says: 'The greater part of the atmosphere is at all times within 15 or 20 miles of the surface and it is probable that the ordinary phenomena of winds, clouds, rain, etc. are confined within much narrower limits.' Yet Dr Knowles Middleton (in his *History of the theories of rain*, 1966) has emphasized that Dalton's paper (in *Nicholson's Journal*, 1803) shows that he did not think deeply enough about the relative density of water vapour at different heights, and that as a consequence his ideas led to confusion.

Dalton recognized that severe cold might be expected after snowfall, and noted the extraordinarily low temperatures on the surface of deep snow on a December night; but he does not take that matter further. It was left to blind John Gough in one of his own later papers to put forward the idea that high pressure over the snow-covered uplands of Scandinavia might be the

cause of the frequent north-east winds of spring that
Westmorland still knows.[10]

Dalton's ideas on rainfall

No-one bred on the edge of the Lake District could fail
to appreciate that more rain falls among the mountains.
At the same time the problem of its measurement gave
rise to many difficulties. Gough took up the problem
and set up a raingauge on Benson Knott, about 1000 feet
above sea level and two miles from Kendal. Generally
one of his sisters helped him with his measurements.
His upland gauge caught less rain than that which he
kept in the town (cf. Gough, in Garnett 1795) and to
all appearance this accorded with Heberden's observations using a gauge on one of the towers of Westminster
Abbey. Dalton corroborated this effect for himself
during 1797-8 on St John's Church in Manchester.
No-one appears to have thought of the possible effect
of over-exposure of the gauge, either on a tower or a
windy upland; although Aaron Copland of Dumfries
was clearly groping towards it. His argument for the
use of square gauges was also printed by this Society
(in Garnett, 1795).

Dalton's fundamental papers on water vapour were
presented in 1801, and soon afterwards we find Gough's
paper disagreeing with these new ideas, and favouring
the older concept of solution. Dalton's reply is tem-
perate and well argued, and Gough did not pursue the
matter further. Yet Dalton was clearly cognisant of
Gough's upland measurements, and in 1819 we find
him stating that he had long been attached to Hutton's
theory of rainfall, published in 1785, according to which
rain resulted from the mixing of saturated, or nearly
saturated air currents differing in temperature. In 1793,
he says, 'it appeared the most plausible of any theory I
had seen', and in 1819 he had become 'the more convinced of its excellence'. This was because it conformed
with expectation based on his knowledge of the rate of
decrease of the vapour content of saturated air with
decreased temperature. It agreed with Gough's demonstration that the ratio between the rainfall caught by his
upland gauge and that in the town below was higher in
summer than in winter. That this was really due to the
greater windiness of the winter months escaped him.

Nobody kept a raingauge nearer to the Lake District mountains until 1833, and no-one is known to have set up a high mountain gauge until Marshall did so on Helvellyn in 1836, and this was unfortunately destroyed. It was only after Dalton's death that Miller of Whitehaven set up the mountain gauges around Scathwaite. Some years earlier, in a paper before this Society Fleming (1831) gave an account of rainfall measurements from 1819 onward along two of the Pennine canals east of Manchester.[11] A gauge at 1500 feet on Blackstone Edge certainly appeared to catch a little more than Manchester, but the highest fall was found at Stubbins, further to leeward. Many years elapsed before the effects of over-exposure on windy uplands on the catch of rain were understood.

Dalton's persistent interest in upland springs, his measurements of the dew-point on mountains, his comment on the cloud that enveloped Sca Fell Pike on a calm day all suggest that he was troubled by the problem of mountain rainfall. Hutton's theory might well appeal to him, for if you live among mountains, some mixing of airstreams converging from different valleys and at different levels can well be understood. Commonly too, more than one cloud-layer is to be seen; one can appreciate Dalton's reluctance to discard Hutton's theory, although Leslie showed in a little-known paper in 1813 that it failed on quantitative grounds.[12] Possibly too Dalton was reluctant to controvert the work of his friend Gough, hampered as Gough was by blindness. We know from his letters to Jonathan Otway how keen he was to visit the spring on the top of Great Gable which had only been known to fail once, in the hot dry summer of 1826.

His effort in 1828 to explain why the measured rain-and-snow-fall on the Great St Bernard Pass was $2\frac{1}{2}$ times as great as that at Geneva is notable; he argues that the pass is still well below the level of the summits.[13] From the measurements known to him he evidently saw no reason to abandon his regard for Hutton's theory.

Why did Dalton only reissue his *Essays*, almost unchanged, in 1834? Perhaps because he was always a teacher, and he at last found that his ideas on meteorology were becoming more widely known, although he

had become a celebrity for other reasons. Mr Greenaway has suggested[14] that Dalton's action arose from
Forbes' critical remarks on the state of meteorology at
the British Association meeting in 1832; made, as Shaw
said, with the natural severity of a young man of
twenty-three. But Forbes clearly regarded Dalton as a
'natural philosopher'; as he said, 'Mr Dalton descends
from his chemistry in the abstract, to illustrate the constitution of the atmosphere and the theory of vapour'.
Forbes' strictures were rather addressed to 'those pro-
fessed meteorologists who enter their journals, with
minute scrupulosity, for a lifetime'. Dalton indeed was
more than forty years older; he did enter his journal; he
still abided by his eighteenth-century naturalist beginnings; but the evidence suggests that he had in reality
grown out of the clothes he was still trying to wear.
Moreover we may note that Dalton was evidently well
disposed to Forbes' work, in his last paper.

That Dalton was aroused to reissue his *Essays* at the
age of sixty-eight can be ascribed to a variety of factors
operative in N.W. England. Meteorology was under-
going a revival; there was a considerable growth of
interest in rainfall measurement, stimulated by the need
to maintain the supply for the Pennine canals, and by
the growing demands in the new industrial towns to
which the drought and consequent distress in 1826
drew attention. From 1829 onward, enthusiasts began
their measurements at Bolton, Oldham and Hyde. In
1833 J. F. Miller began his investigations at Whitehaven; soon, reports began to come in of totals approaching 100 inches in the Lake District. In 1833
Howard produced his own expanded second edition of
The climate of London; in it, he rejected Hutton's
theory, which had been shown to be wanting as early
as 1813 (Knowles Middleton, op. cit.), but Howard in

Plate IIa   Perhaps the best known portrait of John Dalton; engraved after a
portrait (1814) by William Allen. The air pump referred to in
paper 10 is on his right.

Plate IIb   Apparatus from Manchester University Chemistry Department.
1, 2 & 3 Cubical flasks. **4** Water thermometer. **5 & 6** Two bottles
lined inside and out with metal foil. They are probably the remains
of improvised Leyden jars. **7** Specific gravity bottle. **8** Thermometer.

Plate IIa

Plate IIb

1   2   3   4   5   6   7
8

Plates IIIa & IIIb

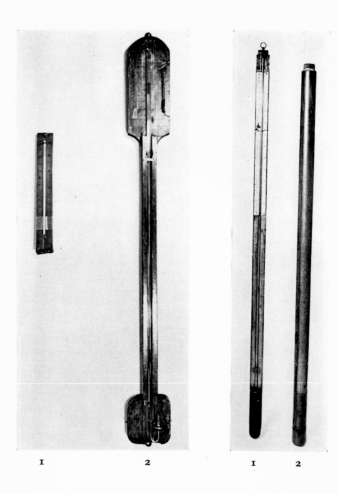

1   2   1   2

Plate IIIc

1   2   3   4   5   6

his turn was 'too full of ideas that rain was a result of the electrical action of clouds on each other'.

Forbes' criticism that far too many collections of observations were being made without adequate design was justified. But we might fairly ask why so many of the contemporary scientific journals were printing those monthly tables of daily readings; indeed, in the *Philosophical Magazine* tables for three stations were printed side by side. Was this not because progress towards the understanding of the movement of the atmosphere could only be made, in the days before the electric telegraph, by careful comparisons of past records at the earliest opportunity?

Dalton's early essays, and his subsequent papers, contained the germs of many ideas that were later developed by others. But, at the age of sixty-eight, it was too late for him to carry out that integration and discussion of his many contributions to the subject, or to make those comparisons of his own observations with those of others, separated either in space or in time, which we should so much have appreciated. Had he done so, we might well have had Buys Ballot's law forty years earlier. Had he linked up the motion of the air, the cooling by expansion of which he was well aware, and the consequences with regard to the water vapour that it contained, we should likewise have had a more satisfactory theory of rainfall forty years earlier; compare his paper in 1800 'on heat and cold produced by the mechanical condensation and rarefaction of air'. Yet it was for others to resolve that fundamental problem that he restated when he was sixty-two:

From observations in Great Britain it appears to be an established fact that more rain falls in the hilly parts of the country

155

than in the plain. But it also appears that the quantity of rain in a low situation is greater than that in an elevated situation in the vicinity.

He had come from a country where from almost any hillock the movement of the clouds and the air can be watched for fifty miles around; where from Black Combe, in Wordsworth's contemporary phrase, 'The amplest prospect of any British ground' can be commanded. It is a country where Dorothy Wordsworth herself noted how often the south wind blew cold before rain, a hundred years before frontal theory emerged. The inspiration of Dalton's early years remained with him, as we can judge from his activities on his annual holiday; but for eleven months of the year his vision was more and more limited, and his time and energy were too much taken up by other pursuits. It was hardly to be expected that in Manchester he could take those further steps to understanding the motion of the atmosphere. Occasionally he was roused; after his return to Manchester from the great visit to France in 1822, he produced a paper 'On the saline impregnation of the rain' after scraping the salt deposit off his window that resulted from a westerly gale on the night of 5 December. He also commented on the evidence of the burning of coal in the growing town. In his 1826 paper on the aurora, he regretted that 'the obscurity of our atmosphere' hindered observation in Manchester. This hints at the confinement of the town; his spirits manifestly rose when he could again busy himself with his friend Jonathan Otway sampling the air on Helvellyn, taking the temperature of Brownrigg Well, looking at the early morning mist on Windermere from Lowwood; always the more satisfied when he could believe the evidence of his own eyes and his own measurements rather than the writings of others. Manchester gave him new and different opportunities, the close laboratory in place of the open air, but also, libraries and keen interested listeners. Occasionally he saw the snowy moorlands, the thunder clouds building over Stockport, the sunset after a 'fine and gleamy day'; but his laboratory called.

We can fitly ask ourselves whether any man could have done more under those conditions, with so little opportunity for co-operative inquiry. We can still read

Dalton's *Essays* and his papers with profit, for we are led to reconsider those fundamental measurements, those basic ideas and mistaken theories upon which Dalton's work was dependent. And we are reminded how much can be learnt by going out and living with the weather, and how much can be done by a logical and thoughtful mind, even under the restrictions of time, space, communications and personal resources with which Dalton had to contend.

Meteorology, as we know, demands co-operation on the largest scale; but the many who lack those opportunities for rapid communication, those expensive instruments that we should like, can derive inspiration from reflecting on Dalton's achievements, fifty years before the electric telegraph enlarged our understanding of motion. And if there were omissions on his part, they remind us of the need to design our experiments and to reflect on the observations that we continue to make. The essentials of the north-west England that he knew are still here.

Acknowledgement: I wish to acknowledge the help of Miss P. A. Marsden in research on the manuscripts of Dalton's meteorological observations. Miss E. Critchley has drawn the diagram.

Notes

1 Sir Napier Shaw, *Manual of meteorology: 1, Meteorology in history* (Cambridge, 1926).

2 T. Robinson, *The natural history of . . . Cumberland and Westmorland* (1709).

3 Gordon Manley, 'George Smith and his Ascent of Crossfell', *Cumberland and Westmorland Archaeological and Antiquarian Society* (1951).

4 T. Garnett, 'Meteorological Observations made on different Parts of the Western Coast of Great Britain', *Manchester Memoirs*, 1st Series, iv (1795) 234.

5 John Dalton, *Meteorological essays* (2nd edn, 1834).

6 John Dalton, 'Observations on the Barometer, Thermometer and Rain, at Manchester, from 1794 to 1818 inclusive', *Manchester Memoirs*, 2nd Series, iii (1819) 483.

7 John Dalton, 'Observations on the Barometer, Thermometer, and Rain, at Manchester, from the Year 1794 to 1840 inclusive, *Manchester Memoirs*, 2nd Series, vi (1842) 561.

8 Gordon Manley, *Quarterly Journal of the Royal Meteorological Society*, lxxxiv (1958).

9 John Dalton, 'Experiments and Observations to determine whether the Quantity of Rain and Dew is equal to the Quantity of Water carried off by Rivers', *Manchester Memoirs*, 1st Series, v (1802) 346.

10 J. Gough (in Garnett's paper, cited above), *Manchester Memoirs*, 1st Series, iv (1795) 234.

Notes **11** Thomas Fleming, 'Account of the Rain which fell on Different Places on the line of the Rochdale Canal', *Manchester Memoirs*, 2nd Series, v (1831) 243.

12 W. E. K. Middleton, *History of the theories of rain* (London, 1965).

13 John Dalton, 'Summary of the Rain, etc. at Geneva, and at the Elevated Station of the Pass of Great St Bernard, for a Series of Years; with Observations on the Same', *Manchester Memoirs*, x (1831) 233.

14 F. Greenaway, 'The Biographical Approach to John Dalton', *Manchester Memoirs*, c. (1958/9) 47.

10

Kathleen R Farrar

Dalton's Scientific Apparatus

Dalton is usually thought to have employed mainly
crude apparatus which he made himself, and when this
study began, it was not expected to yield much information about equipment contemporaneously in
general use. This pessimistic prediction was not fulfilled. His apparatus was, in fact, much less restricted
than nowadays supposed; and his reliance on 'penny
ink-bottles' has been greatly exaggerated.

A large part of the library of Dalton's friend William
Henry is now in Manchester University. This collection contains books and catalogues[1-4] illustrating (and
pricing) the apparatus likely to be available to Henry.
Since Henry and Dalton collaborated in experiments,[5]
and Henry helped Dalton with loans or gifts of apparatus,[6] this information is almost equally relevant to
Dalton. Dalton also had[6] 'a valuable selection of chemical apparatus' from 'Mr Sharpe'[7] to assist him in his
work for the second volume of the 'New System'.
Sharpe's apparatus would probably be mainly for
gravimetric and volumetric analysis, and that from
Henry mainly for pneumatic chemistry. Dalton himself is known to have spent on one occasion[8] the large
sum of £200 on apparatus from the suppliers W. and
S. Jones.[9]

With so much available to him, how has the 'ink-
bottle' legend arisen? The misunderstanding undoubtedly begins with Dalton himself, who took a
pride in minimizing his facilities.[10] When visited by
Pelletan in 1820 he is reported to have pointed to some

miscellaneous pieces in a corner, occupying about the space needed for 'an infant's cradle', and to have remarked 'That's all the apparatus I possess'.[11] The growth of the legend, however, owes much to W. C. Henry, the son of William Henry, who inherited Dalton's apparatus.

There are several statements by W. C. Henry on the crudity of Dalton's instruments and technique.[12] Too much reliance should not be placed on Henry, however, since it is probable that he never examined his inheritance at all. When Dalton died, and for a year afterwards, Henry was in Italy. He had already left Manchester and settled in Ledbury, Herefordshire. He was unable to write his biography of Dalton until after the death of Peter Clare, owing to Clare's reluctance to send him the Dalton manuscripts; since Henry was evidently not prepared to come to Manchester to see them, it is unlikely that he examined the apparatus either.

The following extract from a secretary's report to the Manchester Literary and Philosophical Society[13] supports this surmise, and shows that some of the apparatus was lost at an early date:

> . . . the physical and chemical apparatus of the late Dr Dalton was, at his death, presented to the Society by Dr Charles Henry. . . . From that time to the end of last year, this apparatus remained enclosed in unsightly boxes in a back room of the Society's premises. Here it was almost inaccessible, so that very few persons had any idea of what it consisted, and in course of time it unavoidably became covered with dust, and partly corroded.

This neglect had been due to lack of funds, but a surplus of £30 later became available for attending to it. 'Having been examined and cleaned by competent persons, it was placed, after a small and unimportant portion had been rejected, in a handsome oaken case with glass doors.' (The word 'corroded' is significant here, because it suggests that some of the apparatus had metal parts, and it might be pieces of this type which would be rejected. The bladders so much used in pneumatic chemistry would also have perished during this period.)

The apparatus next appears in the Loan Collection of Scientific Apparatus exhibited in South Kensington in 1876. Roscoe, who selected the exhibits, spoke about them to the Society in 1874;[14] he made no secret of his bias:

The apparatus employed by John Dalton in his classical researches . . . was of the simplest and even of the rudest character. Most of it was made with his own hands, and that which is to be exhibited has been chosen as illustrating this fact, and as indicating the genius which with so insignificant and incomplete an experimental equipment was able to produce such great results. The Society has in its possession a large quantity of apparatus used by Dalton, most of which however, consists of electrical apparatus, models of mechanical powers, models of steam engines, air pumps, a Gregorian telescope, and other apparatus of a similar kind. . . It has not been thought necessary to exhibit these, but rather to show the home-made apparatus with which Dalton obtained his most remarkable results.

In Roscoe's address to the British Association (Manchester, 1887) we have the 'ink-bottle' legend in full flower:

Here, with the simplest of all possible apparatus—a few cups, penny ink bottles, rough balances and self-made thermometers and barometers—Dalton accomplished his great results.[15]

Roscoe could never resist a good story,[16] and this is one of his best; he did not spoil it by telling his audience that Dalton's weights and balances were the same as those used by most of his contemporaries.

Later, the apparatus was photographed by Francis Jones[17] (Figs. 2 to 10). 'Subsequently to 1890', he wrote, 'the most interesting pieces of apparatus were placed in new cases in the library and carefully arranged by Professor Dixon in the positions they now occupy.' The rest of the collection, the teaching equipment, was not listed until 1915, when the Society exhibited it in their house at 36 George Street for the British Association. The catalogue[18] lists two cases in the library and one in a passage. Apart from this, about thirty other items—some by famous instrument makers—are now listed for the first time; an examination of old catalogues[19, 20] suggests that some of them are part of the £200 worth referred to earlier.

As W. and S. Jones were the successors of George Adams who made many of the instruments in the George III collection in the Science Museum, they were a firm of the highest standing; that Dalton traded with them shows his willingness to spend liberally on teaching equipment. This is not surprising, because teaching was his livelihood, and the equipment was a business investment. He enjoyed teaching, and would not have wished to be released from it to spend more time on research.[21] It is possible to regard much of Dalton's work as an aid to teaching; his research familiarized him with his material, and was perhaps partly done with that end in view.

After 1915, little more is heard of the collection.[22] A photograph (Plate IVa) has recently come to light[23] which is evidently of one of the cases of apparatus mentioned above. Most of the pieces can be identified from Figs. 2 to 10. Almost the whole collection was destroyed in an air raid in the early morning of Christmas Eve, 1940.[24] The articles salvaged included a spark eudiometer, a phial, fragments of stoneware from a water thermometer, three earthenware beakers, a glass bottle (Plate IIIc); a model beam engine,[25] and a model pumping engine, now missing. More Dalton relics survived in the Chemistry Department of Manchester University (Plates IIb and IIIb) and in Dalton Hall (Plate IIIa), which was also found to have the atomic models thought to have been missing since 1852.[26]

There is thus no basis for the 'ink-bottle legend' though it is still with us.[27] Its survival is perhaps due to the natural wish to believe that a poor country boy could come into the town and make a name for himself without any initial advantages of training or financial backing. In fact, Dalton lived at a time of transition, and his apparatus reflects this. Broadly speaking, two types of scientific instrument were made in the eighteenth century; the useful kind for navigation, surveying and the like, and others that would now be labelled 'for

---

Figure 2

1 & 2 Mountain barometer with thermometer attached, made for Dalton by the late Mr Lawrence Buchan, a member of the Society. The barometer is enclosed in a wooden case (with screw cap at the top) for convenience in carrying. 3 Manometer tube fixed on a wooden board, divided and numbered by Dalton. 4 Barometer made by Dalton consisting of a glass tube bent at the lower end, which is blown out to a bulb to serve as a mercury reservoir. The barometer is attached by wires to a narrow strip of wood with a cross-piece at the lower end to support the bulb. At the upper end a paper scale is pasted on, with figures in Dalton's writing. The height

of the mercury in this barometer was recently compared with a modern instrument and agreed very closely. **5** & **6** Similar instruments, but containing a little liquid above the mercury, probably indicating that they were used for tension experiments.

Figure 2

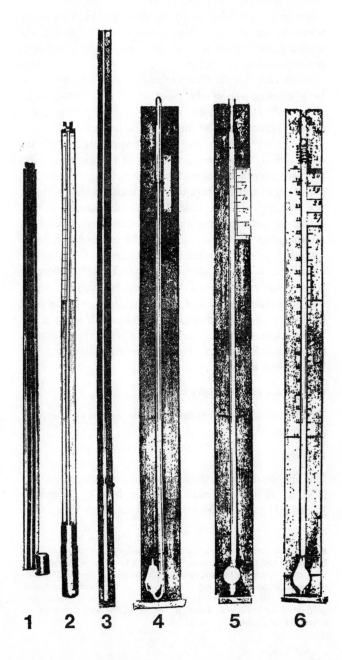

1 2 3 4 5 6

amusement only'. The so-called philosophical apparatus was, for a time, little more than a set of toys for the wealthy, who were smitten with a craze for being entertained by experiments. The elaboration of instruments reached its peak in the extraordinary silver microscope made by Adams for George III. The actual performance of experiments was on the same lines, with a proliferation of 'stage business' more suitable to conjuring than to science.

Frederick Accum (from whom Dalton's balance was bought) was one of the most vocal objectors to this attitude.[28] He ridiculed 'the frivolous regard to show which characterized so many public lectures' and complained that 'Many of the brilliant apparatus which are daily displayed in the laboratories of teaching chemists as instruments of research, serve more to divert the attention of the auditors than to elucidate the truths of the science'. It was indeed at the beginning of the careers of both Accum and Dalton that chemistry began to emerge as a profession, and that lectures began to be attended more for vocational reasons than for entertainment. We find, therefore, that Dalton reflects a passing age with some of his teaching equipment, which was elaborate, showy and expensive; but looks forward to the age of the professional chemist with some of his lecture demonstrations and all of his research apparatus, which, in the words of a fine recent historian, was 'simple but effective'.[21]

Description of the apparatus

Descriptions of non-extant pieces are based on Roscoe[16] and Jones.[17]

Barometers

Dalton had at least three mountain barometers. One (Fig. 2; 2) now lost was made for him by Lawrence Buchan;[29] parts of two others survive (Plate IIIb). One

---

Figure 3

1 & 2 Glass funnels with long stems closed at the ends, graduated by Dalton and used for measuring gases. 3 Graduated bell-jar with bent tube attached, for collecting and measuring gases. 4 Graduated bell jar with brass cap and stopcock, for measuring gases. 5 Conical glass vessel containing mercury. 6 Small phial with graduated tube (broken) fitted to the neck, for measuring gases. (Part of Hope's eudiometer. K. R. F.)

Figure 3

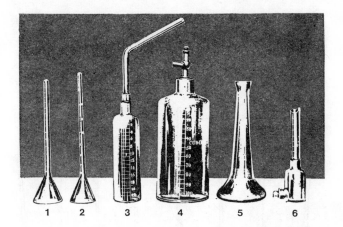

Figure 4

1 Small glass lens, wrapped in a piece of paper on which is marked in Dalton's writing 'Sun's focus 4.2. inches'. **2** Glass specific gravity bottle. **3** A common pair of scales used by Dalton. **4** A specific gravity bottle, marked 1,000 grains capacity. **5** Lead counterpoise for specific gravity bottle, stamped '175', wrapped in paper marked 'bottle balance'. **6** Set of brass grain weights from 1,000 to 20, in wooden box (two missing). **7** Glass specific gravity bulbs with figures engraved on each. These are contained in a wooden case on the lid of which is a table of values, 'o = 1·000, 1 = 1·001, 2 = 1·002' etc. **8** Set of brass grain weights from 1,000 to 20 grains, in wooden box.

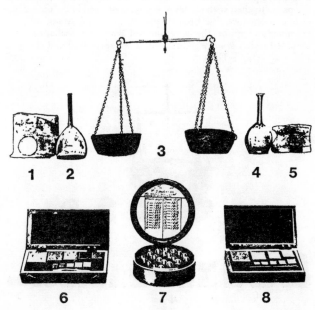

Figure 5   **1, 3, 4, 5, 6, 7 & 8** Seven water thermometers of different materials (stoneware, brass, iron, tin, lead, etc.) for determining the temperature of the maximum density of water. *Nicholson's Journal*, 1804, p. 94. **2** Stoppered phial with the bottom cut off and with tube fitting the neck, for collecting and measuring gases.

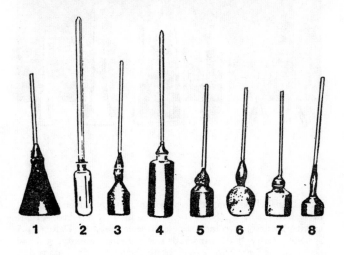

Figure 6   **1** Dalton's pocket balance with beam four inches long and having the pans attached with common string, contained in tin case. **2** Set of four French weights from 10 grammes to 1. **3** Boxes of weights, grammes and grains, the larger ones of brass, the smaller of platinum. **4** Leaden grain weights made from sheet lead and stamped with numbers by Dalton.

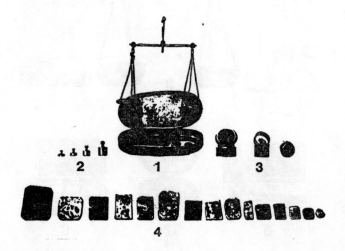

1 A maximum and minimum alcohol thermometer on wooden scale (one bulb broken), made by H. H. Watson, Bolton. **2** A maximum and minimum thermometer used by Dalton and stamped with maker's name, J. Ronchetti, 29 Balloon Street, Manchester. **3** Mercury thermometer attached to strip of wood stamped with the date 1823, apparently made and graduated by Dalton. **4** Mercury thermometer with file-marked graduations on the glass stem. **5** Mercury thermometer with long stem and wooden scale. **6** Glass tube used by Dalton for measuring the tension of carbon disulphide vapour. There is a paper scale attached on which in Dalton's handwriting may be seen 'Sulphuret. carb.' There is a cork at the upper end apparently used for supporting this portion of the tube in a water bath. **7** Bent glass tube. **8** Small glass tube bent at lower end with paper scale attached. **9** Mercury thermometer attached to strip of wood, made and graduated by Dalton and stamped J.D. 1823. The freezing point of this instrument was tested in 1876 by Mr Baxendell, who found that it had not altered since the original graduation. I have retested the freezing point (June 1904) and find it about ⅓ of a degree Fahrenheit *below* the mark on the stem.

Figure 7

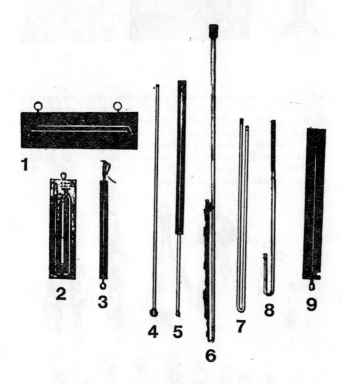

Figure 8   **1** A differential thermometer. **2** Balance used by Dalton, made by Accum. **3** A wet and dry bulb hygrometer, made by H. H. Watson, of Bolton.

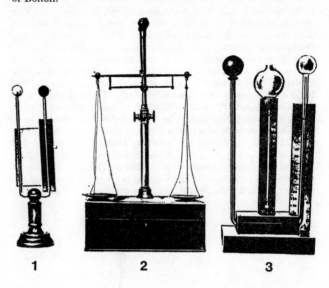

1   2   3

Figure 9   **1 & 2** Phials containing platinum and amalgam of tin and mercury. **3** A glass alembic. **4** A Florence flask, with cork and valve for determining the specific gravity of gases. **5** A spark eudiometer of thick glass, with copper wires fitted to the neck. **6 & 7** Two phials, one containing an amalgam of bismuth and mercury. **8–19** Phials, containing respectively iodine, cochineal, mercury, gunpowder, mercury, grana sylvestra cochineal, quercitron bark, resin, mercury, madder, lead and mercury, and creosote.

1   2   3   4   5   6   7

8   9   10   11   12   13   14   15   16   17   18   19

1, 4 & 6 Portions of Pepys' apparatus for the analysis of gases. **Figure 10**
1 is the eudiometer, with elastic ball attached. For analysis of air, a solution of nitric oxide in ferrous sulphate is used to absorb the oxygen. See paper by W. H. Pepys in the *Philosophical Transactions* for 1807, p. 247. (See also the present paper. K. R. F.) **7** A glass bottle with brass cap.

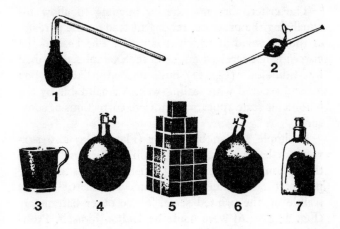

Cross-section of the cistern of an eighteenth-century mountain **Figure 11** barometer of French make. (Reproduced from *The History of the Barometer* by kind permission of Dr W. E. Knowles Middleton.)

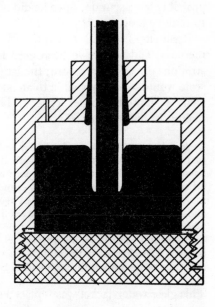

is an empty case; the other lacks part of the case, but shows the tube, cistern and scale. Like the lost specimen, it has a thermometer, near the top of the scale. When carried, the cistern end was held in the hand, and the other end was fitted with a ferrule.

The cistern has no exterior opening to allow for equalizing the pressure, relying instead on the porosity of the boxwood of which it is made. The base of the cistern is not screwed on, as in the examples described by Middleton[30] (Fig. 11), but is pushed on like a pill-box lid and secured with sealing-wax. A small table by the barometer scale appears to indicate corrections of some sort.

A simple siphon barometer (Plate IIIa) also survives; it has a characteristic bulb in the short arm of the siphon. A wooden casing usually protects the lower part of the instrument. The name Ronchetti[31] is just legible on the printed scale. Three other barometers (Fig. 2; 4, 5, 6) were made by Dalton himself. Probably both Dalton and Ronchetti bought the tubes ready made from a glassblower; in 1791 they cost 9*d*. each.[32]

Jones says that barometer 4 agreed closely with a modern instrument. Dalton's earlier barometers were probably less accurate, since he did not boil his mercury to remove moisture.[33]

Barometers 5 and 6 contained liquid above the mercury, and may have been used for lecture demonstrations of vapour pressure; the large figures and clear scale would be easily visible to an audience. A teaching chart[34] showed another type of barometer used by Dalton in his research:[35]

I take a barometer tube perfectly dry and fill it with mercury just boiled, marking the place where it is stationary; then having graduated the tube. . . . I pour a little water (or any other liquid the subject of the experiment) into it, so as to moisten the whole inside; after this I again pour in mercury, and carefully inverting the tube, exclude all air. . . . I next take a cylindrical glass tube open at both ends, of 2 inches diameter and 14 inches in length, to each end of which a cork is adapted, perforated in the middle so as to admit the barometer tube to be pushed through and to be held fast by them.

This glass water-jacket was replaced at higher temperatures by a metal one, and readings made on the unenclosed limb of the siphon. But since barometers 5 and

A case of Dalton's apparatus. **1** Apparatus with metal fittings
attached to a small metal flask through a stopcock. **2** Flask with
metal cap and stopcock.

1   2

The British Association meeting in Manchester 1887: (left to right,
standing) J. Wislicenus, G. Quincke, E. Schunck, C. Schorlemmer,
J. P. Joule: (seated in front) Lothar Meyer, D. I. Mendeleev, H. E.
Roscoe.

Plate V The internal structure of a segment of a receptor from the retina of the rhesus monkey as seen under the electron microscope (Pedler).

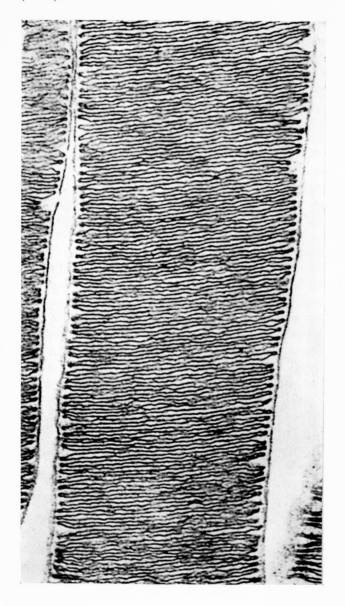

6 are fixed to a wooden scale, and have a bulb instead of an open limb, they could not have been used for experiments of this type; it may be that they were kept ready made up, in case an experiment on the lecture-bench failed. Dalton[36] mentions 'a barometer with a few drops of ether on the mercury that has continued with unvaried efficacy for eight or nine years', and says that ether bought in London, Edinburgh, Glasgow or Manchester appeared to be very uniform as shown by experiments of this type.

The long manometer tube (Fig. 2; 3) was used to study pressure changes on heating mixtures of air and vapour at between one and two atmospheres. The sealed end of the tube was dipped into a vessel containing water at the desired temperature; the mixture of air and vapour was confined by a mercury thread which could vary from 1/10″ to 30″ in length.[37] The apparatus was not practical at pressures greater than two atmospheres.

A siphon barometer was used in a similar way. The closed limb, containing a little ether, but no air, was quite short (9″), while the open end was 36″ long. The tube was filled with mercury to within 10″ of the top, and the closed limb immersed in a water-bath.[38] Two types are illustrated (Fig. 7; 6 and 8); 6 was used for experiments on carbon disulphide, for it was labelled 'Sulphuret carb.'. A paper scale was attached to the open limb, and the upper supporting cork still remained. The use of 7 is unknown. There is no example of yet another type of manometer used by Dalton for pressures above two atmospheres.[39] In this, as in 8, the tube was a siphon with a short closed limb with air and vapour enclosed in it. The long limb had air enclosed in the upper 10″ and hermetically sealed by drawing out a fine capillary, allowing it to cool, and quickly sealing off. Pressure changes in the limb containing ether could then be followed by measuring volume changes in the side containing air.

Thermometers and other meteorological instruments

Dalton certainly bought thermometer tubes, as the account books show[32] and he went on making thermometers until at least 1823, for two (Fig. 7; 3 and 9) were stamped with this date, 9 having his initials as

J D—N

well. Baxendell tested 9 in 1865,[40] and Jones in 1904 found a correction of about 1/3°F at 32°F.

Two thermometers (Fig. 7; 4 and 5) have stems about two feet long, suggesting that they were used for lecture purposes. Two maximum and minimum thermometers (Fig. 7; 1 and 2) were made by H. H. Watson and by Ronchetti. Another thermometer (Fig. 7; 8) has a large bulb compared with a modern instrument.

Differential thermometers (Fig. 8; 1) were air thermometers designed to show small variations in temperature. Two bulbs were connected by a piece of tubing bent twice at right angles. Most of the tube was filled with a coloured liquid, the levels of the liquid in both halves of the tube being the same when the instrument was kept at an even temperature. One of the bulbs appears to have been blackened, and this would mean that under conditions of changing temperature, the levels in the tubes would no longer be the same. In the words of Accum, it 'is peculiarly calculated for experiments on radiant caloric'.[41] Accum charged a guinea for this apparatus. The two maximum and minimum thermometers and the wet and dry bulb hygrometer are further examples of the good quality of Dalton's meteorological equipment. A thermometer (Plate IIIa; 1) is said to have come from Dalton's house in Faulkner Street,[42] so that he must have used this towards the end of his life. The scale, which is marked in degrees Fahrenheit and Réaumur, is certainly not home-made.

In his early investigations (about 1787–92) Dalton used a very crude hygrometer made of whipcord running over a pulley and weighted at the free end. Measurements of length changes gave him a rough measure of changes in relative humidity over short periods, but there was also a progressive stretching over the whole five year period.[43] He also had, eventually, a wet and dry bulb hygrometer by Watson (Fig. 8; 3).

Even in the earlier years there is mention of better equipment, There was the 'very good theodolite by Dollond' with which Dalton observed the aurora on 13 October 1792; this may have belonged to his friend Crosthwaite, who determined the altitude of Bassenthwaite Lake with what appears to have been the same instrument.[44]

It was probably Dalton's 'water thermometers' which gave rise to the ink-bottle legend (Fig. 5; except 2, which is a device for collecting and measuring gases). Their purpose was to determine the temperature at which water exhibited its maximum density. Dalton knew that he would need to take account of the expansion of the thermometer vessel, so he had them made of a variety of materials, mostly with known coefficients of expansion. The vessels were fairly large, one or two ounces in capacity.

Dalton says:[45]

Common brown inkstands, which go by the name of Nottingham ware answer very well for one species, but they require to be well painted without, as they are not otherwise watertight. I have a few of Queen's ware, made purposely in Staffordshire, which constitute another species of earthenware; some of them are glazed in and out; others unglazed, but these being painted without are made water-tight, and expand the same by heat as the glazed ones: Of glass, common thermometer tubes, with larger bulbs than ordinary are sufficient. I have the metallic vessels made in the shape of cylindrical tin canisters, conical towards the top, and at the summit a small cylindrical tube, such as to take a thermometer tube. The glazed earthen ware and the metallic require mostly to be painted before they are quite tight.

Results were recorded for two vessels of brown earthenware, and one each of Queen's ware, flint-glass, iron (thin plate), tinned iron, copper, brass, pewter and lead. One of the brown earthenware bases was salvaged (Plate IIIc; 6). A complete water thermometer, probably the pewter one, survives in the Chemistry Department of Manchester University (Plate IIb; 4). This shows the black cement used to fix in the thermometer tube and traces of the black paint used to seal cracks.

The inkstands seem to have been used simply to extend the range of materials. The other containers show that Dalton could call upon craftsmen to make simple apparatus for him if he required it.

We know little of Dalton's rain-gauges. One at Kendal had a funnel 10″ in diameter;[46] he wrote about rain-gauges in a letter to Sarah Hudson,[47] giving a diagram (Fig. 12).

Cubical flasks

There were some small glass vessels (Plate IIb; 1, 2 and 3) which are sometimes thought to be ink-bottles.

This is doubtful; they have thin walls, and seem to be too fragile for this. On the other hand, they could be heated with less danger of cracking than a thicker vessel. Although they have not so far been found in any contemporary plates, they must have been standard, commercially available equipment, for there are some similar ones in the Oxford Museum of the History of Science.

Two bottles

These (Plate IIb; 5 and 6) are of about 8 oz. capacity, and retain the remains of metal foil coatings both inside and out. They are probably Leyden jars. It is possible that they were an improvisation of the type mentioned by Priestley.[48]

The alembic

Fig. 9 shows a collection of reagent and specimen bottles and three pieces of chemical apparatus. The alembic, 3, was a piece of standard equipment (there is a similar one in the Science Museum). Because of the ground glass fitting, it was easier to clean than a retort, and sublimate could be collected from the upper part without having to break the apparatus.

The presence of this piece implies that of others. Fig. 13 shows the use of an alembic, and its support and heating apparatus.[2] The conventional support in Dalton's time was a brass ring with a screw fitting for adjusting its position on a brass rod. The burner is a small Argand lamp; these burnt oil, and were the 'Bunsen burners' of their day, filling a gap between large furnaces and candles. A lamp and stand arrangement of this type is preserved in the Science Museum. The 'little lighted furnace' which features in a story of Dalton's old age was probably an Argand lamp.[49] Fig. 14 shows a free-standing lamp furnace.[50]

The cost of a matrass (round-bottomed flask) with an alembic fitted by grinding was from one to one and a half guineas, and a lamp furnace with various fittings could cost anything from 8*s*. 6*d*. to four guineas in 1805.

A 'Florence flask' (Fig. 9; 4) also appears in Fig. 13.

Dalton's diagram of a simple raingauge.   **Figure 12**

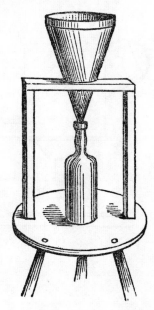

Apparatus from Accum's catalogue of 1805. **1** Alembic. **2** Stand   **Figure 13**
with sliding rings. **3** Small lamp furnace. **4** Florence flask.

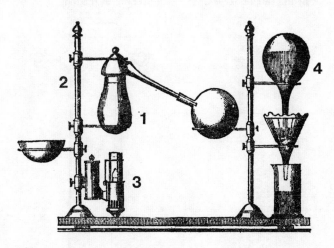

Figure 14   Large lamp furnace.

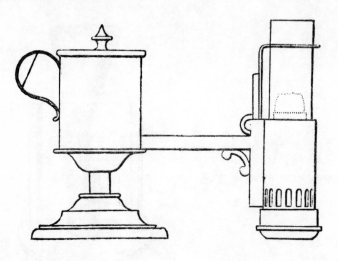

Figures 15 & 16   **15** Apparatus for producing water by sparking a mixture of hydrogen and oxygen.   **16** Form of Volta's eudiometer with two electrical connections at the top.

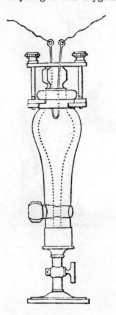

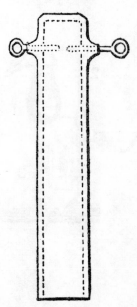

Type of Volta's eudiometer described and used by Dalton.   **Figure 17**

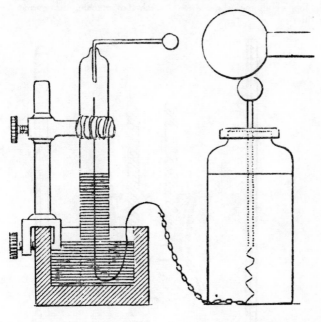

18 Graduated funnel. This was a type of eudiometer devised by Dalton.

19 Bell jar and flask used in pneumatic chemistry.

Figures 18 & 19

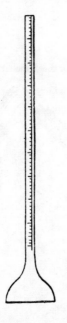

20 (left) Hope's eudiometer. 21 William Henry's modification of Hope's eudiometer, showing the method of attaching the graduated tube.

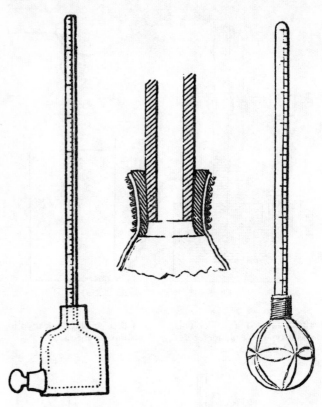

Part of Pepys' eudiometer, showing the detachable graduated tube.

Figure 22

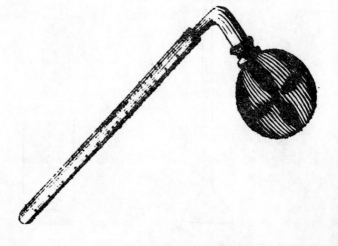

The spark eudiometer

This is an apparatus for exploding gases on a prepara-
tive scale, and was usually used to demonstrate the
synthesis of water from hydrogen and oxygen. One of
these survived in part (Plate IIIc; 3). The wires have
now gone; they appear to have been sealed in by
cement. The lower opening may originally have had a
brass cap with a screw fitting, as was usual in pneumatic apparatus. Dalton probably discarded this model
when the better type (Fig. 15[50a]) came in, about 1820;
the latter was designed to screw on to an air pump, and
it would be expected that earlier types were similarly
designed.

Analytical eudiometers in which gases were sparked
(Volta's eudiometers) were thick-walled graduated
tubes widening to a funnel shaped opening at the base.
Some had two hook-like wires cemented in at the top
(Fig. 16[51]), others had only one wire at the top, while the
second lead came in through the mercury trough and
up through the base of the instrument (Fig. 17[52]). This
was the model described by Dalton,[53] who used Volta's
eudiometer frequently; he probably had a number of
them since they were liable to be broken by the explosion of the gases they contained—and even by
spontaneous shattering.

With Volta's eudiometer, Dalton obtained very good
results when he sparked ether with oxygen[54] and its
accuracy in skilled hands would only be limited by the
accuracy with which it could be calibrated and read.
The tubes are usually rather wide for their lengths, with
the proportions of modern measuring cylinders, but
errors need not have been greater than about 2–3 per
cent.

Other types of eudiometer are shown in Fig. 3; 1,
2 and 6. The two funnels 1 and 2 are like one shown
by Henry (Fig. 18[55]) who says that Dalton used graduated funnels of this type for the estimation of the oxygen
content of air by reaction with nitric oxide. 6 is a fragment of a Hope's eudiometer, though it was not
recognized by Roscoe or Jones.

This (Fig. 20) and a modification of his own devising
(Fig. 21) are described by Henry.[56] Hope's eudiometer
had a graduated tube into a phial with a stopper in the

side. The gas was placed in the tube and the phial was filled with an appropriate solution. Pressure was equalized by easing the stopper from time to time. In Henry's modification an elastic bottle was used instead of a phial. It seems possible that Fig. 10; 1 shows this, and not the eudiometer of Pepys[57] which had a specially adapted measuring tube (Fig. 22[58]) and was accompanied by a complicated measuring device which Pepys thought would increase its accuracy. The elastic bottles in Fig. 10; 4 and 6, are not like those shown by Pepys, and are more likely to have been general pneumatic apparatus like the brass capped bottle 7.

Other apparatus on Plate Va

The earthenware cup 3 is said to have been used for holding mercury, and three cups of this type were salvaged (Plate IIIc; 1, 2 and 5). The purpose of the blocks, 5, is unknown.

Balances, weights and hydrometers

Dalton's analytical balance by Accum (Fig. 8, 2) is the same as that depicted on Accum's bill-head;[59] Accum, who was one of the best chemical operators in the country, must have thought it to be a good advertisement for his wares. He charged 18*s*. to £1 15*s*. for an 'accurate' balance, but an 'assay balance' like Dalton's cost from 10 to 15 guineas.[3] Roscoe may have thought it a rough balance because the pans are suspended by string, but this was usual at the time.

There was also a cruder balance (Fig. 6; 1) and various kinds of weights, including some of brass (Fig. 6; 2) in the range 1 to 10g. The small boxes (Fig. 6; 3) contain weights which are fractions of both grains and grams, the larger ones being of brass and the smaller of platinum. The smallest of these, and a paper of wire weights mentioned by Roscoe were 0·01 grain weights, suggesting that the best balance could weigh (in modern terms) to the nearest milligram. Since Dalton seldom dealt with samples weighing less than 10 grains, his weighing error is unlikely to have exceeded 1 per cent. The weights are in conformity with the specifications laid down by Faraday.[60]

Dalton appears to have relied on specific gravity for standardizing his solutions. A specific gravity bottle survives (Plate IIb; 7) and there were others (Fig. 4; 2 and 4; 5 is a counterpoise). He also used specific gravity bulbs ('philosopher's bubbles'); the set shown (Fig. 4; 7) is as large as the largest set in the Science Museum. The 20 bulbs cover the range from 1·000 to 1·020;[61] they cost from £4 to £8 a set.[4] Faraday says that they were rarely used in chemical research and it is possible that these were lecture equipment.

No apparatus which survived his death gave any information about the methods Dalton used for volumetric analysis.

Pneumatic apparatus

Apart from the elastic bottles with screw fittings, at least four pieces of brass fitted glass apparatus survived; these are a cubical bottle with a brass cap and small additional fitting (Fig. 10; 7), a graduated bell-jar (Fig. 3; 4) and two other objects (Plate IVa).

The cubical bottle is unusual; nothing like it can be found in any book or catalogue so far examined. It could be one of the cubical bottles already mentioned, which may have been kept for luting into brass caps as required. Some pieces in Oxford have brass fittings roughly luted into position by means of a dark cement.

The graduated bell-jar, and balloon flasks like that in the upper right-hand part of Plate IVa are often illustrated in books of the period (Fig. 19).[62] The flask is fitted with a stopcock, which would have a screw thread for the attachment of other components.

The apparatus left of centre in Plate IVa has a brass fitting on each of the diametrically opposite necks. There is a long rod through the upper fitting, possibly a support. The lower fitting has a stopcock and something which could be either a bladder or (more probably) a metal vessel. A rather similar copper vessel with a screw fitting, but larger and with a neck, is in the Oxford Museum of the History of Science. The purpose of the apparatus is unknown and the difficulty of identification is increased because screw fittings were interchangeable, and the fact that two pieces of equipment were attached to each other is no guarantee that they were originally used in conjunction.

Brass fitted apparatus has considerable significance in the history of the development of equipment. In modern apparatus leak-proof joints are of ground glass and the parts of an apparatus are interchangeable. Before this, joints were made by means of rubber bungs and tubing. Earlier still, there was the brass fitted apparatus of pneumatic chemistry. *It resembled modern ground-glass apparatus in having interchangeable joints.* The apparatus examined in Oxford bore the names of both Knight and Newman, while some was unsigned and differed from the products of both of these makers. Nevertheless all of these pieces could be fitted to each other. *Any* male thread would fit *any* female thread, and a blowpipe with Newman's name on the box, had one tap stamped with his own name and another with 'Knight/Foster Lane'.

Brass fitted apparatus seems to have shown some improvement during its rather short useful period. A rather fragile Florence flask seen in Oxford was joined to a bell-jar through flimsy brass fittings which had become loose. This was similar to an apparatus in a portrait[59] of Accum who left England in 1822. Pieces with Newman's name on the other hand tend to be of thick glass with stout, firmly fixed fittings. Newman's active period[63] was 1816–38, so that these heavier fittings appear to be of late date.

Some brass fitted apparatus would probably be made to order, but there was a wide range available on demand. Glass bell-jars, 'with best stopcocks, connecting piece, jet and pipe' cost $2\frac{1}{2}$ guineas, flasks with appropriate fittings were £1 12s. 6d., while the male and female joints were 2s. 6d. A brass stopcock, if large, could be priced as high as a guinea.[2] Bladders mounted with ferrules to fit this apparatus were 3s. to 4s. and 'elastic gum bottles' of the type Dalton had were from 8s. to 12s.[4] Knights claimed that they had 'a great variety' of fittings in this range.

Accum's catalogue of 1812–13 offers bell-glasses with stopcocks and globes for weighing gases for as much as £8 3s.—rather a fancy price for those days. There are two superb examples in Harvard,[64] which may have been supplied by Accum, since the University traded with him. They bear the inscription 'Pixii père et fils, rue de Grenoble St Germain 18 à Paris'.

Evidently this easily assembled, readily interchangeable apparatus was widely made and even more widely sold. It must have originated in either England or France, the two countries where pneumatic chemistry had its beginning, but its origin is still obscure.

There are a number of references to this type of apparatus in Dalton's works, the earliest in a paper read in 1800.[65] Dalton used a large spherical glass receiver, capacity 'above one gallon', and with a brass cap and stopcock.

Dalton[66] mentions a Florence flask with a stopcock, to which he connected a bladder. Later he described a receiver of 400 cubic inches capacity, open at the top and fitted with a brass cap, for attaching a bladder to the receiver; he used it to investigate the gases formed on burning sulphur[67] and phosphorus[68] in air. In his experiments on ether he mentions balloon flasks of 253 and 404 cubic inches capacity, fitted with brass caps and stopcocks.[69] The enormous flask of 2 cubic feet capacity does not seem to have been brass fitted.[70]

Dalton's air pump figures in the portrait by Allen (Plate IIa). It is small and plain compared with some of the ornate ones which have survived.

The apparatus at Manchester Grammar School

A round flask, brass fitted and of rather less than a litre capacity was preserved in Manchester Grammar School with some other objects thought to have belonged to Francis Jones,[17] a former chemistry master. The flask could be screwed easily to a tap by Newman, and must therefore be of early nineteenth-century origin. With the flask were two barometer tubes similar to that in Dalton's barometer by Ronchetti (Plate IIIa, 2), and a box of slides relating to the history of chemistry. It is possible that Jones used this flask and the barometer tubes as lecture specimens.

Acknowledgements: I wish to thank the following for their help in the production of this paper: Mr R. Littlemore for photographic assistance; the staff of the Oxford Museum for the History of Science for permission to examine their exhibits; my husband, Dr W. V. Farrar, for helpful advice; and Dr W. E. Knowles Middleton for permission to reproduce Figure 1. I also wish to thank the High Master of Manchester Grammar School for permission to examine the school's apparatus.

Notes

1 F. Accum, *A system of theoretical and practical chemistry* (2 vols, London, 1803). Annotations in William Henry's copy show

that Henry used, or considered using, some of the illustrations from this as a basis for those in his own book.

2 F. Accum, *Catalogue of chemical preparations, apparatus and instruments for philosophical chemistry* (London, 1805).

3 F. Accum (and Garden), *Catalogue of the apparatus and instruments employed in experimental and operative chemistry* (London, 1812 or 1813, date partly illegible). Note the change of adjectives qualifying 'chemistry'.

4 R. and G. Knight, *Catalogue of apparatus and instruments for philosophical, experimental and commercial chemistry* (London, 1811).

5 J. Dalton, *A new system of chemical philosophy*, i, parts I and II (Manchester, 1808 and 1810) 440-1.

6 Ibid., ii (Manchester, 1827) viii.

7 See D. S. L. Cardwell, supra, p. 3.

8 W. W. Haldane Gee, H. F. Coward, and A. Harden, *Manchester Memoirs*, lix (1915) no. 12, 1-66.

9 E. G. R. Taylor, *The mathematical practitioners of Hanoverian England, 1714-1840* (Cambridge, 1966). Entry 858.

10 Dalton also claimed that he could carry his library on his back; at his death it consisted of more than 750 volumes, according to the sale catalogue (Salford, 1844).

11 H. Lonsdale, *The worthies of Cumberland. John Dalton, F.R.S.* (London, 1874) 246. W. H. Wollaston made similar remarks, equally implausible, about his own apparatus.

12 W. C. Henry, *Memoirs of the life and scientific researches of J. Dalton* (London, 1854) 29: 'Dalton never possessed the refined instruments . . . essential to rigorous experimental determinations'; 38, 'His instruments of research, chiefly made by his own hands, were incapable of affording accurate results'; 179 (quoting Sedgwick), 'without any powerful apparatus . . . with an apparatus, indeed, many of them might think contemptible' Dalton had achieved 'a name not perhaps equalled by that of any other living philosopher of the world'.

13 *Manchester Memoirs*, i (1860) 53. The Manchester Lit. & Phil. Soc. is referred to in the rest of this paper as 'the Society'.

14 H. E. Roscoe, ibid., xv (1875-6) 77.

15 Idem., B.A. Report (1887) 1.

16 Idem., *Life and experiences* (London, 1906). At the exhibition of 1876, Roscoe was introduced to Queen Victoria as 'Mr Dalton'.

17 F. Jones, *Manchester Memoirs*, xlviii (1903-4), no. 22, 1-5.

18 C. L. Barnes, ibid., lx (1915-16) ii-viii.

19 G. Adams, *Lectures on natural and experimental philosophy* (5 vols, London, 1799). This includes a catalogue (in vol. 5) of Adams' successors, W. and S. Jones.

20 A catalogue of Ebsworth is bound with a list of the library of a mathematical society based in London, but not the same as the present Mathematical Society. This book (in Manchester University Library) contains MS. additions and a printed list of instruments and apparatus, some of it chemical, for the use of members. The work presents some problems and is currently under examination. Ebsworth (9, Entry 1320) appears to have been the successor of Dudley Adams. Dalton had a Hadley's sextant (18) signed D. Adams, London, so that this catalogue would indicate the latest prices likely to be paid by Dalton, whereas the previous catalogue (19) would show the earliest; there is surprisingly little difference.

21 J. R. Partington, *A history of chemistry*, iii (London, 1962) 758.

22 Some of it may have been exhibited in the Museum Room set up in 1936; a leaflet was printed describing this exhibition, but no copy can be traced.

23 Found in the Society's files, and loaned to the writer by Mr A. L. Smyth. Its history is not known.

24 *Manchester Memoirs*, lxxxiv (1939–41) xxiii, xxxv–xxxvii.

25 A. P. Hatton and J. W. Flowett, ibid., cvi (1963–4) no. 8, 1.

26 Henry, op. cit. (12) 124.

27 *New Scientist*, xxxi (1966) 493.

28 C. A. Browne, *Journal of Chemical Education*, ii (1927), 829, 1008, 1140.

29 Buchan was elected to the Society in 1810, and died in 1859, aged 84. 'He was a man of liberal views and large intellectual capacity'; see *Manchester Memoirs*, i (1857–60) 146, 246.

30 W. E. Knowles Middleton, *The history of the barometer* (Baltimore, 1964) 146–7. See fig. 2.

31 Taylor, op. cit. (9) entry 1689, gives Joshua Ronchetti's addresses as 29 Balloon Street and 43 Market Street, Manchester.

32 Cash account 1792–3; includes expenses from previous years (microfilm in Manchester Central Library).

33 Henry, op. cit. (12) 13, 225.

34 Gee, Coward and Harden, op. cit. (8) give details of sheet 31, which had a logarithmic curve representing Dalton's Law for the increase of vapour pressure with temperature and a diagram of a barometer tube containing mercury with water above it. The tube has a heating jacket surrounding its upper part; the lower part was bent, and graduated for measurement of pressure.

35 J. Dalton, *Manchester Memoirs*, v (1802) 535.

36 *Idem.*, op. cit., (5) 20–1.

37 Idem., op. cit., (35) 571.

38 Ibid., 565.

39 Ibid., 566.

40 J. Baxendell, *Manchester Memoirs*, iv (1865) 133.

41 F. Accum, op. cit., (3) 14.

42 Written notice on the wooden scale. A thermometer is listed in the sale catalogue (Salford, 1844).

43 J. Dalton, *Meteorological essays* (London, 1793) 32.

44 Ibid., 65, 200.

45 Idem., *Nicholson's Journal*, x (1805) 93–5.

46 Idem., op. cit., (43) 35.

47 H. Lonsdale, op. cit., (11) 65.

48 J. Priestley, *A familiar introduction to the study of electricity*, 2 vols (London, 1777) 1; Plate II, k.

49 F. Greenaway, *Manchester Memoirs*, c. (1958–9) 7.

50 W. Henry, *The elements of experimental chemistry* (6th edition, 1810), Plate V, fig. 46.

50a Ibid. (9th edn, 1823) 244.

51 Ibid. (6th edn, 1810), Plate II, fig. 28.

52 Idem., ibid., Plate IX, fig. 84.

53 J. Dalton, op. cit., (5) 274.

54 Idem., *Manchester Memoirs*, viii (1819) 446–82.

55 W. Henry, op. cit., (50) 415, and Plate II, fig. 24.

56 Ibid., 191–2, and Plate II, figs. 20 and 21.

57 W. H. Pepys, *Phil. Trans. Roy. Soc.* (1807), 247.

58 S. Parkes, *Chemical catechism* (London, 10th edn, 1822) Plate II, fig. 27.

59 R. J. Cole, *Annals of Science*, vii (1951) 128.

60 M. Faraday, *Chemical manipulation* (London, 1829) 27–8.

Notes

61 The inscription in the lid (partly erased) seems to read H. (or W.) B. Watson. This may be a mistake for H. H. Watson, or may refer to a different instrument maker.

62 W. Henry, op. cit., (51) Plate II, fig. 22.

63 Taylor, op. cit., (9) Entry 1396.

64 I. B. Cohen, *Some early tools of American science* (Harvard, 1950) appendix III, figs. 36 and 37.

65 J. Dalton, *Manchester Memoirs*, v (1802) 515–26 (read 27.6.1800).

66 Ibid., (5) 235.

67 Ibid., 390–1.

68 Ibid., 413.

69 Ibid., (54) 459, 461.

70 Ibid., 480.

11

Robert Fox

Dalton's Caloric Theory

It is only natural that we should pay particular attention to those of Dalton's scientific contributions which have proved to be of lasting value, but I make no apology for drawing attention briefly to one aspect of his work, his theory of heat, which does not fall into this category for the simple reason that it was wholly and fundamentally wrong. In doing so I hope to go some way towards redressing the balance in favour of Dalton the physicist, while not of course denying his prime importance to the field of chemistry.

Dalton himself would probably be surprised that this work should now be treated as something of a digression, for to him the subject was one of the greatest importance, especially in the years immediately preceding the first appearance of his *New system of chemical philosophy*. His preoccupation with heat and related matters in this period, approximately the first decade of the nineteenth century, is well known and it can come as no surprise for anyone who has examined his early papers[1] and such accounts as we have of his note-books[2] and unpublished lectures[3] to find the first part of volume one of the *New system*[4] almost entirely devoted to a lengthy account of the author's theory of heat, with the exposition of his chemical atomic theory taking a poor second place. In Dalton's mind of course the two were not unrelated, but whereas much of his atomic theory, by its essential correctness, has been able to survive, his views on heat, suffering as they did from a firm and lifelong[5] adherence to the

Figure 23

Dalton's diagram illustrating his theory of heat (from the *New system,* Manchester, 1808, p. i). Also shown are sketches of the new scale of temperature which Dalton was advocating at this time.

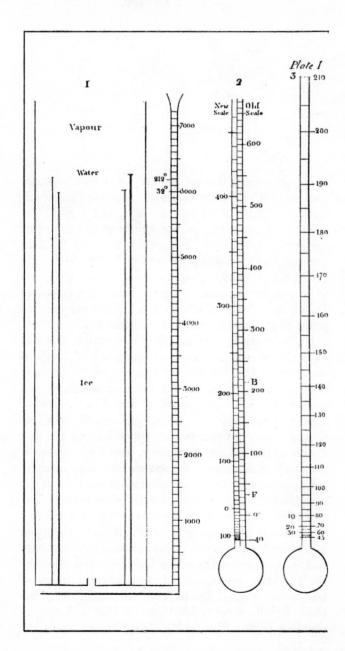

EXPLANATION OF THE PLATES.

PLATE I. Fig. 1. is intended to illustrate the author's ideas on the subject of the capacities of bodies for heat. See page 3. There are three cylindrical vessels placed one within another, having no communication but over their margins; the innermost is connected with a lateral and parallel tube graduated, and supposed to represent the degrees of a thermometer, the scale of which commences at absolute cold; if a liquid (supposed to represent heat) be poured into the tube, it will flow into the inner vessel, through an aperture at the bottom, and rise to the same level in the vessel and the tube. Equal increments of heat in this case are supposed to produce equal increments of temperature. When the temperature has arrived at a certain point (suppose 6000°) the body may be supposed to change its solid form to the liquid, as from ice to water, in which case its capacity for heat is increased, and is to be represented by the second vessel. A considerable portion of liquid must then be poured into the tube before any rise will be perceived, because it flows over the margin of the innermost vessel into the lateral cavity of the second; at length it reaches the level, and then a proportional rise will ensue, till the body becomes converted into an elastic fluid, when the thermometer again becomes stationary—whilst a great portion of heat is entering into the body; now assuming a new capacity.

Fig. 2. is a comparative view of the old and new divisions of the scale of the mercurial thermometer. See Table, page 14. The interval from freezing to boiling water is 180° on both scales, and the extremes are numbered 32° and 212° respectively. There are no other points of temperature in which the two scales can agree.

Fig. 3. is a view of the divisions of a water thermometer, conformably to the new scale of the mercurial; the lowest point is at 45°; the intervals from 45° upwards, to 55°, 65°, 75°, &c. are as the numbers 1, 4, 9, &c. Also, 30° and 60° coincide, as do 20° and 70°, &c.

PLATE II. Fig. 1. represents an air thermometer, or the expansion of air by heat; the numbers are Fahrenheit's, and the intervals are such as represented in the 7th column of the table, at page 14.

Fig. 2. is the logarithmic curve, the ordinates of which are erected at equal intervals, and diminish progressively by the ratio ½. The intervals of the absciss or base of the

E e

erroneous caloric theory, have suffered a well-deserved oblivion.

In the history of theories of heat Dalton has a prominent place as the last important exponent of principles first taught by William Irvine, a talented pupil of Joseph Black who lectured at Glasgow from 1766 until his death in 1787. Irvine had published nothing on the subject in his own lifetime[6] and the considerable, though by no means universal, support which his views had won in Britain during the last quarter of the eighteenth century was almost entirely a result of the two editions of *Experiments and observations on animal heat* by the English physician Adair Crawford[7] which appeared in 1779 and 1788.[8] Crawford had developed Irvine's ideas with particular reference to the origin of the heat evolved in the bodies of warm-blooded animals and in combustion and had derived explanations which, if they lacked support other than his own very suspect experiments, were still sufficiently convincing, in Dalton's eyes at least, to be adopted by him in all essential respects long after Crawford's death in 1795.[9]

The Irvinist principles, as I shall call them, without wishing to detract in any way from Crawford's contributions, are best illustrated by the analogy of a cylinder of uniform cross section filled with a liquid, the liquid in the cylinder representing the heat in a body in degrees above the 'natural zero of temperature', to use Dalton's term,[10] and the cross sectional area of the cylinder would be proportional to its specific heat. As a typical example of the way in which these principles could be applied, consider the change of state from ice to water, illustrated in Fig. 23.[11] An Irvinist would argue, and in this particular case he would not be without experimental support,[12] that the specific heat of ice, or on our analogy the cross section of the cylinder, suddenly increased when the temperature reached the melting point. Thus, if the temperature, or level of the liquid in the cylinder, were not to fall, it was only to be expected that some additional ('latent') heat would have to be added. Sudden changes in specific heat could of course equally well be applied to account for the heat absorbed in vaporization and also for heats of chemical reaction. In an exothermic reaction, for example, it followed that the total heat capacity of the products must always be less than that of the reactants and it was therefore only too predictable that Crawford's explanation of the most important reaction of this type, respiration, should have been supported by his experiments, which showed the specific heat of inhaled air, and more especially of oxygen, to be appreciably greater than those of carbon dioxide and water vapour, the products of respiration.[13]

These then were the fundamental beliefs underlying all Dalton's work on the theory of heat. They were not original and they could have been held by virtually any British scientist of the late eighteenth century. After 1800, however, this was hardly the case, since criticism, especially from France,[14] had now cast serious doubt on the truth of Irvine's principles and it is clear that by 1806 even Dalton himself felt that Crawford's theory of animal heat had declined in popularity.[15] In fact, although he does not appear to have realized it, Dalton was unique among nineteenth-century writers in placing sufficient trust in the opinions of Irvine and Crawford not merely to accept them but also to extend them and apply them to new problems. The earliest instance of this, dating from June 1800, occurs in his interpretation of his own observations on the heating which accompanied the sudden entry of air into a vacuum.[16] In attributing the rise in temperature to the fact that the specific heat of empty space was greater than that of an equal volume of air Dalton was applying his Irvinist beliefs in a quite novel fashion and his claim that he had merely adopted an already familiar explanation was entirely misleading. For, although earlier writers[17] had certainly explained the phenomenon in terms of the presence of heat in the vacuum before the entry of air, they were not Irvinists and so had neither estimated the magnitude of the specific heat of the void nor even assumed that it had one.

In this example there is evidence that Dalton's views on heat were already taking a highly individual turn, but the most original of his contributions, those concerning the sizes of gas particles, were yet to be made. Their originality was largely the result of one important respect in which he differed from Irvine and Crawford, namely in his uncompromising belief in the physical reality of caloric, the weightless and highly elastic fluid of heat which he supposed to surround the atoms of all bodies, constituting virtually all their bulk, especially in the case of gases, while contributing nothing to their weight.[18] Irvine by contrast, with a caution only to be expected in the pupil of one with such positivistic tendencies as Joseph Black,[19] appears to have expounded his principles independently of any opinion as to the nature of heat,[20] while Crawford had expressed only tentative support for the material theory.[21] However useful the concept of the fluidity of heat might have been for both men as an aid to thought, neither could have shared Dalton's wholehearted conviction on the matter. Although I cannot enlarge on the background to this contrast here, it does seem relevant to point out that Dalton made no important contribution to the theory of heat until the first decade of the nineteenth century, by which time the dominance of caloric over the rival vibrational theory was probably greater than at the time when Irvine and Crawford developed their views. In Dalton's day, we should recall, Lavoisier's chemistry was generally interpreted as giving strong support to caloric.

In developing what were already familiar principles in a manner which demanded the literal acceptance of caloric theory Dalton was thus making a quite new departure. It was one which gave hope of success with problems which could not otherwise have been solved or even tackled and Dalton gave a good illustration of the power of this new approach in October 1801 in his demonstration that the diameter of the particles of any gas being heated at constant pressure increased in proportion to the absolute temperature.[22] T, in other words, was shown to be proportional to $V^{\frac{1}{3}}$ (on the assumption that the particles were spherical and that adjacent particles were in contact) and not, as we should now expect for a perfect gas, to V. A special interest attaches to this piece of work since it was the first in which Dalton applied his new found belief in the fundamentality of gases. Earlier in the same paper he had announced his celebrated discovery that all gases were expanded equally by heat and had demonstrated the implications which this held in the context of the prevailing 'Newtonian' picture of stationary gas particles held apart by repulsive forces. He saw his discovery as evidence that in gases, and in gases alone, these repulsive forces had completely overcome the naturally attractive forces between the particles of ponderable matter which gave liquids and solids their characteristic structure and also their widely varying expansion coefficients. Since Dalton, like virtually all his contemporaries, attributed the repulsive forces to caloric, it was a natural extension to suppose that gases were the only substances in which the inter-particle forces were wholly the result of caloric and hence to conclude:

. . . that general laws respecting the absolute quantity and the nature of heat, are more likely to be derived from elastic fluids than from other substances.[23]

That all Dalton's most important work on caloric theory concerned matter in the gaseous state obviously had a great deal to do with this statement.

Dalton's derivation of the expression relating particle size and temperature is examined in greater detail in the Appendix and it must suffice to say here that it was considerably longer than his own somewhat cryptic account would suggest and appears to have involved both his own Irvinist-style caloric theory and Newton's purely mathematical demonstration that Boyle's law could be explained if it was supposed that the repulsive forces between the adjacent particles of a gas expanding isothermally were inversely proportional to the distance between them.[24] Since it also contained one other quite unsubstantiated premise as well as a careless slip, it is fortunate that the few writers who commented on it,[25] though sceptical, do not seem to have examined it very thoroughly.

We can only assume that Dalton himself recognized the weakness of his argument, for at some time between January 1805 and 1807[26] he abandoned it and never returned to the problem. But the subject of particle size and in particular its dependence on the nature rather than the temperature of a gas was shortly to gain a new and far greater significance with the emergence of his atomic theory. From the start size was as much a characteristic of the Daltonian atom as weight. By 6 September 1803, when the first table of particle weights appeared in his notebook, Dalton had already rejected his earlier 'confused idea'[27] that under similar conditions of temperature and pressure the particles of all gases were of the same size[28] and by 19 September the first list of fourteen gas-particle diameters had been drawn up.[29] In view of his later descriptions of gas particles composed of huge atmospheres of caloric surrounding a small heavy central atom,[30] it may seem surprising that it was not until the early months of 1806 that he began to examine the implications of his new concept in the light of his Irvinist theory of heat. Was it not immediately obvious that the diameters were related to the quantities of heat in different gases and hence also to their specific heats? One reason for the delay may well lie in Dalton's 'first theory of mixed gases'[31] which he held at this time and which even led him to doubt for a while whether the repulsive forces between particles should be attributed to caloric at all.[32] It was only towards the end of 1805,[33] when he finally abandoned this theory, that he unequivocally restored to caloric its customary rôle and, even more important, gave variations in particle size between different gases a special importance as the basis of his amended or 'second' theory of mixed gases.[34]

With this new and eminently satisfactory application of particle size fresh in his mind and with the difficulties which his first theory raised for caloric now removed Dalton returned to the subject of heat between March and June 1806. According to Roscoe and Harden[35] some fifty pages of notes attest to his interest in this period and it is significant that he paid considerable attention to the relationship between the sizes of the particles of various gases and the quantities of caloric which they contained. The earliest comment appeared in a short manuscript article 'On heat' dated 23 May 1806.[36] Here Dalton maintained that, at a given temperature and pressure, the atmospheres of caloric were largest and densest round those atoms which had the greatest attraction for the fluid. In another note,[37] quite separate from this article but evidently written at about the same time, we find Dalton, in search of a more specific relationship, rejecting the possibility that the density of caloric in any gas was proportional to the diameter of its particles. Unfortunately he offered no explanation for this rejection so that we can only guess at the considerations which, by 1 June and on the very next page after this last note,[38] had led him to try a quite different approach. His revised opinion, that under similar conditions the density of caloric was the same in all gases, irrespective of the size of their particles, seems to have been preferable to that which he had held a few days earlier in just one respect, namely in that it predicted specific heats in rather better, if not good, agreement with the experimental values given by Crawford in 1788.[39] It is therefore in a concern to reconcile the consequences of his caloric theory of gases with the results of Crawford's experiments, or at least with his explanation of heats of reaction, that I feel we must look for an understanding of the motives for this work. So far as I am aware, Dalton's views on the state of caloric in gases led to no other consequences which were capable of independent verification. Admittedly the volume specific heats obtained by Crawford were by no means equal, as would have been expected if Dalton had been correct, but still less did they increase with increasing particle size,[40] the corollary of Dalton's earlier opinion.

Dalton was still working on the problem during the printing of the *New system*,[41] so that it is not surprising that the definitive version of his views which appeared in part one of the book[42] showed yet another fundamental change. Believing as he now did that equal quantities of heat were contained not in equal volumes of gases, and still less in equal weights, but rather in equal numbers of particles, it followed that the specific heat by weight of any gas, elementary or compound, should be inversely proportional to the weight of its ultimate particles. In his conviction that a relationship of this type existed at all he was clearly guided by his belief in the essential simplicity of gases,[43] but the justification for the particular choice which he made was slight, consisting essentially of an involved and far from conclusive argument based wholly on Irvinist principles. The experimental evidence was equally inadequate. In fact, of the six gases for which a comparison between the predicted and experimental specific heats was possible, Dalton found real support for his speculations only in the case of atmospheric air and it was therefore no coincidence that he should now have specifically excluded air from the general criticism of the accuracy of Crawford's results which had appeared in a chapter of the *New system* printed off earlier.[44] His confident, if negative, claim that there was no 'established fact' which could disprove his treatment was only too true in 1808, but it reflected the scarcity and deplorable standard of earlier experiments on the specific heats of gases rather than any intrinsic merit in his own work. Within a few years this unsatisfactory, though forgivable, state of affairs had changed and the very bases of Dalton's argument, his Irvinist theory of heat and his belief in the correctness of Crawford's explanations of animal heat and heats of reaction, had become quite untenable, at least for anyone less committed and more open-minded than Dalton.

The first blow came with the French Institute's prize competition in physics for 1812. In their fine prize-winning entry two young physicists, François Delaroche and Jacques-Étienne Bérard, established as correct values for the specific heats of gases which could not conceivably be reconciled either with Crawford's theory of heat or with Dalton's predictions and which showed moreover that the specific heat of a gas could not be proportional to the quantity of heat which it contained.[45] An equally vigorous attack on Irvinist principles came in 1819 from Dulong and Petit[46] in the very same paper in which they announced their conclusion that the specific heats of all metallic elements were inversely proportional to their atomic weights. Like Delaroche and Bérard they argued that experiment did not support the existence of any connection between a change in heat capacity and the emission or absorption of heat in a chemical reaction, but they went further in singling out Dalton's speculations for special criticism.

Dalton's reaction to these attacks did not appear until 1827. Then, writing in an appendix to volume two of the *New system*,[47] he finally acknowledged the correctness of Delaroche and Bérard's experiments, though only after repeating them himself and with the reservation that any breakdown of the proportionality between specific heat and the total quantity of caloric in gases was to be attributed merely to the variation in their specific heats with temperature and so did not provide sufficient reason for the rejection of Irvine's principles, at least for solids and liquids, in which this variation did not seem to occur. To Dulong and Petit he was understandably less gracious, first casting doubt on the constancy of their atomic heats and then claiming that he had partially anticipated their discovery! Just how ludicrous the latter claim was, despite W. C. Henry[48] and the *Dictionary of national biography*,[49] should be obvious to anyone who reads Dulong and Petit's criticisms of the Irvinist theory and in particular of Dalton's interpretation of it. That Dalton should have even made the claim suggests either that he was deliberately trying to obscure the issue or, more probably, that here as so often in his scientific work he had seriously misunderstood the writings of others.

Dalton's cause was now all but lost, yet it would be wrong to conclude without some reference to the brave show of defiance which he made in 1842 when he reproduced his views on caloric in the second edition of the *New system* exactly as they had appeared in the first, not even omitting Crawford's long discredited experimental results. They must have made quite extraordinary, if not unintelligible, reading and it is doubtful to what extent Dalton himself was really convinced of their truth. In any case the work of a seventy-six year old is an all too easy target, but this repetition of his views only two years before his death seems to reflect the same independence of mind which was already apparent in the early 1800's. Even then he had developed a version of caloric theory which, although based on familiar if unsubstantiated principles, was undeniably original. In fact its originality was its greatest weakness, for it turned his attention to problems such as the capacity of the void and the theoretical prediction of specific heats which held no interest for anyone who did not first share his views on caloric. Indeed to his contemporaries, whether in 1800 or 1842, Dalton's work on the theory of heat must have seemed almost as wrongheaded and irrelevant to current problems as it does to us now.

Appendix

It is impossible to know exactly how Dalton derived his relationship between particle size and temperature, but the following is one possible approach. Dalton considered the expansion of air at constant pressure between 55°F and 212°F, a process which he would presumably have had to treat in two stages. In the first, the heating of the air at constant volume from 55°F to 212°F, the total heat content would have increased from, say, Q_{55} to Q_{212}, while the inter-particle force, originally F_{55}, would have become F_{212}. Since Dalton assumed, explicitly though without justification, that this force was proportional to Q, it followed that $\frac{F_{212}}{F_{55}} = \frac{Q_{212}}{Q_{55}}$. His Irvinist views would now have allowed him to go one stage further, for he could argue that $\frac{Q_{212}}{Q_{55}}$ was in turn equal to $\frac{T_{212}}{T_{55}}$, the ratio of the absolute temperatures before and after the heating. In order to relate this ratio to the increase in volume which would have occurred if the air had been allowed to expand at constant pressure, it was necessary to consider a second process, the isothermal expansion of the air to the point where the pressure, and hence also F, fell to the values which they had before the heating. Dalton must have supposed, and here he was giving Newton's purely mathematical demonstration the status of a physical truth, that the force between the gas particles varied in inverse proportion to the distance (d) between them, so that $\frac{F_{212}}{F_{55}} = \frac{d_{212}}{d_{55}}$, where d^3_{55} and d^3_{212} were, of course, proportional to the volumes which the air would have occupied at 55°F and 212°F respectively had it been heated at constant pressure in a single process. It followed simply that $\frac{T_{212}}{T_{55}} = \frac{d_{212}}{d_{55}}$ and hence, when Dalton's own experimental values for the expansion were inserted, that the absolute zero was at − 1540°F. Dalton, strangely, made only an approximate calculation, but his figure of − 1515°F was still in 'more than fortuitous' agreement with Crawford's (app. − 1500°F). It should be noticed that even here he had not abandoned his belief in the correctness of the more traditional Irvinist method of determining the zero. By 1808, when he placed it at about − 6000°F, he relied solely on the latter method (see Dalton, op. cit., (4) 82–99).

1 Conveniently listed in A. L. Smyth, *John Dalton 1766–1844: A bibliography of works by and about him* (Manchester, 1966) 9–12.

2 See especially Roscoe and Harden, *A new view of the origin of Dalton's atomic theory* (London, 1896) 58–80.

3 R. A. Smith, 'Memoir of John Dalton and History of the Atomic Theory up to his time', *Manchester Memoirs*, xiii (1856) 254–6; A. W. Thackray, 'Documents relating to the Origins of Dalton's Chemical Atomic Theory', *Manchester Memoirs*, cviii (1965–6) 36 and 39–40; W. W. Haldane Gee, 'John Dalton's Lectures and Lecture Illustrations', *Manchester Memoirs*, lix (1914–15) 4–10 and Plate 1.

4 J. Dalton, *A new system of chemical philosophy* (Manchester, 1808) i (Part 1).

5 Although Dalton was far more committed in the last of his major scientific works, the *New system* (2nd edn, London, 1842), than in the first, his *Meteorological observations and essays* (London, 1793) 18–19.

6 For our knowledge of Irvine's opinions we rely principally on Crawford, op. cit. infra (8), and on the *Essays, chiefly on chemical subjects, by the late William Irvine, M.D., F.R.S.Ed., and by his son, William Irvine, M.D.* (London, 1805) 1–189.

7 Convenient biographical sketches of Irvine (1743–87) and Crawford (1748–95) appear in the *Dictionary of national biography*.

8 A. Crawford, *Experiments and observations on animal heat, and the inflammation of combustible bodies* (1st edn, London, 1779; 2nd edn, London, 1788).

9 Dalton, op. cit., (4) 75. See also his paper 'On Respiration and Animal Heat', *Manchester Memoirs* (2nd Series) ii (1813) 15–44, where he vigorously defends Crawford.

10 Among other terms used by him at various times to indicate the absolute zero were 'the point of total privation of heat', 'absolute cold' and 'zero of cold'.

11 From Dalton, op. cit., (4) Plate 1 and p. 217.

12 Dalton, along with most of his contemporaries, adopted Richard Kirwan's figure of $0·9$ for the specific heat of ice, where that of an equal weight of water was unity, although by 1792 Johan Gadolin had obtained the far better figure of $0·52$ (*N. Acta R. Soc. Sci. Upsaliensis*, v (1792) 28–9). For Kirwan's work see J. H. de Magellan, *Essai sur la nouvelle théorie du feu élémentaire* (London, 1780) 176–7. Another figure available to Dalton was that of William Irvine, who had shown the specific heats of water and ice to be 'in a ratio not greater than 10 to 8' (Irvine, op. cit., (6) 54).

13 Crawford, op. cit., (8) 31–53 (1st edn); 144–273 and 489 (2nd edn).

14 The most notable and effective critics were Lavoisier and Laplace who, in their 'Mémoire sur la Chaleur', *Mémoires de l'Académie Royale des Sciences* (1780) 381–6, used their own data concerning specific heats and heats of reaction to expose the unreliability of the well known 'Irvinist' method of determining the absolute zero which had been first described in Magellan, op. cit., (12) 175–6 (see Crawford, op. cit., (8) 449–56 (2nd edn), for a more detailed account of the method). In demonstrating that the values for the zero obtained by applying the method to five different reactions varied considerably, Lavoisier and Laplace were making the first attack on an extremely vulnerable point in the Irvinist doctrines. It is not surprising that similar criticisms soon followed from Armand Séguin, in the *Annales de Chimie*, v (1790) 231–57, and from Gadolin, op. cit., (12) 1–49.

15 Dalton, *Manchester Memoirs* (2nd Series) ii (1813) 24.

16 J. Dalton, 'Experiments and Observations on the Heat and Cold produced by the Mechanical Condensation and Rarefaction of Air', *Manchester Memoirs* (1st Series) v (1802) 526. His statement that the volume specific heat of the void was 'less' than that of air was clearly an error and it was corrected in all the versions of the paper which appeared in other journals.

17 Notably M. A. Pictet in his *Essay on fire*, trans. by 'W.B.', (London, 1791) 29. This and H. B. de Saussure's *Essais sur l'hygrométrie* (Neuchâtel, 1783) 129 and 231–3, were evidently the sources for Dalton's knowledge of earlier explanations of this type of phenomenon, although he had probably not read J. H. Lambert's *Pyrometrie oder vom Maasse des Feuers und der Wärme* (Berlin, 1779) to which Saussure and Pictet owed a large, and fully acknowledged, debt.

18 See, for example, the passages from Dalton's notebook dated 23 May and 12 June 1806 which are quoted in Roscoe and Harden, op. cit., (2) 71 and 73–4. Also Dalton, op. cit., (4) 143–4 and *New system* (Manchester, 1810) i (Part 2) 548 and Plates 7 and 8.

19 On this aspect of Black's work see D. McKie and N. H. de V. Heathcote, *The discovery of specific and latent heats* (London, 1935) 27–30, and, more recently, D. S. L. Cardwell, 'Reflections on Some Problems in the History of Science', *Manchester Memoirs*, cvi (1963–4) no. 9, p. 8.

20 Irvine, op. cit., (6) 71.

21 Crawford, op. cit., (8) 115–16 (1st edn); 435–6 (2nd edn).

22 J. Dalton, 'On the Expansion of Elastic Fluids by Heat', *Manchester Memoirs*, v (1802) 601.

23 Ibid., 600. The opinion is repeated in Dalton, op. cit., (4) 68.

24 Newton, *Principia*, Book 2, Proposition XXIII.

25 See, for example, the anonymous comments in *Nicholson's Journal* (2nd Series) iv (1803) 223–4 and those in T. Thomson, *A system of chemistry* (4th edn, Edinburgh, 1810) 571–4.

26 The $V^{\frac{1}{3}}$ law appeared in the syllabus for Dalton's lectures of 1805 delivered in Manchester (see Thackray, op. cit., (3) 36), but was rejected explicitly in 1808 in the *New system*, p. 12. Dalton's rejection of the law was implied in the syllabus for his Edinburgh lectures of April 1807 (Thackray, op. cit., (3) 39), where he wrote that on the new scale of temperature which he was now advocating 'the expansive force of air increases in geometrical progression with equal increments of heat'.

27 Dalton, op. cit., (4) 188.

28 This rejection is clearly implied in the passage from p. 246 of Vol. 1 of Dalton's notebook quoted in Roscoe and Harden, op. cit., (2) 27.

29 Ibid., 41.

30 For references see note 18.

31 The term used by L. K. Nash in his paper 'The Origin of Dalton's Chemical Atomic Theory', *Isis*, xlvii (1956) 101–16 to denote Dalton's first attempt to explain the uniform diffusion of gases through one another.

32 Dalton, *Manchester Memoirs* (2nd Series) i (1805) 436 and op. cit., (4) 189. See also the notes for his 1810 Royal Institution lectures quoted in Roscoe and Harden, op. cit., (2) 16.

33 In his paper 'The Origin of Dalton's Chemical Atomic Theory: Daltonian Doubts resolved', *Isis*, lvii (1966) 44–5, A. W. Thackray argues convincingly for September 1805 as the date of the origin of Dalton's 'second theory of mixed gases'.

34 First described in Dalton, op. cit., (4) 187–92.

35 Roscoe and Harden, op. cit., (2) 71.

36 Ibid., 72.

37 Ibid.

38 Ibid., 73.

39 Crawford's results are conveniently listed in Dalton, op. cit., (4) 66.

40 The particle diameters which Dalton adopted at this time were probably very similar to those listed in his notebook on 14 September 1805 (see Thackray, op. cit., (33) on the dating of this table). Although he did modify his particle weights for oxygen and nitrogen between November 1805 and August 1806 (ibid., 55), the method of calculation, as described in Roscoe and Harden, op. cit., (2) 24–5, made the effect of such changes on the calculated diameters small.

41 Dalton, op. cit., (4) 66.

42 Ibid., 68–75.

43 For references see note 23.

44 Thus compare his comments on pp. 63 and 67 of this work.

45 F. Delaroche and J. E. Bérard, 'Mémoire sur la détermination de la chaleur spécifique des différens gaz', *Annales de Chimie*, lxxxv (1813) 156–76.

46 A. T. Petit and P. L. Dulong, 'Recherches sur quelques points importans de la théorie de la chaleur', *Annales de Chimie et de Physique*, x (1819) 397–8 and 408.

47 Dalton, *New system* (Manchester, 1827) ii, 268–71, 280–8 and 293–7. Dalton's reaction to Dulong and Petit's law is considered at greater length in a paper on the law now in preparation.

48 W. C. Henry, *Memoirs of the life and scientific researches of John Dalton* (London, 1854) 68.

49 *Dictionary of national biography*, article 'John Dalton'.

I should like to say a few words in favour of Crawford. At that time both his theories and experiments did, in fact, constitute 'the main line'. True, his calculations on absolute zero were defective and by the beginning of the nineteenth century Dalton and the younger Irvine were the only men to take them seriously, but as Professor Partington pointed out, Crawford's experiments on the specific heat of gases, though perhaps deplorable, were better than those of Lavoisier and Laplace for example and were remarkably good for the time. Of course the calculation of absolute zero by means of gas expansion was not then unknown. Martine had calculated a value from Amontons' figures as early as 1740, though there is good reason to believe that Amontons himself was not aware of the method on which Martine based his calculations.

While Amontons' work was not too well known in Britain, Martine's was very influential in Scotland, particularly through the medium of Dr Black's lectures, but the significant factor in the renewal of interest in this sort of calculation was probably the discovery of the Gay-Lussac–Charles' Law. Turning for a moment to the Scottish chemists—Black, Cullen, etc.—I find them fairly strongly committed, at least by implication, to material views of the nature of heat. They were, I think, positivists in the same sense as Newton; that is, when it suited them.

I entirely agree with Mr Fox in his assessment of the value of Dalton's writings on heat. It is, however, perhaps worth mentioning that at least in regard to the question of temperature changes

G R Talbot

G R Talbot associated with the compression and expansion of gases Joule took Dalton's work very seriously, as did Clement and Desormes in their entry for the 1812 competition; an entry which was however rejected and not published until 1819. It was in this essay that they claimed actually to have determined the specific heat of the void.

Encounters with
John Dalton

Many of the papers in this volume deal with the reactions of men who had Dalton's written word in front of them, or were reflecting on his ideas, criticizing them, learning from them, or building on them. Dalton, however, was not just a name on a title page, but a man people met and lived with. This paper will deal, therefore, with situations in which people had Dalton before their very eyes. Our most important intellectual activities occupy only a tiny proportion of our time. Most of the encounters I shall describe took place in that other, larger, sphere of life, the domestic and social.

In Dalton's early life they were not without effect on the progress of Dalton's thought but in his later years when he was producing no new work of any value they interest us only as reflecting the history of science at large. Since the scientific aspects are being dealt with in detail I shall, with one exception, confine myself to biographical matters.

One can think of Dalton's early life as alternating between periods of assimilation into a group or community, and periods marked by short striking confrontations with people whose attitudes sharply affected his own.

The quality of his early life can only be appreciated by a visit to his birthplace. Today, the village of Eaglesfield does not seem very far from the high road and from substantial centres of Cumberland commerce, but if one stands in the village street and allows the imagination to dissolve the asphalt road under one's feet, to banish the modern agricultural machines, and all the signs of twentieth and even nineteenth-century convenience, one will soon feel the chill of remoteness. It would have been impossible, it seems, for the life of any child in such surroundings as they once were to be anything but narrow and without horizon. Such thoughts must, however, be qualified by an appreciation of certain positive features of the eighteenth-century provincial life which have passed away. At a time when charity, the succouring of bodily needs, was still largely a matter of private benefaction, education, the nourishment of the unprovided mind, was still also a matter for private initiative. Since education was always seen to have two aspects, instruction and moral enlightenment, religious movements and educational movements went together, with the result, in our context, that the accident of being born into a Quaker family gave Dalton the chance of being well-taught.

The anecdotes of Dalton's early life[1] tell us very little that can be relied upon. His first teacher was one John Fletcher, a young man doing just what Dalton was to do later, helping out at a school and struggling with pupils not much younger than himself. But soon Dalton came under the influence of the first true scientist of his acquaintance, Elihu Robinson, a well-to-do Quaker, a leading figure in the locality, an amateur observer of nature, and a devotee of primitive observational meteorology. Dalton was admitted to his house, which must have been a world apart to the son of a poor weaver.

Dalton's recollections of his early days were vague. In 1841, at an age when we are supposed to recall our childhood with clarity, he had to confess in a letter to a relative by the name of Robinson, one of several of that name to whom his connection was fairly definite, that although he had referred to Elihu Robinson as 'cousin' the relationship was by no means clear.[2] These Quakers would no doubt have helped each other, as their convictions led them to help anyone in need, material or spiritual, but whether the early patronage of Dalton was solely a family matter, or whether it arose from clearly visible merit, is less definite than the early biographers seemed to think. Whatever the cause we must be grateful, as Dalton was grateful.

We do not know how much of the private apartments of Elihu Robinson's house Dalton saw, but he was sent for often enough to receive his first grounding in mathematics. Dalton was not picked out alone as a prodigy. There was another pupil, William Alderson, older than Dalton, but not so clever. Dalton used Alderson's name in some draft legal documents[3] he drew up at the age of fifteen so they must have been well acquainted. But although they corresponded they drifted apart bit by bit and only met again in old age. Dalton remembered his boyhood companion, and Alderson was deeply moved by the consideration of one who had by then achieved so great eminence.

In 1781 Dalton moved to Kendal, to teach, to lecture and to grow to manhood. We have no direct account of his competence or manner, but the evidence of his lecture attendance books suggests that he was not a compelling personality. Over and over again he began a course with good attendance of twenty or so. Within a few lectures, his attendance was down to three or four, and sometimes petered out.[4] Those of us who have laboured in the stony vineyard of adult education know this experience only too well, and we can sympathize with Dalton's disappointments. We can also understand why Dalton could persevere. He felt compelled to go on teaching, casting bread on the waters, not certain who amongst his pupils might benefit. The casual student, coming to a lecture to occupy time might soon drop away, but the best stayed on recognizing that they were getting something of value. When it came to lecturing to earnest students in Manchester, the matter made up for the defects in manner, and Dalton was a success, so much so that he was invited to come to Manchester permanently.

Other papers in this volume deal with the Manchester world, with the reaction of the Henry family and the rest of the Manchester circle amongst whom Dalton lived all the rest of his life. Let me deal with some people to whom meeting Dalton was an isolated occurrence.

The outstanding meeting is that with Thomas Thomson in 1804, when, according to Thomson, Dalton gave him an account of his atomic theory.

In 1804 Thomson travelled from Glasgow to Greenock, then by sea to Liverpool and overland to

Manchester to visit Dr William Henry, who had been his pupil in Edinburgh. Dalton's name was already known from his papers on gases, so there was every reason for them to meet. On 26 August Thomson dined with Thomas Henry and drank tea with William Henry in company with Dalton.[5] Thomson's diary reports that Dalton had been occupied with experiments on carburetted hydrogen, had found three species, olefiant gas, composed of an atom of hydrogen and an atom of carbon, gas of the marshes, composed of two atoms of hydrogen and one of carbon, and oxide of carbon, composed of an atom of carbon and one of oxygen. Thomson goes on 'He has suggested the following ingenious method of ascertaining the constituents of bodies'. Then follows a note of Dalton's symbols. It was evidently on this note that Thomson relied for his assertion twenty years later that Dalton deduced his theory from this work on hydrocarbons. The diary note, however, established nothing of the sort, merely that Dalton had a general method, which had been applied most recently to the hydrocarbons. We all know how much easier it is to talk about the day's work than the year's work, and it seems to me that this is what happened over William Henry's tea-cups.

Dalton had already made a reputation outside Manchester through his work on gases, and he had been to London to buy instruments. In 1803, he went on another kind of mission which, for a provincial, was of some distinction, to lecture at the Royal Institution.

The minutes of the meeting of the Managers of the Royal Institution[6] record only the bare facts of the invitation made at the recommendation of its 'Committee of Sciences', the composition of which we do not know.

Long after this, the Evening Discourses at the Royal Institution became events of some importance, focussing attention on growing points in science, and having a sense of occasion. In 1803 it was not yet so. The lectures Dalton was to give were characteristic of the early phase of the Royal Institution's life, when it was still working out Rumford's early ideal of informing the middle-class about the effects of science on daily life. Davy although already popular was still not at the height of his reputation. It was not Dalton the modest provincial who might expect to learn from Davy, but Davy who might expect to learn from Dalton, the senior and more experienced man.

The Chairman at the meeting of Managers which agreed the final programme arrangements with Dalton on his arrival was Charles Hatchett, who was himself engaged at that time to work on the proportionate composition of minerals.

From here on we look for the first crossing of the paths of Dalton and Wollaston. The two men had been born in the same year within a month of each other. A comparison of the character and aptitudes of these men would make a chapter in the history of society as well as of science. Wollaston came from a family with a tradition of learning, his father being a clergyman and a Fellow of the Royal Society, his grandfather a writer on natural theology.

Henry Lonsdale, the most discursive of Dalton's biographers, asserted that Wollaston[7] had been one of those responsible for bringing Dalton to London. I have not been able to substantiate this. One can only suppose that Wollaston would have attended Dalton's lectures which were part of the season's events for the seriously science minded in the London of the day, when there was no separation or at least not a sharp separation, between the formal communication of science and the less formal lectures of the series of which Dalton's formed part. In view of the special rôle Wollaston played in the future of Dalton's theory, the possibility that they met earlier than 1809 deserves careful inquiry.

Wollaston had followed the career Dalton had once dreamt of, medicine at Caius College, Cambridge, eventually a successful practice in London. The rebuffs given to Dalton in his ambitions had only served to spur him on to success in an alternative career. Wollaston, failing to achieve advancement in medicine, withdrew into a life of study, from which, it must be admitted he managed to make a comfortable profit when he had his platinum processes to exploit. In his experimental work he was excellent, but not the peer of Davy. In his theoretical speculation he was too cautious to take the leap which he seems to have been ready to take to an atomic theory of his own. Partington has said that it is doubtful if Wollaston would ever have had the courage to publish this theory, even if it had occurred to him. I cannot endorse this. The man who could write the Bakerian lecture of 1812[8] with its brilliant handling of three-dimensional atomic problems, its searching speculation about the architecture of crystals, its broad generalizations, could hardly have drawn back from an atomic theory if he had been convinced of its soundness.

Thomson thought his own publication of Dalton's theory in 1807 had made Wollaston refrain from further investigations. It seems more likely to me that Wollaston was already, before he read Thomson, possessed of some theory of proportion very close to an atomic theory. I should like to suggest that the most likely source of this was Dalton's Royal Institution lectures, and that the interplay of the minds of Dalton and Wollaston did not begin in 1808, but in January 1804 with a Dalton lecture on the composition of matter.

The evidence is of the most tenuous, but worth examining briefly. We have lost the full syllabus of Dalton's first Royal Institution lectures, but we have had in the past two years the syllabus of some lectures of 1805. This syllabus was part of a damaged mass of paper, recovered from the Dalton papers, war-damaged in 1940, which were catalogued at the Science Museum as lecture-syllabuses of 1808. When I re-examined these recently, taking each page apart, one of them turned out to be a syllabus of 1805. It had been known that these lectures had been based on the Royal Institution lectures. Dalton had evidently not had time to reorganize his thoughts, so we can suppose this syllabus represents what the Royal Institution audience heard in 1803–4.

Mr Thackray,[9] who examined these documents soon after I did, has published them as part of his excellent survey of unedited Dalton. He has come to the conclusion that Dalton's chemical atomism developed only slowly after the germination of the idea in 1803, and that nothing was yet clear in Dalton's mind in 1805. I differ from him in thinking that the 1805 syallabus, if compared with the later syllabuses, shows that Dalton had the composition of water very much in his mind at one crucial point in Lecture 15, and that this was probably his first exercise in calculating an atomic weight.[10] We know from Dalton's editing of his own papers that he was much given to extending his thoughts each time he worked on previous material. In his letters about his London lectures he refers to his presentation of his 'recent ideas', which included at that date the after-thoughts on atomic weights which terminate so dramatically the paper of 21 October 1803. Taken with Lecture 15 of the 1805 syllabus, this suggests to me that Wollaston could have heard about Dalton's atomic theory before Thomson did. Four years later Wollaston, with Thomson, gave the Dalton system the experimental support which took it out of Dalton's hands into the general stream of science.

Dalton mentions very few names as personal acquaintances in his early correspondence except his uncle, but after the publication of his *New system*, he writes more and more often about his leading contemporaries. He lectured again at the Royal Institution in 1809.[11]

He thought Davy was 'coming very fast into his views on chemical subjects'. He attended meetings of the Royal Society although not yet a Fellow, and dined with several scientific clubs. He was pleased to be able to talk chemistry with Davy and with Wollaston, whom he thought one of the cleverest men he had yet seen but there is no clue whether this was their first meeting. He met Blagden, Tennant and others at the house of Sir Joseph Banks, and was much impressed with the size of the party, forty or so in number, many more than he could ever have seen at a purely scientific gathering in Manchester.

Dalton's name was, at this time, still as well known for his early physical work as for his atomic theory, and he did not count among the great ones, but twelve years later the prolonged debate on his later ideas had made his name even more widely known, especially in France, where, in spite of disagreement with his scientific views, his intellectual quality was honoured, more than in his native country. He had been elected a corresponding member of the Académie des Sciences in 1816.

In 1822 he paid a memorable visit to Paris.[12] The

contrast between his accounts of the social life of the London scientific circle and that in Paris is striking.

In London, the meetings he describes are entirely masculine, and limited to public eating places. If he visited private houses he saw libraries, but described no practical work. In Paris, on the other hand, he met Gay-Lussac at the Arsenal, Biot at his laboratory, and was shown experimental work by Thenard and Ampère; Cuvier showed him work in the museum of the Jardin du Roi. The culmination of his visit was the excursion to Arceuil, where there came face to face two of the most influential thinkers of their time, chemists as different as could be, Dalton and Berthollet. The two men epitomize the differences between the scientific worlds of Britain and France at the time: Dalton, carrying out his scientific work piece-meal in the intervals of a daily avocation which can hardly be called scientific, having only the most tenuous relation with industry, and none with official government circles; Berthollet fully occupied in scientific and technical work, adequately rewarded, through official channels, supporting and supported by manufactures of great economic importance.

At least this is true of the earlier phase of Berthollet's career. By now industry had so far advanced in Manchester that Dalton's fellow-citizens, who were alive to the possible contribution science might make to their work and had men like Peter Ewart to show how this could be done, found Dalton a sad disappointment. They could come to him for simple analysis of water and elementary descriptions of rocks, but nothing directly influential on the course of industry ever came either from his laboratory or his pen. Indirectly and in the long term his influence was profound and revolutionary but the quick returns were not for his immediate companions.

Dalton seems to have had that ease with young people which makes some men born teachers. Dr Charles Clay[13] told the Manchester Literary and Philosophical Society in 1884 how he had once, in 1817, helped Dalton by collecting some firedamp from a coal mine. He was apprenticed to a surgeon, a Mr Kinder Wood, who had sent him to Dalton's lectures. Dalton wanted some firedamp (methane) and Wood put him in touch with the owner of a mine where firedamp was rife. Young Clay was sent on the errand, and insisted on going down the mine himself, with bottles filled with water, supplied by Dalton. He emptied the bottles, re-sealed them, returned to the surface after his oppressive and dangerous mission. When he got back to Manchester he reported to Dalton.

The Doctor received me very kindly, and the quiet twinkle of his eye showed his satisfaction, which was greatly increased when he learned the particulars of my travels. He eyed the bottles with great satisfaction; he looked at the corks closely sealed, and seemed puzzled. I asked him what he was going to do with them? 'Well,' he said, 'I am thinking how I am to get the corks out without mixing it, more or less, with the atmosphere. I want to put the air into that receiver on the shelf of that pneumatic trough.' I said, 'I think I could do it'. He looked at me and said, 'How?' I said, 'File the bottle-neck round, and then a smart tap under the water I think will do it'. He said 'Capital, thou shalt try'. He gave me some coppers to fetch a file, and I soon filed a bottle-neck round, then held it under the shelf of the pneumatic trough, a gentle tap with the handle of a knife, and the air-bubbles very speedily rose into the receiver. The other bottles were beheaded, and very soon I took leave of the Doctor, who was apparently well pleased, and on parting said, if there was anything in his lecture which I did not understand, he wished me not to hesitate, but ask him, and he would always willingly assist me, and he was as good as his word; in fact, he showed me many little kindnesses afterwards, and so ends my small reminiscence of Dr Dalton.

This is a touching portrait of a man who knew how to interest the young, to give a scientific experiment roundness and meaning, leading the young student by challenging him to find a solution to a problem, rather than by showing him a solution.

Men who have this gift with children often have another one, which may well spring from some ability to convey confidence. They get on well with women, in a sexless but appreciative way which makes them agreeable companions. Dalton had a high respect for women all his life and many friendships with them. He heard of the death of the daughter of Cuvier with deep sorrow.[14] She had reacted very favourably to the English visitor when he came in 1822 and had shown him the sights of Paris. Perhaps he could never have faced the responsibility of marriage. Had he not written on divorce in 1789?[15]

Frank Greenaway

*Encounters with
John Dalton*

It seems unlikely that the marriage state would be rendered happier, were divorces much more easily to be obtained. For, the condition of the female sex in general would evidently be greatly depressed by it, without any equivalent advantage to the other sex; as in the case in most uncivilized countries, where haughty tyranny united with abject submission, affords few instances of that conjugal felicity, which is only to be obtained from mutual love and esteem. In short anything that has a tendency to lessen the dignity of the fair sex, in my opinion, is unlikely to increase the happiness of the marriage state.

It is difficult to measure the rise and fall of his intellectual power for two reasons: one was the irregular unsystematic nature of his early education, which had not brought before him consistently the whole range of scientific knowledge, even such as it was, of his time. His early Quaker acquaintances were none of them very interested in chemistry so far as we can discover, none of them was a medical man nor a university-trained mathematician. His undoubtedly powerful mind was therefore forced to exercise itself on problems of a much lower order than would have been encountered if his young life had been similar to that of some of his great contemporaries.

For example, he came upon chemistry almost by accident, the accident of the arrival of Thomas Garnett, then at the height of his power, before that tragically afflicted man came to his public disintegration at the Royal Institution.[16] He gave lectures of his own on chemistry after this, but it was not until he felt obliged to produce a comprehensive chemical work that he began to develop a system of chemical philosophy. By then Garnett was broken and dead, apparently leaving no benefit to posterity. But if a good teacher is to be immortalized in his pupils, Garnett had, unknown to himself, already done all that was demanded of him by opening Dalton's eyes to another view of matter. So when Dalton came to speak at the Royal Institution, something of sad, dead Garnett was still alive.

There is a second reason why it is difficult to judge the rise and fall of Dalton's intellectual power. This is the decision to attempt to produce a new system of chemical philosophy at a time when specialization was already setting in a norm for scientific work.

None of his Manchester contemporaries could help

him because none had the specialist knowledge to bring a sense of proportion to any criticism, none was able to teach this middle-aged philosopher the discipline of writing scientific texts in the modern manner. So we cannot judge at all easily whether the clumsy inadequacy of his later work was the result of a loss of power or of the frustration of lack of adequate training. One test would be the way he taught his students, but he had none. It is true that he had many young pupils, sent to him for the most elementary instruction but no-one came to him as an adult to learn advanced techniques. His only teaching to grown-up professional students took the form of a few lectures in pharmaceutical chemistry, which differed little in plan or content from the stock lectures he gave to the amateur public. Only one pupil acquired any scientific name: James Prescott Joule, but he came as a child, to learn little and to be taken away when Dalton's first stroke in 1837 began to destroy him.

In 1832 the year of Joule's first study under Dalton we see Dalton exhibited in extraordinarily contrasting lights, within the space of a day.

At the British Association meeting the award of an honorary degree at Oxford, in the company of Faraday, Brewster and Robert Brown marked him out as a scientist held in the highest esteem. But the night before, the young J. D. Forbes[17] showed that everything Dalton had stood for in his beloved science of meteorology was superseded by new needs and a new outlook.

The British Association had grown out of discontent partly with the politics of science partly with its practice. Dalton had been invited to attend the first meeting at York by Brewster who had corresponded with him about his colour-blindness. Dalton had also been in touch with Babbage, who against all appearances had some views in common with Dalton on the communication of science. But the regard of a few influential men, whatever it could do in the way of public honours, could not outweigh the criticism of younger men, able to judge his work with expert knowledge.

Forbes attacked Dalton where he was most vulnerable, recognizing the value of his qualitative thinking, but demanding the virtual re-establishment from the beginning of a science of meteorology on a new basis of exact experimental study. A passage in Forbes' report shows how Dalton had become identified with chemistry even by those who, had they taken the trouble, should have seen that Dalton had begun as a physicist:

> The most interesting views which have been given in this science, and the most important general laws at which it has yet arrived, have for the most part been contributed by philosophers who, in pursuit of other objects, have stepped aside for a moment from their systematic studies, and bestowed upon the science of Meteorology some permanent mark of their casual notice of a subject which they never intended to prosecute, and which they soon deserted for other and more favoured paths of inquiry. Mr Dalton descends for a moment from his chemistry in the abstract, to illustrate the constitution of the atmosphere and the theory of vapour . . .

This is grotesque misjudgment of Dalton's real development, and of his real contribution to meteorology, but Dalton behaved in an equally ill-judged way in what he did to rebut Forbes' criticism. Instead of arguing the value of the work on vapours, which he was possibly not himself capable of estimating, he chose to reprint in 1834 the *Meteorological essays* of 1793. In his biography of twenty years later, W. C. Henry is uniformly kind, even laudatory about Dalton, except in this one act, which he could consider as nothing but folly. But then as early as 1832, Henry knew that Dalton had shot his bolt intellectually.

So Dalton's most famous pupil, the young James Prescott Joule, came to the feet of a man who had nothing left of greatness to give of himself, but had already become no more than a living legend.

Except for his long service to the Manchester and Literary and Philosophical Society (dealt with by another contributor) Dalton rendered to his fellow citizens of Manchester only one service, that of lending dignity to the town by being a well-known figure comparable in reputation with the great names of London and Edinburgh. Admiration can sometimes be frustrating unless one can show it in concrete form and the Manchester citizens felt that the national honour paid in the form of a pension, and the academic honours paid by Oxford ought to be matched by Manchester itself. They had no university to award degrees, no source of meritorious emolument. So a decision was taken to make a statue. It must be greatly regretted that an alternative suggestion, to build and equip a Dalton house, was rejected. It would have represented the man better than the imitation Newtonesque statue eventually made. But the incidents of the making of the statue are amusing.[18]

Francis Chantrey received the commission, and Dalton went to London to sit for the modelling of the head. He was now at ease in the company of London celebrities, but they had changed. Wollaston, the clever one, had died in 1828, after suffering borne with fortitude. Davy had died within six months of him. In them had gone two transmitters of the eighteenth-century legacy of experimental chemistry. Dalton outlived them but only physically. He had no intellectual place in the world in which Faraday was the centre. In the year he received the pension, W. C. Henry wrote to an inquirer that the ageing man was spent, whether he realized it himself or not. But Dalton could still relish a new observation of manners. To Chantrey's studio he went, to be fascinated by the master's methods. First rough drawings made with the camera obscura, then a rough modelling made by pupils, and only at a later stage the hand of Chantrey himself at work. To Chantrey's studio also came Faraday, by now the master of physical science. It is a pity we do not know if they conversed with each other and with Chantrey. It would have been interesting to know how Dalton would have talked to a man who had made his early reputation with a head of Satan and was now making a fortune giving a synthetic immortality to respectability. Is it not ironic that Dalton outlived the sculptor who was to give him a marble life?

While he was in London Dalton was presented at Court. We do not know who had this extraordinary idea first, possibly Charles Babbage, who, as an odd character himself, no doubt felt drawn to the odd character from Manchester. Even if we can believe only half the stories of that presentation, the occasion must have been exceptional. Dalton could not wear court-dress: his Quaker faith forbade him to carry a sword, although the sober black would have been unexceptionable. So he went in academic dress, and his account book shows that, like so many others still have to do, he paid 'a guinea for the loan of a doctor's gown'. The scarlet was, to his colour-blind eyes, as drab as any other garment, but to the rest of the levee he stood out. It is said that one good Bishop was disturbed to find a Quaker admitted to the Citadel of Orthodoxy; it is said that William IV was faintly disturbed at hearing Dalton came from Manchester, a home of Radicalism. Anyone less likely than Dalton to disturb the political scene is hard to imagine, but William IV might have been surprised at a vision of the future which would have shown him that this rough-spoken misfit had already done more to determine the future of England and the world than he or anyone else present

The close of Dalton's life followed a familiar pattern: a man whose powers are failing gaining at last an ease and comfort that would have released his energies for greater production if only they had been given him earlier.

From the first stroke he suffered in 1837, at the age of sixty-nine, his judgment began to fail, and he wrote the papers rejected by the Royal Society which led to his bitter outburst, recollecting the dead ones, Davies Gilbert and the others who had understood and supported him. When the British Association met in Manchester in 1842, Dalton was too infirm to act as President. The chair was taken by Lord Francis Egerton who described Manchester as Dalton's birthplace. The mistake is understandable. Manchester had made Dalton even though Dalton cannot be said to have made Manchester, at least not the Manchester of his day. Modern Manchester, with its science-based industries might be said to be in part Dalton's creation, but that is another story.

Notes

1 The biographies of Dalton have been compared in F. Greenaway, 'The biographical approach to John Dalton', *Manchester Memoirs*, c (1958–9) 1–99.

2 H. Lonsdale, *The worthies of Cumberland: John Dalton* (London, 1874) 284–5.

3 A. L. Smyth, *John Dalton: a bibliography* (Manchester, 1966) *item 142*, 25.

4 Smyth, op. cit., *item 127*, 23.

5 Anon., *Glasgow Medical Journal*, v (1857) 69, 121.

6 Minutes referring to Dalton appear at 5 September 1803 (minute 6), 28 November (minute 12), 5 December (minute 9), 12 December (minute 15).

7 Lonsdale, op. cit., 232 (Lonsdale includes in the sponsors Rumford, who had by this time broken his connection with the

Royal Institution, so Lonsdale's assertion may be entirely unsound).

8 Greenaway, op. cit., (1958) 86–7.

9 A. W. Thackray, 'Documents relating to the origins, of Dalton's atomic theory', *Manchester Memoirs*, cviii (1965–6) 21–42.

10 Greenaway, *John Dalton and the atom* (London, 1966) 145–7.

11 Lonsdale, op. cit., 240 ff.

12 Ibid., 258 ff.

13 C. Clay, 'A reminiscence of Dr Dalton', *Chemical News*, (1884) 59–60.

14 Lonsdale, op. cit., 262.

15 Smyth, op. cit., items 22, 23, list Dalton's early magazine contributions.

16 K. D. C. Vernon, 'Foundation and early years of the Royal Institution', *Proceedings of the Royal Institution*, XXXIX, Part IV (1963) 364–402.

17 Greenaway, op. cit., (1958) 41–2.

18 Greenaway, op. cit., (1966) 191.

J T Marsh

Dalton wore the 'plain dress' of Friends (Quakers) and also used the Quaker form of speech. In addition to being a member of the 'Lit. Phil.' for fifty years, he was a regular attender for fifty years at the Manchester Meeting of the Society of Friends (twice on Sundays) in the building first facing South Street and later Mount Street; when the latter was built in 1830, he gave £50 to the building fund. He attended Quarterly Meetings at Manchester, Liverpool and Preston. Sometimes he walked from Manchester to Stockport to attend Meeting; (presumptive evidence of Quaker activity!) On two occasions he went to London Yearly Meeting, and on one of these he petitioned unsuccessfully for music in Meeting under certain limitations.

Although not active in the vocal ministry of meetings for worship, generally held in silence, he was a good 'committee Friend', particularly in educational matters, and visited some Friends Boarding Schools on examining day. He left £500 to Ackworth School and £500 to Wigton School.

He must have been a popular and weighty Friend, for women Friends used to tease him about going into the Gallery at Quarterly Meeting wearing his green coat; his coat was drab and he was colour blind. (The 'Gallery' could be compared with the Front Bench in Parliament.)

A J Pacey

Mr Greenaway mentioned J. P. Joule as the only pupil of Dalton's to achieve any sort of eminence in science, and so I wonder how he assesses Eaton Hodgkinson (1789–1861) and his relationship with Dalton.

Hodgkinson was a mathematician whose main interest was the theory of structures and the strength of materials; from 1847 he was Professor of the Mechanical Principles of Engineering at University College, London. His reputation had been made in the two years prior to that appointment by his part in the design of the tubular railway bridge over the Menai Straits. In collaboration with William Fairbairn, he provided the theoretical and experimental data which Robert Stephenson needed to build the Menai Bridge, and so he helped to make possible what was perhaps the greatest single achievement of civil engineering during the nineteenth century.[1]

Hodgkinson is said to have been a pupil of Dalton's during his early twenties, when Dalton is supposed to have helped him in the study of such authors as Lagrange, Laplace and Euler.[2] But it is not clear how detailed this study was, or what works by these authors were involved. The mathematics used by English engineers was very elementary at this time, especially in comparison with what was done in France, so Hodgkinson would perhaps not need to reach a very high standard in his studies with Dalton before he began to produce relatively original work. But I would welcome comments on Dalton's possible contribution here, for there can be no doubt that Hodgkinson's advances in engineering theory were of the greatest significance.

1 It has been so described by Professor A. W. Skempton in *Newcomen Soc. Trans.*, XXXVI (1963–4) p. 83.
2 Robert Rawson, 'Memoir of the late Eaton Hodgkinson', *Manchester Memoirs*, 3rd Series, ii (1865) 152.

Frank Greenaway

I would be grateful for help from any mathematician. Dalton had some reputation for skill in mathematics, but I am unable to find that he did anything of any value. Dalton may have gone on teaching an out-dated style of mathematics and I wonder if that would have been of any value in the engineering work described. Mathematics training for any advanced work at that time would have had to be received from some teacher other than Dalton.

Elizabeth C Patterson

A Note Concerning Benjamin Silliman's Meeting with John Dalton:

Fulton and Thomson in their definitive biography of Silliman[1] give an account of his European tour as a young man. After landing at Liverpool, Silliman travelled to Manchester, where he was 'greatly impressed' with the museum and the 15,000-volume library of Manchester New College. The most memorable event of his Manchester visit was his attendance at one of Dalton's popular lectures after his meeting the natural philosopher. Silliman writes of his surprise at finding attractive young ladies and laymen of varied interests in the large audience at the Manchester Literary and Philosophical Society—an audience that rivalled in size that at the local theatre. 'Dr Dalton,' he continues, 'exhibited one experiment which I never saw so well performed before. A wire made several circuits around the room, being attached to the wall; its circuit was interrupted at small distances by the cutting of the wire, the room was darkened, and when a powerful electric discharge was passed through the wire, it exhibited a brilliant corruscation at every interruption.'[2] Silliman then comments with interest on the simplicity of the glass apparatus Dalton had used to establish his famed gas law.

This lecture with its spectacular demonstration had a marked influence on Silliman's own polished later lecture style. 'Having studied the devices of Dalton and other popular lecturers in England and having had a long apprenticeship before his classes at Yale, he had developed an effective method of presentation which rarely failed to please.'[3]

1 Fulton, J. F., and Thomson, E. H., *Benjamin Silliman* (New York, 1947).
2 Ibid., 47.
3 Ibid., 173.

Mr Greenaway has given us a fascinating account of his 'Encounters with Dalton' and has ably indicated the need for a thorough revaluation of Dalton's character, life and work. Any new study will have to be based not only on a reappraisal of Dalton's published papers and the one-sided Victorian biographies, but also on the small number of still surviving unpublished manuscripts. These manuscripts, which include letters, lecture notes and other more miscellaneous papers, are important for the way they help to give substance to Dalton's still shadowy form. In a forthcoming article ('Fragmentary remains of John Dalton, Part 1: Letters', *Annals of Science* (in the press)) I am publishing some 24 letters of Dalton's in their entirety and providing brief details of a further 16. Letters to Charles Babbage, J. B. Biot, J. L. Gay-Lussac, Sir John Herschel and Thomas Thomson are among those included.

Arnold Thackray

J D—Q

E L Scott

Dalton and William Henry

In 1808, when John Dalton published the first part of his *New system*,[1] he dedicated it to the professors and others who had recently received him with interest and approbation in Edinburgh and Glasgow, and also to the members of the Manchester Literary and Philosophical Society who had 'uniformly promoted his researches'. Two years later, when the second part was published, his dedication was more personal. He singled out the Vice-President of the Manchester Society, William Henry, to whom, with Humphry Davy, the work was 'respectfully inscribed, as a testimony to their distinguished merit in the promotion of chemical science, and as an acknowledgement of their friendly communication and assistance'. In 1827, when the first, and as it turned out, only, part of the second volume came out, though he changed his dedication again, he nevertheless acknowledged in his preface 'the continued and friendly intercourse with Dr Henry, whose discussions on scientific subjects are always instructive, and whose stores are always open when the promotion of science is the object'.[2]

Thus, from the outset, the student of Dalton is brought to the realization that, of all his relationships, that with William Henry was in a special category. This view is strengthened and confirmed not only by the frequent references to Henry met with in the works of Dalton, but also by the equally numerous references to Dalton found in the works of William Henry.

The purposes of the present paper are, first, to

examine the background against which this relationship developed, and secondly, to explore its nature and consequences and inquire what light it might throw on the perplexities which still surround our conceptions of Dalton.

Not only did William Henry occupy a singular place among the friends and associates of John Dalton, but for a long period the Henry family held a unique place in scientific and medical circles in Manchester. When William Charles Henry—William Henry's son, and the author of the first full-length and, in many ways, unsatisfactory biography of Dalton—died in 1892, he was referred to in a press obituary as 'the last of his race of three eminent Manchester men of chemical science'.[3] Both his father and his grandfather, Thomas Henry, as well as himself, had been fellows of the Royal Society. All three had been members of the Manchester Literary and Philosophical Society—Thomas Henry was a founder-member and president for nine years—and all had been medical practitioners in Manchester and members of the honorary staff at the Manchester Infirmary.[4]

The Henrys' ancestry, and hence their social and educational backgrounds, were very different from Dalton's. Thomas Henry's paternal grandfather had commanded a company of infantry in Ireland under James II. During the disturbances that followed the campaign, he was assassinated—his son, Thomas Henry's father, being then barely a year old. The child was brought up and educated under the care of Viscount Bulkeley. When he was nearly twenty-one he was brought to Wales where he married the daughter of a clergyman. 'They sought the means of support by jointly engaging in the education of females, and for many years conducted a respectable boarding school, first at Wrexham in North Wales, and afterwards in Manchester.'[5]

Thomas Henry was born in Wrexham and educated at the grammar school there. He had early inclinations to the Church, and to this end it was planned that he should go to Oxford. Indeed, William Henry tells us that the date of departure was fixed and a horse provided for the journey. Thomas Henry's parents, however, had a large family and were not well-to-do; their dismay at the expenses involved and 'the uncertainty of eventual success' increased as the day drew nearer. Whilst they were hesitating, their dilemma was solved by the offer of a Mr Jones, a Wrexham apothecary, to take Thomas as an apprentice, and 'to this measure, though deeply feeling the disappointment of long indulged hopes, he could not deny the reasonableness of assenting'.[6]

He stayed with Mr Jones until the latter's death, when he became articled to an apothecary in Knutsford. When his apprenticeship expired he became the principal assistant to an apothecary in Oxford, where he apparently made many friends among the students and attended anatomical lectures at which John Hunter was employed as a demonstrator. In 1759 he returned to Knutsford to set up in business on his own. Here he married Mary Kinsey and five years later he moved to Manchester, where he succeeded to the business of a surgeon-apothecary in St Ann's Square.

William Henry wrote that the only book which his father remembered 'to have been put in his hands by either of his masters, was the Latin edition of Boerhaave's Chemistry . . . a work which, whatever may have been its merits, was certainly not calculated to present that science to a beginner under a fascinating aspect. His reading was, therefore, entirely self-directed. . . .'[7]

In 1767, three years after Thomas Henry settled in Manchester, Thomas Percival moved there from Warrington. This was to prove an event of great significance in Henry's life. The two men became firm friends, and at some period they were near neighbours in King Street. In the preface of the volume of essays which Thomas Henry published in 1773,[8] he confessed that his interest in experimental science had largely been fostered by Percival; he referred warmly to the latter's friendship and medical care. Moreover, in spite of his early inclinations, he embraced Percival's Unitarianism.

The history of science and education in Manchester is inextricably woven with the history of the dissenting movements. In particular, it is inseparable from any account of the struggle to obtain facilities for the higher education of those to whom, because of their inability to subscribe to the tenets of the Established Church, so many doors were closed. From these struggles arose the Warrington Academy, in which Priestley taught, the short-lived Manchester College of Arts and Sciences, in connection with which Thomas Henry gave lectures on chemistry, calico-printing, bleaching and dyeing, and the Manchester Academy, in which Dalton taught for seven years and to which William Henry went at the age of twelve.

In 1775 Thomas Henry was elected a fellow of the Royal Society, on the recommendation of Priestley and Sir John Pringle, who was then its president. It was at about this time that Henry was in communication with Priestley over some observations which both he and Percival had made on the effects of carbon dioxide on vegetation, which were contrary to those obtained by Priestley himself.[9]

We must not, however, be detained in the present paper by the work of Thomas Henry—except to mention one more event which, because of its consequences, is pertinent to any study of William Henry and the standing of the Henrys in Manchester. In 1771 Thomas Henry had sent to the Royal College of Physicians 'An account of an improved method of preparing Magnesia Alba',[10] magnesium carbonate being then much in vogue for the treatment of gastric disorders. It is difficult to determine the degree of originality which Henry could claim for his process; at all events he was prevailed upon by the president of the College and other medical men to commercialize his process. 'Henry's Magnesia' became a lucrative proprietary medicine. It earned him considerable wealth and also a nickname—he became familiarly known as 'Magnesia' Henry. In the rôle of apothecary, Thomas Henry's undoubted originality lay in his advocacy and practice of the medical use, in certain cases, of calcined magnesia—the use of the carbonate itself having certain disadvantages.[11]

The chemical manufacturing business thus started grew and prospered. It provided William Henry, in due course, with the means and independence to carry out his own chemical investigations, inspired initially by his father's experiments and subsequently by the lectures of Joseph Black, under whom he studied chemistry during his first year at Edinburgh University.

William Henry, Thomas Henry's third son, was born in Manchester in 1774, a few months after Priestley's discovery of oxygen. In the same year Ralph Harrison, then minister at the Cross Street Unitarian Chapel, and an ex-pupil of Warrington Academy, started a school and gained a considerable reputation as a teacher.[12] William Henry, in due course, became one of his charges, and when Harrison was appointed as the first professor of classics and belles-lettres at the newly-opened Manchester Academy in 1786, the young Henry 'had made such rapid progress as to be permitted, though considerably under the customary age for admission, to follow his preceptor to his enlarged sphere of competition. . . .'[13]

On leaving the Academy, in 1790, William Henry succeeded Edward Holme as companion and secretary to Thomas Percival—who, because of weak eyesight and liability to violent headaches, liked to engage a young man with medical ambitions to read to him and write his correspondence from dictation. William Henry clearly benefited from the influence of this intelligent, humane and versatile man, and the access to his considerable library. During the five years which he spent in Percival's house he began his preliminary studies in medicine, and on leaving, and before entering Edinburgh University in 1795, he spent a short period in Manchester Infirmary for observation and practical instruction.

The Manchester Literary and Philosophical Society had been founded in 1781, having grown out of weekly meetings which for some years had been held in Percival's house, for the discussion of scientific and philosophical subjects. Of the twenty-four original members, thirteen were medical men.[14] Some of those most instrumental in its foundations were Unitarians—notably Percival himself, Thomas Henry and Thomas Barnes, who had become the Minister at Cross Street in 1780. Some of the early meetings were held in Cross Street Chapel school-room. However, discussions of 'Religion, the practical Branches of Physic, and *British* politics' were expressly forbidden by the rules of the Society.[15]

It would appear that at early meetings of the society members were more ready to listen to papers than to provide them, and, by way of encouragement, a gold medal was offered to the author (not necessarily a member) of the best paper on an experimental subject; a silver medal was to be given to any member under twenty-one for the best paper on a literary or philosophical subject. The latter was awarded to Thomas Henry, junior—William's elder brother—who chose as his subject 'The controversy between Henry Cavendish and Richard Kirwan on the cause of the diminution of common air in phlogistic processes'.[16]

Thomas Henry, junior, apparently a young man of considerable promise, assisted his father in the lectures which the latter gave under the auspices of the Manchester College of Arts and Sciences, founded in 1783. In 1793, together with two of Priestley's sons, he emigrated to America,[17]—apparently he died while still a young man. A few years after Thomas' departure, his father took William into partnership, and after one year he left the university—in W. C. Henry's words, 'in deference to prudential considerations'—in order to help his father in his apothecary's practice and in running the family business.

In the same year that Thomas Henry, junior, left England for America, John Dalton left Kendal for Manchester, to take up the appointment of professor of natural philosophy and mathematics at the Manchester Academy (or 'New College' as it became known). He had been recommended to Thomas Barnes, then principal, by John Gough—that remarkable man, blinded by smallpox at the age of three—who had befriended and tutored Dalton in his early years. Both Gough and Dalton had been brought up as Quakers, but, according to McLachlan, Gough had turned Unitarian. 'As a Quaker', says McLachlan (and the only one to have taught in a Nonconformist academy), '[Dalton] was at home amongst non-subscribers to creeds, and lovers of religious liberty'.[18]

Dalton joined the Manchester Society in 1794, having been proposed by Thomas Henry, Thomas Percival and Robert Owen. He attended his first meeting on 3 October and on 31 October read his first paper 'Extraordinary Facts relating to the Vision of Colours, with Observations'.[19]

It is from some time after this that we can probably

date the beginning of the friendship between William Henry and Dalton. In 1794 Henry was only twenty, Dalton was twenty-eight. To a young man of twenty on the outset of his career eight years is a considerable seniority. Dalton was then a man of some standing— he had his teaching post at New College and his *Meteorological essays*[20] had just been published. Possibly William Henry first met Dalton through his father, who was then vice-president of the Manchester Society. William Henry was not elected to the Society until 29 April 1796, becoming librarian the same year and secretary the following year.

As we have seen, Henry's interest in chemistry had been quickened by his year's work at Edinburgh under Joseph Black, for whom he conceived an intense admiration.[21] By the middle of the year following his return from Edinburgh he had prepared and presented his first paper, submitting it, through his father, to the Royal Society.[22] This was a rebuttal of the views expressed some nine years earlier in a paper read by William Austin, giving an account of some experiments on sparking 'heavy inflammable air'. From these, Austin had concluded that carbon was not an element, but a combination of 'the phlogisticated and heavy inflammable airs', heavy inflammable air being 'itself a compound of the lighter inflammable and phlogisticated airs'.[23] By a critical examination of Austin's experiments and by some further experiments of his own, Henry attempted to show that Austin's conclusions were unjustified.

The paper has little intrinsic value, and twelve years later, at the end of a paper on the analysis of ammonia, Henry gave an account of some experiments which he had 'lately made in conjunction with Mr Dalton', and which led him to doubt the accuracy of some of his former conclusions. He remarks that it was to be lamented that experimentalists did not more often retrace their labours.[24] William Henry subsequently made the study of the gaseous hydrocarbons his special interest, and one suspects that it was his influence which started off Dalton's researches into the combining proportions of hydrogen and carbon in August 1804.[25]

In the winter of 1798–9 William Henry gave a course

of public lectures on chemistry in Manchester, for which a forty-page syllabus was printed and sold for a shilling.[26] The course was repeated the following winter, and in the November of 1799 Henry's introductory address was published in Manchester under the title *A general view of the nature and objects of Chemistry, and of its application to arts and manufactures*. A. W. Thackray[27] has recently pointed out that Dalton would have been interested in the following passage:

... The water of the ocean, for example, is raised into the atmosphere by its chemical combination with the matter of heat; but the clouds that are thus formed, maintain their elevated situation by virtue of a specific gravity, less than that of the lower regions of the air ...[28]

The passage might also have stimulated Dalton's interest in chemistry, for Henry had used the example to demonstrate the inadequacy of 'natural philosophy' alone (which, being concerned with 'sensible motion' excluded chemistry) to explain certain phenomena; the concurrence of the two sciences was therefore sometimes necessary.

Very early in Henry's syllabus is a section on heat—followed immediately by one on gases which, he says, consisted 'partly of solid gravitating matter and partly of an extremely subtile fluid, which impresses on our organs the sensation of heat and is termed Caloric'.[29]

The nature of heat was a live issue at the time, for in 1798 Rumford's 'Inquiry concerning the source of the heat which is excited by friction' had been read to the Royal Society,[30] and Davy's 'Essay on heat, light and the combinations of light' had been published in Beddoes's collection for 1799.[31] (This was the essay which contained Davy's often-quoted experiment on melting two pieces of ice by friction.)[32] A critical review of Rumford's and Davy's experiments, in the course of which he upheld the concept of heat as material, was sent by Henry to Beddoes late in 1799 for inclusion in his next collection of essays. However, no more were published, and Henry's paper was not printed until 1802, having been read to the Manchester Society in June 1801.[33]

Some eight years ago F. Greenaway expressed the belief that Henry's adherence to the caloric theory of heat strongly influenced Dalton: 'Henry was not the only one to believe in the material nature of caloric, but what he believed Dalton was likely to accept.'[34] He was inquiring why Dalton did not adopt a kinetic theory of heat which would have been so much more in keeping with his 'Newtonism'.

This was, of course, an allusion to Dalton's concept of the structure of gases, on which he based his novel theory of mixed gases. The presentation of this in 1801 called forth such a thunder of disapproval that the rumblings had not died away by the time the *New system* was published seven years later.

Dalton first announced his 'New Theory of the Constitution of mixed Aeriform Fluids and particularly of the Atmosphere' in a hastily written[35] letter on 14 September 1801, which was published in the October issue of *Nicholson's Journal*.[36] In the same month he read to the Literary and Philosophical Society an expanded and clearer version of this; he also read two other papers, on evaporation and vapour pressure. When these were printed in 1802, Dalton took advantage of his position as secretary to the Society—a post he had taken over from William Henry in 1800—to include material from an earlier paper on the thermal expansion of gases, read in April 1800 and previously unpublished.[37] He also added an introduction to the four essays, in order to show how all the material was relevant to his main thesis, which was that:

> When two elastic fluids, denoted by A and B, are mixed together, there is no mutual repulsion among their particles: that is, the particles of A do not repel those of B, as they do one another. Consequently, the pressure or whole weight upon any one particle arises solely from those of its own kind.[38]

Dalton based his conception of the nature of gases on Newton's principle that if an elastic fluid made up of mutually repulsive particles obeys Boyle's law, then the forces between the particles are reciprocally proportional to the distances between their centres; he chose, however, to ignore Newton's observation that whether in fact elastic fluids *do* consist of particles which repel each other was a physical question to be decided.[39] His concern was to show how the principle, hitherto applicable only to homogeneous fluids, could be adapted to a system of mixed gases in such a way as to explain certain observed facts—in particular, that the atmosphere consisted of a number of gases of different densities uniformly distributed. He gave reasons for rejecting the widely held view that the gases were chemically combined.

It was this rejection of a firmly entrenched position, more than anything else, that brought about the storm of protest. Writing to Dalton a few years later, William Henry said:

In the discussions . . . which took place in this Society, on your several papers, the doctrine was opposed by almost every member interested on such subjects, and by no one more strenuously than myself. . . .[40]

It was not long before Dalton's views were also assailed in print—notably by Thomas Thomson, Murray, Berthollet and John Gough, all of whom regarded air as a chemical compound. Partington recently wrote:

Dalton had to press his correct opinions in the face of very formidable opposition from most of the leading scientists and from the text-book writers of the time, and the chorus of disapproval might well have overawed a less determined and original man.[41]

However, Dalton was soon to receive support from Henry, who, though originally belonging to the opposition, subsequently found reasons for changing his mind. Earlier in 1801, he had published the first edition of his *Epitome of chemistry*,[42] based on the series of experiments he had used to illustrate his lectures. Immediately after publication, he presented a copy to Dalton.[43] In it he refers to atmospheric air as 'a mixture, or rather a combination, of two different gases'.[44] The phrase does not suggest that Henry was strongly committed to a particular view at that time.

In 1802, both he and Dalton were working on the solubilities of gases in water. Dalton was led to this by his investigations into the proportions of the various gases in the atmosphere.[45] Henry's experiments eventually enabled him to state the law that now bears his name:

. . . *under equal circumstances of temperature, water takes up, in all cases, the same volume of condensed gas as of gas under ordinary pressure. . . .*[46]

Earlier, however, he had carried out an abortive investigation into 'the order of affinities of gases for water',[47] probably, as has recently been suggested, in order to counter Dalton's arguments.[48]

At all events, a perusal of Henry's paper, and the paper eventually read by Dalton,[49] shows clearly that the friendship between them had ripened to the extent that each was kept informed of the other's results and progress, and, moreover, that mutual aid was sought and readily given. In particular, when Henry expressed doubt as to the accuracy of certain of his figures, owing to 'a suspicion that due attention had not always been paid . . . to the quality of the unabsorbed residuum' of gases, Dalton suggested that the amount of any gas absorbed by a given quantity of water was 'exactly proportional to the density of the gas *considered abstractedly from any other gas with which it may accidently be mixed*' (my italics). Henry carried out further experiments which, he says, confirmed Dalton's idea, and early in 1803 wrote a short appendix (from which the above passages are quoted) in order to give his corrected figures, and, one presumes, to give Dalton the credit for his suggestion.[50] He became convinced, with Dalton, that the absorption of gases by water was a purely mechanical process, and, moreover, that his later results could be most easily explained by the acceptance of Dalton's theory of mixed gases.

Accordingly he wrote off to *Nicholson's Journal* in June 1804, in the form of a letter to Dalton, his 'Illustrations of Mr Dalton's Theory of the Constitution of Mixed Gases', in which he stated, for general consumption, his change of view.[51] Moreover, he therein provided Dalton with a succinct expression of his theory—that '*mixed gases neither attract nor repel each other, and that every gas is as a vacuum to every other gas*'.[52]

One of Dalton's most persistent critics was John Gough. Of the long dispute between Gough and Dalton, William Henry's son misleadingly wrote:

Dalton . . . not unmindful of former kindnesses, though evidently pained by the temper of Mr Gough's criticism, did not permit himself to retaliate upon one whom he regarded as his benefactor. . . . He replied with unruffled calmness to all that bore the character of argument. . . .[53]

Unhappily, Gough did not content himself with argument, but made a personal attack on Dalton, implying that his 'self-love' blinded him to the flaws in his argument.[54] The following passage illustrates the level to which the controversy subsequently descended. It occurs in a reply by Dalton to a letter in *Nicholson's Journal* from Gough, consequent upon Henry's expressed change of view:

> Oxigen repels oxigen, but not azote: This is a postulatum; and being admitted, it follows, that if a measure of oxigen be put to one of azote, the oxigen finding it porous, must enter the pores, and *vice versa*, till the two gases severally making their way into the interstices of the other, at last obtain a perfect equilibrium, and then press with equal force on all the surrounding bodies, and no longer press on each other. This is so plain and obvious an inference, and so little involves mechanical consideration, that I should have justly incurred blame for insulting my readers with the appearance of mathematical demonstration in the case. As well might I have attempted, from the elements of Euclid, to demonstrate to a cottager, that if he put a sieve over his chimney the smoke would still escape, though interruptedly; or to a chemist, that if he drilled holes in an exhausted receiver, it would in time be completely filled with air.[55]

A few days later, Henry sent his own reply to Gough—much more polite, patient and reasoned in tone.[56] He began disarmingly by saying that nothing had been further from his intention, when he sent his earlier letter, than to enter into controversy regarding a doctrine, to the defence of which he might naturally be supposed to be less competent than its author. In fact, Henry was far more competent than Dalton to defend any arguable view; his exposition was much more convincing, in this case, than Dalton's mixture of exasperation and facetiousness, and though it failed to convince Gough,[57] it must have been beneficial to Dalton's prestige.

The encouragement alone, thus given to Dalton, would be a fact of some importance, in view of the subsequent development of Dalton's thought, but the stimulus given to Dalton to continue his investigations into the solution of gases may well have been crucial. At the end of Dalton's paper on this subject comes his first published table of atomic weights, preceded by a brief note from which it might be inferred that his 'inquiry into the relative weights of the ultimate particles of bodies' was undertaken expressly for the purpose of answering the question posed at the beginning of the paragraph—'Why does water not admit its bulk of every kind of gas alike?'[58]

George Wilson, of Edinburgh, made this inference in 1845, the year after Dalton died. In the earliest biographical sketch of Dalton, published anonymously in the *British Quarterly Review*,[59] he was the first to point out that the account of the origin of Dalton's chemical atomic theory given by Thomson, in his *History of chemistry* in 1831,[60] could not be supported. Though Wilson reached his conclusion (that 'the first glimpse of his "Atomic Theory" was obtained by Dalton in the course of certain researches into the solubility of the different gases in water') simply on his reading of Dalton's published works, the same view was taken by L. K. Nash in 1956[61] after a careful analysis of the entries in Dalton's notebooks which Roscoe and Harden had given in their *New view of the origin of Dalton's atomic theory* in 1896.[62]

It is, however, no part of the purpose of the present paper to enter the debate over the origin of Dalton's concepts, or indeed over what was truly original in his contributions to chemistry. Nevertheless it is pertinent to inquire what light William Henry's writings throw on these questions. Henry and Dalton were closely associated for over thirty years; their collaboration over the experiments on the absorption of gases in water has been singled out for some detailed treatment for obvious reasons—a perusal of Henry's papers and Dalton's *New system* furnishes plenty of further evidence of their presence at each others' experiments on a variety of subjects. One might expect that if anyone knew the ramifications and general trend of Dalton's thought, William Henry did. Moreover, the meeting between Thomas Thomson and Dalton in 1804,[63] from which sprang the first published account of Dalton's chemical atomic theory[64] and the account of its origins already mentioned, took place in William Henry's house.

Yet the only reference to the history of Dalton's ideas from Henry's pen is the tantalizingly short extract from his private journal, written in 1830 after a conversation with Dalton and quoted by W. C. Henry:

Mr Dalton has been settled in Manchester thirty-six years. His volume on meteorology, printed but not published before he came here. At p. 132 *et seq* of that volume, gives distinct anticipations of his views of the separate existence of aqueous vapour from atmospheric air. At that time the theory of chemical solution was almost universally received. These views were the first germs of his atomic theory, because he was necessarily led to consider the gases as constituted of independent atoms. Confirmed the account he before gave me of the origin of his speculations, leading to the doctrine of simple multiples, and of the influence of Richter's table in exciting these views.[65]

William Henry's references to Dalton's chemical atomic theory, in the various editions of his own textbook are cautious. The first notice, of two pages, appeared in the first two-volume edition in 1810, after ten pages devoted to Berthollet's views, and is introduced thus:

In opposition to the theory that chemical affinity has a tendency to unite bodies in unlimited proportions, a hypothesis has lately been proposed by Mr Dalton, which appears more consonant to the general simplicity of nature. . . .[66]

This brief notice is supplemented by four pages in an appendix, which include a table of atomic weights.[67]

Henry's move towards the rejection of Berthollet's views is more definite in the next edition, where a longer account of Dalton's ideas is given, and Berthollet's theory, which, Henry says, 'promised, on its first development, to form a new era in chemical philosophy', is here said to be 'at variance with the doctrine of definite proportions, which every day gathers strength by the accumulation of new and well-established facts'.[68]

Henry's own position is clearly revealed in his final appraisal of Dalton's ideas, published in his last edition in 1829:

In every science it is necessary clearly to distinguish between what is certain and what is merely probable; the laws of combination, in definite and multiple proportions, appear to me to belong to the former class; but the generalization, which explains those truths by speculations respecting atoms, must be acknowledged, in its present state, to be entirely theoretical.[69]

In the statement which Henry prepared, at the request of Charles Babbage, as part of the campaign to

secure a pension for Dalton, he spoke of Dalton's having 'drawn from observed phenomena new and ingenious views; upon these views he has founded distinct conceptions of a general law of nature, and he has
traced out the conformity of that law with an extensive
class of facts'. Babbage seems to have been aware of the
unsatisfactory vagueness of this passage and apparently
used Henry's statement as the basis for his own, in
which he wrote that:

the great discovery of Mr Dalton and that which will in-
separably connect his name with the history of physical
science is the 'Law of Definite Proportions'. It is this law
which has . . . connected chemistry with number and thus
rendered it an exact science.[70]

Henry felt strongly that governments should enable
those who had proved themselves able investigators to
carry on their work untroubled by the anxieties of
earning a living. In a further letter to Babbage on the
subject of Dalton's pension he wrote of exempting
Dalton from 'the low and irksome duty of teaching the
very elements of science, to which he is doomed unless
something is done to prevent it, for the rest of his life'.[71]

Henry's own experimental work was interrupted by
the demands on his time made by his business, and
until he relinquished it, an extensive medical practice.
He had returned to Edinburgh in 1805, and obtained
his M.D. in 1807 with a dissertation on uric acid. The
following year he was appointed honorary physician to
the Manchester Infirmary, but resigned this post in
1817, the year after his father died.

The death of Thomas Henry in 1816 meant that a
new president had to be appointed to the Manchester
Literary and Philosophical Society. William Henry insisted that Dalton should fill the vacancy, and declined
to allow himself to be nominated, as some members
wished.[72]

At about the same time, Henry's candidature had
been sought for the vacant chair of chemistry at Glasgow. He confessed himself gratified by the suggestion
and pleased by the prospect, but regretted that he was
'compelled, by a variety of circumstances, to forego all
intention' of proposing himself for a situation more
agreeable in almost every respect to his taste and habits
than the sphere in which he was then moving.[73] He

wrote of a large and increasing family and his 'great exertions', attended with all the success he could have expected, to increase his chemical manufacturing business.

He also referred to his 'habitual delicacy of health' and, in particular, to recent attacks of haemoptysis. In childhood Henry had sustained a serious injury, as a consequence of which he suffered acute neuralgic pains throughout the rest of his life. W. C. Henry also wrote of his father's 'habitual infirmity of health and feelings of oppression arising from the slow and imperfect motion of the digestive functions'.[74]

In a letter written in 1832 to John Davy,[75] Henry spoke of having lately been 'precluded from working at any of the more refined operations of chemical investigation by the disqualification of most essential members, the hands'. He referred to tumours on the inside of the sheaths of the tendons which irritated the adjacent nerves, causing pain which, he says, had twice driven him 'to the necessity of excision'. In the same letter, incidentally, he said that he suspected that Dalton, like most other men who had lived upwards of sixty years, had 'shot his shaft'.

Unable to do experimental work, Henry turned his attention more to literary pursuits. One of his projects was a history of chemical discovery since 1750. This was, however, never accomplished, for in 1836, as a result of worsening health and insupportable pain, he committed suicide.[76]

Thus, the task, for which he was surely more qualified than any other man, of writing Dalton's biography fell, in the event, to his son. There are still many problems which engage us as to the origins and directions of Dalton's thought. It is tempting, if perhaps pointless, to inquire if William Henry could have supplied us with any of the answers.

Notes

1 J. Dalton, *A new system of chemical philosophy* (i, Part 1, Manchester, 1808; i, Part II, Manchester, 1810; ii, Part I, Manchester, 1827; no more published).

2 Ibid., ii, preface, p. viii.

3 *Manchester Evening News*, 9 January 1892.

4 See E. M. Brockbank, *Sketches of the lives and work of the honorary medical staff of the Manchester Infirmary* (Manchester, 1904).

5 W. Henry, *Manchester Memoirs*, 2nd Series, iii (1819) 204–40 (205–6).

6 Ibid., 207.

7 Ibid., 207–8.

8 T. Henry, *Experiments and observations* . . . (London, 1773); for the full title see J. R. Partington, *A history of chemistry* (London, 1962) iii, 691.

9 See J. Priestley, *Experiments and observations on different kinds of air* (London, 1774–7) iii, 306–24 and 369–75; also T. Henry, *Manchester Memoirs*, ii (1785) 341–9.

10 *Medical Transactions of the Royal College of Physicians*, ii (1772), 226–34; reprinted in T. Henry, op. cit., (8).

11 '. . . on account of the great quantity of air which enters into its composition. Whenever it meets with an acid in the stomach they immediately unite; but in forming this union, all the air contained in the Magnesia is discharged with a great degree of effervescence, and recovering its elasticity sometimes occasions very uneasy sensations in weak bowels. inflating them and distending them overmuch, inducing griping pains, and above all a sense of debility or sinking, which is not easily described' (T. Henry, op. cit., (8) 48).

12 See A. Gordon, *Dictionary of national biography*, xxv, 37.

13 W. C. Henry, *Manchester Memoirs*, 2nd Series, vi (1842) 99–141 (102).

14 See *Complete List of the Members and Officers of the Manchester Literary and Philosophical Society from its institution* . . . (Manchester, 1896).

15 See *Rules, established for the government of the Literary and Philosophical Society of Manchester* . . . (Manchester, 1782).

16 *Manchester Memoirs*, ii (1785) 513 (Extract from Minutes, 11 May 1785).

17 See F. W. Gibbs, *Joseph Priestley* (London, 1965) 218 f.

18 H. McLachlan, 'John Dalton and Manchester', *Manchester Memoirs*, lxxxvi (1945) 170 f.

19 *Manchester Memoirs*, v (Part I) (1798) 28.

20 J. Dalton, *Meteorological observations and essays* (London, 1793).

21 W. C. Henry, op. cit., (13) 106.

22 W. Henry, 'Experiments on carbonated hydrogen gas; with a view to determine whether carbon be a simple or compound substance', *Phil. Trans. Roy. Soc.*, lxxxvii (1797) 401–15; read 29 June 1797. A copy of this paper, inscribed by Henry, is in a collection made by Dalton and now in Manchester Central Library (S and A 331/4).

23 W. Austin, 'Experiments on the Analysis of the Heavy Inflammable Air', *Phil. Trans. Roy. Soc.*, lxxx (1790) 51–72 (69).

24 W. Henry, *Phil. Trans. Roy. Soc.*, xcix (1809) 430–49; the section containing a re-appraisal of his 1797 paper begins on p. 446.

25 See Roscoe and Harden, *A new view of the origins of Dalton's atomic theory* (London, 1896) 62 f.

26 *Syllabus of a Course of Lectures on Chemistry* (Manchester, n.d.).

27 A. W. Thackray, 'The Emergence of Dalton's Chemical Atomic Theory; 1801–08', *Brit. J. Hist. Sci.*, iii (Part I) (June, 1966) 7.

28 W. Henry, *A general view* . . . (Manchester, 1799) 10.

29 Ibid., 39.

30 *Phil. Trans. Roy. Soc.*, lxxxviii (1798) 80–102.

31 *Contributions to physical and medical knowledge, principally from the West of England*, collected by Thomas Beddoes (Bristol, 1799), 5–38; also in *Collected Works* (ed. J. Davy) (London, 1839–40) ii, 5–23.

32 Commenting on the formidable difficulties of this experiment, Andrade (*Nature*, cxxxv (1935) 359–60) wrote 'no doubt the whole effect observed by Davy was due to conduction'.

33 W. Henry, 'A review of some experiments which have been supposed to disprove the materiality of heat', *Manchester Memoirs*, v (Part II) (1802) 603–21. In December 1800 Davy had referred to his own paper as one of his 'infant chemical speculations' (*Nicholson's Journal*, 1st Series, iv (1801) 395).

34 Greenaway, 'The biographical approach to John Dalton', *Manchester Memoirs*, c (1958) 1–98 (85).

35 See Thackray, op. cit., (27) 7, note 42.

36 *Nicholson's Journal*, 1st Series, v (1801) 241–4.

37 See A. N. Meldrum, 'Dalton's Physical Atomic Theory' *Manchester Memoirs*, lv (1911) no. 5.

38 'Experimental Essays . . .', *Manchester Memoirs*, v (1802) 535–602 (536). W. Henry's paper defending the materiality of heat (33) immediately follows, though read in June 1801.

39 See Partington, *A history of chemistry* (London, 1962) iii, 767; see also Dalton, *New system*, i, 168.

40 *Nicholson's Journal*, viii (1804) 297.

41 Partington, op. cit., 777.

42 W. Henry, *An epitome of chemistry in three parts* (London, 1801).

43 Letter from Dalton dated 5 April 1801 to J. Fell (Science Museum, Inventory No. 1954—355).

44 W. Henry, op. cit., (42) 20.

45 See *New system*, i, 182–3.

46 W. Henry, *Phil. Trans. Roy. Soc.*, xciii (1803) 29–42 (41).

47 *Nicholson's Journal*, viii (1804) 299.

48 See Thackray, op. cit., (27) 10.

49 Dalton, 'On the Absorption of Gases by Water and other Liquids', *Manchester Memoirs*, 2nd Series, i (1805), 271–87; see also *New system*, i, 182 f.

50 *Phil. Trans. Roy. Soc.*, xciii (1803), 274–6; though undated, it appears between papers dated 24 February 1803 and 23 April 1803.

51 *Nicholson's Journal*, viii (1804) 297–301.

52 Ibid., 298.

53 W. C. Henry, *Memoirs of the life and scientific researches of John Dalton* (London, 1854) 11.

54 *Manchester Memoirs*, 2nd Series, i (1805) 405.

55 *Nicholson's Journal*, ix (1804) 89–90.

56 Ibid., 126–8.

57 A list of references to the contributions by Gough and others to the controversy over Dalton's Theory of Mixed Gases is given by A. N. Meldrum, *Manchester Memoirs*, lv (1911) no. 5, 18–22.

58 Dalton, op. cit., (49) 286–7.

59 *British Quarterly Review*, i (1845) 157–98; it was later reprinted in a volume of Wilson's essays, *Religio Chemici* (Cambridge, 1862) 304–64.

60 T. Thomson, *The history of chemistry* (London, 1830–1) ii, 291.

Notes   **61** L. K. Nash, 'The origin of Dalton's chemical atomic theory', *Isis*, xlvii (1956) 101–16.

62 Roscoe and Harden, op. cit., (25).

63 Anon., *Glasgow Medical Journal*, v (1857) 123.

64 T. Thomson, *A system of chemistry* (3rd edn, Edinburgh, 1807) 424–9.

65 W. C. Henry, op. cit., (53) 62–3.

66 W. Henry, *Elements of Experimental Chemistry* (6th edn, London 1810) i, 81.

67 Ibid., ii. 475–8.

68 W. Henry, *Elements* . . . (7th edn, London 1815) i, 48.

69 Ibid., (11th edn, London, 1829) i, 53.

70 British Museum, 'Babbage Collection', Add. MS. 37186 ff., 260–4. The statement referred to and quoted in full by W. C. Henry (op. cit. (53) 174 f.) which appears to have been written by a secretary (ff. 262–3) is attached to a covering letter from William Henry (f. 260–1). A note in Henry's handwriting is added to his formal statement. F. 264 is a part of a draft in Babbage's handwriting incorporating some of Henry's material (see e.g. ff. 299–300 for comparison). Thus it appears that the statement as such, by William Henry, was not, in fact, forwarded to Lord Grey.

71 British Museum, 'Babbage Collection', Add. MS. 37187, f. 229. (Letter dated 18 November 1832 from William Henry to Charles Babbage.) It is said that once, in reply to an inquiry, Dalton said that 'teaching was a kind of recreation, and if richer he would not probably spend more time in investigation than he was accustomed to do' (see G. Wilson, op. cit., (59) 348).

72 E. M. Brockbank, *The book of Manchester and Salford* (Manchester, 1929) 39.

73 See K. Loewenfeld, *Manchester Memoirs*, lvii (1913), no. 19.

74 See W. C. Henry, op. cit., (13) 101–2, 135.

75 Letter to John Davy, dated 31 January 1832 (Royal Institution Library).

76 *Manchester Guardian*, 3 September 1836; *Annual Biography and Obituary*, xxi (1837) 78–83.

J R Ravetz   Mr Scott's mention of Wilson's interpretation of the genesis of Dalton's ideas does raise a most intriguing question on the historiography of Dalton. It appears that it was left for Nash, more than a century later, to rediscover Wilson's interpretation by a laborious study of manuscript sources. It would be interesting to know whether Wilson's interpretation was widely known in his time, and, if so, by what stages it came to be forgotten.

E. L. Scott   There are, I think, two points here. Wilson's view first appeared in 1845 in an anonymous 'essay review' of Dalton's published works, occasioned by his death the previous year. It therefore lacked the authority and impact of Thomson's account, which had appeared in his *History of chemistry* in 1831. Moreover, Thomson had claimed that this was Dalton's *own* account of how he had arrived at his atomic theory (i.e. as a consequence of his 'discovery' of the law of multiple proportions, resulting from his analyses of marsh gas and olefiant gas). W. C. Henry, after a somewhat vacillating examination of the question, came finally to the acceptance of Thomson's account as being substantially correct, and this account may be found unquestioned (for example, in von Meyer's *History of chemistry* (1891)) up to the time of Roscoe and Harden's re-examination of the subject in 1896 (and even beyond that date in 'popular' histories of chemistry).

The second point is that Wilson's interpretation of what Dalton had written in his 1805 paper was a *possible*, but not a *necessary* one. Dalton certainly made it clear that he had *applied* his findings regarding 'the relative weights of the ultimate particles of bodies' to his investigations into the different solubilities of gases in water, but the implication that he had arrived at these findings as a *result* of his solubility experiments is by no means clear.

*Dalton versus
Prout: The
Problem of Prout's
Hypotheses*

There has been a good deal of unwarranted confusion among commentators as to what exactly Prout's hypothesis was. In fact there were *two* hypotheses. One, that atomic weights, or specific gravities, were *integral* multiples of the atomic weight or specific gravity of hydrogen (the whole number rule); and two, that hydrogen was the prime matter, or less specifically, that there were only one or two ultimate elements from which all the known chemically undecompounded bodies were constructed. It is important always to draw these distinctions since a chemist could adopt one of these hypotheses without necessarily accepting the other. It will be useful to refer to the former hypothesis as 'the integral multiple weights hypothesis', or more simply, 'the multiples hypothesis'; and to the latter as 'the *protyle* hypothesis', or 'unitary hypothesis', and its commitment as 'reduction'. For example, it has been shown recently that Prout adopted the unitary hypothesis in 1810, five years before he derived the notion of the multiples hypothesis. Again, although Thomas Thomson made several statements in support of a reduction of the elements before he became acquainted with Dalton's theory,[1] in supporting and making propaganda for Prout's integral multiple weights hypothesis, he held no brief for the *protyle* hypothesis as formulated by Prout.

It would not be practicable to examine either of these hypotheses at any length in this paper. Recently there have been a number of excellent studies of the theory of elements,[2] but Prout's integral multiple weights hypothesis has not attracted the same attention. This is also a large theme since it encompasses the history of atomic weight determinations. This paper will be restricted to the examination of Dalton's attitude towards both hypotheses.

William H Brock

Dalton versus Prout: The Problem of Prout's Hypotheses

I. *Dalton's attitude towards the protyle hypothesis*

Although the connections between Daltonian atomism and the two Greek corpuscular theories of matter, the Democritan atomic theory and the Empedoclean corpuscular theory, are only indirect, it is nevertheless useful to view Dalton's theory, *qua* matter theory, as an amalgamation of these two corpuscular traditions. Thus, chemical change, according to Dalton, was explained in terms of a number of qualitatively-different (Empedoclean) and quantitatively-different (Democritan) particles. These particles, or atoms, were not omnipresent elements like Empedoclean 'roots', but the smallest parts of Lavoisier's undecompounded bodies. Dalton's theory, therefore, included many elements, and hence many different types of atom, as the invariants of chemical change. In some ways, by amalgamating Newtonian corpuscular physics with Lavoisier's pragmatic chemistry, Dalton was closer in spirit to Empedocles than to the atomism of Democritus. Yet there were many nineteenth-century exponents of a corpuscular chemistry who were closer to Democritus's atomism of a universal, unique matter. This school, while it was unable to share the empirical advantages enjoyed by the multi-element viewpoint nevertheless enjoyed the encouragement of conceptual simplicity and the prospect of a physical or mathematical chemistry.[3]

The theory of the elements in the nineteenth century became a dialogue between the school of multi-element chemists and the various schools of reductionists who included physicists as well as chemists. Since Dalton had built the multi-element viewpoint into the postulates of his atomic theory these reductionists to some extent inevitably felt obliged to reject the form of atomism proposed by Dalton. It is possible to detect two basic types of scepticism towards Dalton's theory before 1860.

William H Brock

*Dalton versus
Prout: The
Problem of Prout's
Hypotheses*

1. The Textbook Tradition.[4] This was a straight-forward 'facts versus hypotheses' positivism which is found in most British chemistry textbooks during the period 1810–60. It was an eighteenth-century tradition that chemistry and physics were separate disciplines, and Lavoisier's rejection of 'metaphysical' speculation concerning the nature of matter led, in the case of Dalton's theory, to an insistence on a separation between the atomic hypothesis and the empirical laws of chemical combination.

2. The Proutian or Unity of Matter Tradition. This was a world-view of long-standing tradition which required a physical and chemical molecular theory of matter. It held that Dalton's postulation of 'many elements—many different atoms' was wrong. In offering their criticisms, chemists of this persuasion were not rejecting atomism, or rather a corpuscular physics; but they were rejecting an Empedoclean physics for a Democritan one. It is the second of these forms of scepticism with which this paper is partly concerned.

Siegfried has pointed out in a series of articles[5] that Lavoisier's pragmatic definition of the element was intellectually disquieting since it left chemists with the problem of deciding whether a chemically undecomposable substance was a real element, or whether time would show that it was a compound substance. Humphry Davy experienced this dilemma in a most acute form, and he consequently refrained from referring to Lavoisier's simple substances as elements at all, and adopted instead the non-committal phrase, *undecompounded bodies*. Davy's romantic appreciation of the simplicity, harmony, and design of Nature, made him feel instinctively that chemists had embraced too many 'elements', and he hoped for an explanation of Dalton's laws of definite and multiple proportions in either the discovery of bodies that really were *un*-decomposable, or in terms of point atoms with attractive and repulsive powers; rather than with an atomic hypothesis that was bound up with the perhaps insuperable limitations of chemical analysis in its unquestioning acceptance of a multiplicity of elements.[6]

Dalton, although he saw the point of Davy's feeling, just would not allow it as a reason for denying his atomic theory. Not that Dalton was any Lavoisierean empiricist. In the spirit of Berthollet, he urged that a person armed with an hypothesis 'is more likely to have a proper bent given to his investigations than one who makes a number of experiments without any fixed object in view'.[7] Berzelius and Thomson would have agreed. However, the danger was, as in the case of Thomson, that enthusiasm for a particular hypothesis, or particular world-view, could lead to what Babbage and Prout were to call 'Procrustean Science'.[8] With Davy, Prout and Thomson, Dalton shared an obsession with the rôle of hydrogen and oxygen in the scheme of chemical combinations;[9] but unlike them, he did not see these two elements as potential candidates for an improved and simplified chemical picture.

In his 18th lecture to the Royal Institution on 30 January 1810, Dalton rejected Davy's unitary philosophy, and claimed mistakenly that Newton had also rejected it.

I should apprehend that there are a considerable number of what may be properly called *elementary* principles, which never can be metamorphosed, one into another, by any power we can control.[10]

When Berzelius wrote that he believed all atoms were of the same size (so that, as Dalton pointed out, atomic weights were equivalent to relative densities), Dalton denied it vehemently. 'Atoms', he replied to Berzelius, 'are of *unequal sizes*, and the size may be in direct proportion to the weight, or otherwise'.[11] It is intriguing to reflect that it is easier to imagine the 'elements' as polymerized *protyle* if the atoms of different 'elements' have different sizes than if with Berzelius they are imagined to be of equal size. As it happened, although they disagreed over sizes of atoms, both Dalton and Berzelius agreed that the existence of many elements meant the existence of many different species of atom.

In the form known as 'Prout's hypothesis', the unity of matter viewpoint is attributed not to Humphry Davy, but to William Prout. But as previously indicated, Prout was already committed to the unity of matter before the publication of Davy's *Elements of chemical philosophy* in 1812 publicized the reductionists' cause.

From the evidence of an undergraduate essay of 1810, it is clear that Prout's belief in the unity of matter was developed from a peculiar amalgamation of

the non-atomic qualitative physics of Aristotle in which
there was a prime matter that gave constancy to a world
of changing forms, with eighteenth-century corpuscular philosophy in which the 'integrant particles' of
the chemist were made up from large numbers of
'constituent particles'. The further evidence of the
confused manuscripts of Prout's lecture notes on animal
chemistry which were delivered in London in 1814
show that he retained this commitment to the unity of
matter after he had learned of Dalton's atomic theory;
by which time he would also have become aware of the
reductionist speculations of Davy, Thomson, and
others.[12]

From Thomson, and to a lesser extent Berzelius,
Prout acquired a knowledge of the importance of
atomic weights and specific gravities. It was their publications, together with the publication of Wollaston's
table of synoptic equivalents, which led to Prout's paper
on specific gravities in which the integral multiple
weights hypothesis was first formulated.[13] These mathematical relations, which attracted the enthusiastic
attention of Thomson, were for Prout, as he revealed
in 1816,[14] an indication of the unity of matter to which
privately he had been committed for several years. The
simplicity for which many natural philosophers had
been searching since Lavoisier had defined the concept
of the element was over; back to the pre-Socratics,
everything was one—hydrogen!

Such an hypothesis was obviously exciting. After a
slow beginning, catalyzed by Thomson, it inevitably
stimulated analytical work.[15] For if chemists could
show by exact and improved methods of analysis that
atomic weights were integral multiples of the atomic
weight of hydrogen within the limits of experimental
error, then this would provide a means for correcting
atomic weights and support (but not prove) the world-
view that everything was hydrogen.

Another point immediately emerges. If Prout's
protyle hypothesis were true, then the status of Dalton's
multi-element atomic theory would be threatened. An
atomic theory of matter would still be possible, but the
theory which Dalton proposed would have to give way
to the older corpuscular physics by being transformed
into a chemical molecular theory. In fact, as we all

know, this transformation occurred in spite of the vicissitudes of the theory of elements; perhaps because the hands of chemists were forced by other even more pressing experimental and theoretical issues. Nevertheless, it would be a useful historical exercise for someone to examine whether the debates between the schools of multi-element chemists and reductionists promoted an environment in which the compromising chemical molecular theory could be quietly developed and adopted.

II. *Dalton's attitude towards integral weights*

It does not seem that Dalton ever commented directly on the integral multiple weights hypothesis. On two occasions when he might have been expected to discuss it he did not do so. Before these are examined, however, one problem must be cleared away. Reference to Partington's useful tabulation[16] of Dalton's various lists of atomic weights for the period from 1803 to 1827 shows that, although fractions were not excluded, the majority of his values were integral even though sometimes qualified by a $\pm$ sign. However, it would be wrong to infer from this that Dalton supported the multiple weights hypothesis. Although, for example, Dalton's weights in Parts I and II of his *New system* (volume 1) were almost entirely integral, reference to the text shows that he continually used qualifying expressions like 'nearly', 'about', 'not less than . . . nor more than', and 'between'.[17] In other words, his values were chosen to be within the limits of his estimated experimental error.

Curiously, in his *History of chemistry*, Thomson wrote that Dalton 'was of opinion that the atomic weights of all other bodies are multiples of hydrogen',[18] and specifically cited the *New system* of 1808. Earlier, Ludwig Meinecke had expressed a similar view.[19] Benfey believes that it is inconceivable that this judgment was an error of memory on Thomson's part because he was such an ardent supporter of both Dalton's theory and of 'Prout's hypothesis'. The same historian noticed that Thomson seemed to withhold Prout's name deliberately from the discussion; perhaps because of the vicious nature of Berzelius's attack on his *First principles*.[20] Indeed, it seems possible that

Thomson, who was still smarting from Berzelius's blows when he wrote the *History*, may have wished to accord a certain sanctity to the multiples hypothesis by fathering it on the originator of chemical atomism.

Needless to say, Dalton did not mention the integral multiples hypothesis anywhere in the *New system* (least of all in Part I). Even if Dalton at one time believed in integral weights, and gave Thomson this impression in early conversations, he cannot have retained the belief for long. The most probable explanation for Dalton's use of such weights throughout his career is that like Davy he felt that:

> I have usually given *whole numbers*, taking away or adding fractional parts, that they may be more easily retained in the memory. When the number was gained from experiments in which a loss might be supposed, I have added fractional parts, so as to make a whole number.[21]

But unlike Prout, and to a lesser extent Davy, Dalton did not try to link this pedagogic and experimental simplification[22] to the question of the number of elements. There was no need for him to do so since he was firmly committed to many elements.

That Dalton did not support the integral weights hypothesis can also be inferred from the absence of any positive support for it when in 1816 and in 1830 he had the opportunity to speak his mind.

1. In a paper read to the Manchester Literary and Philosophical Society on 18 October and 27 December 1816, 'On The Chemical Compounds of Azote and Oxygen', Dalton had occasion to discuss the composition of air. As an example of the confusion among chemists over whether air was a mixture or a chemical compound, he cited a recent anonymous author (in fact Prout) who had said that chemists appeared *always* to have thought of air as a mixture and never examined it as an example of chemical combination.[23] That Prout indeed said this appears to be an indication of his lack of training in chemistry, or lack of familiarity with its literature.

Dalton's citation proves that he had read Prout's first anonymous article. His pedestrian, but logical mind would not have been attracted to Prout's paper which was badly written, very confused, and full of blunders. In addition, since Dalton did not support

Gay-Lussac's volume relations, he would have paid little attention to Prout's recommendations concerning the relation between specific gravity and atomic weight,[24] and his observation of integral weights on the hydrogen scale. Dalton showed no signs of having read Prout's correction of February 1816 which contained the *protyle* speculation,[14] and although Thomson had revealed Prout's identity in May 1816,[25] this does not seem to have come to Dalton's attention. References to Prout by name do not appear in any of Dalton's writings; but as we shall find, there is some evidence for their collaboration during the 1830's.

2. The other opportunity concerns Dalton's unpublished paper: 'Chemical Observations on certain atomic weights as adopted by different authors with remarks on the Notation of Berzelius'. This was read to the Manchester Society on 15 October 1830,[26] that is during the critical period between the publication of Thomson's *First principles* in 1825 in favour of multiple weights, Berzelius's outspoken attack on Thomson's scientific and analytical reputation in 1827, and Edward Turner's analytical papers in favour of non-integral Berzelian atomic weights of 1832 and 1833.[27] Unfortunately, the anticipation awakened by Dalton's title that in his paper will be found an explicit opinion of Prout's integral multiple weights hypothesis is not fulfilled. However, some conclusions may be drawn from it.

The manuscript of this lecture has been badly damaged by fire, and is incomplete. Since the bottom third of each sheet is destroyed, about seven lines, or fifty-six words, have been lost per page. The continuity of Dalton's argument is therefore badly upset. This is unfortunate since, tantalizingly, the paper appears to be of historical importance in connection with the origins of Dalton's theory.[28]

At the beginning of his argument Dalton recalled conversations with Davy at the Royal Institution in 1804 on the way in which the oxides of nitrogen and their mutual relationships were explained by the atomic theory. Davy, said Dalton, had been interested but not very encouraging, and later he had unhappily fallen a victim to the French disease of 'volumes'. Thomson, Dalton continued, had also been interested in his ideas since 1804, 'but his system of atoms *as it now stands*, does not appear to me to be fixed upon a stable foundation'.[29] This may be interpreted as a more or less specific rejection of the philosophy behind Thomson's *First principles*[30] and in particular, a rejection of the integral multiple weights hypothesis.

Although Dalton felt that Wollaston's positivist distinction between experimentally-determined 'equivalent weights' and hypothetical atomic weights was puzzling, Berzelius's system of combinations was 'very perplexing on account of its being founded on that of volumes in accordance with Davy's [*sc*, system], & yet having a special regard to atoms'.[31] Here one would expect him to have commented on the divergences between Thomson's and Berzelius's *values* for atomic weights. Surprisingly, Dalton did not do so. Instead he criticized Berzelius on the score that he had used *volumes* and thoroughly confused matters with his double atoms; Thomson, despite his philosophy, had at least decently stuck to *atoms*.

This is rather confusing since both Berzelius and Thomson used Gay-Lussac's law of combining volumes as evidence for the determination of atomic weights. But Thomson had not adopted Berzelius's rule that *atom* and *volume* were interchangeable expressions, or that equal volumes of gases under the same physical conditions contained the same number of atoms. For Thomson, and most of his British compatriots, the latter rule was broken in the case of oxygen which was assumed to contain twice as many atoms per unit volume.[32] This effectively gave the formula HO for water instead of Davy's and Berzelius's H_2O, and many other formulae similar to those which Dalton deduced from his rules of combination.

Despite this limited support for Thomson, Dalton found himself in agreement with Berzelius over the atomic weights of eleven elements, including carbon, nitrogen, sulphur and lead. All of these had fractional weights in Berzelius's 1826 table.[33] Presumably Dalton knew what he was saying, even though his last full published list, in 1827, gave values for these elements that were not even remotely similar to those of Berzelius.[34] But if Dalton is taken at his word this is firm evidence that he was against integral weights. The manuscript continues from this point by way of discussing chemical notation, Richter's equivalents, and rules of combination; but it does not seem likely that Dalton would have had another opportunity in the lecture to be more explicit.

With the creation of the British Association for the Advancement of Science in 1831, there arose what could have been new opportunities for Dalton to discuss the multiples hypothesis. In appendices to the outdated second volume of his *New system*, which finally appeared at the end of 1827, Dalton revealed a concern for the accurate determination of the specific gravities of dry gases. 'The greatest *desideratum* at the present time', he wrote:

is the exact relative weight of the element hydrogen. The small weight of 100 cubic inches of hydrogen gas, the important modifications of that weight by even very minute quantities of common air and aqueous vapour, and the difficulties in ascertaining the proportions of air and vapour in regard to hydrogen, are circumstances sufficient to make one distrust results obtained by the most expert and scientific operator.[35]

'Several writers', he complained, 'and some of considerable eminence' who had derived incredible specific gravities to four or five decimal places had gone wrong because they had not understood 'the effect of aqueous vapour in modifying the weights and volumes of gases'.[36]

This is probably a reference to the important controversy between Thomson and Rainy, to which we now turn.

The bulk of Thomson's *First principles* was concerned with the experimental determinations and calculations of the specific gravities and atomic weights of all the known elements and many of their compounds. The experimental imprecision of Thomson's methods is well known,[37] and there is also a certain amount of evidence that he adjusted a few results to conform with the integral multiples law.[38] He believed that he had uncovered a number of remarkable mathematical relations between the various atomic and molecular weights of substances.[39] Although none of these relations would be considered very significant today, they show what Thomson meant and understood by the

'First Principles of Chemistry'. It seems clear that he hoped to discover rules of affinity from the numerical principles he uncovered—principles which were the real basis for chemists' gross classifications of substances by their chemical properties. Yet it would have been difficult to avoid concluding from his generalizations that the physical basis for the relations, and for chemical affinities, was that matter was made from hydrogen and oxygen. However, Thomson was not explicit concerning this possibility; like Mendeleev later, he merely noted down relations between atomic weights without commenting on their physical cause. As a physicist, Dalton was never particularly interested in the relations between chemical elements, or their compounds. Prout and Thomson were; in effect they were searching for a periodic law, and like Mendeleev and Lothar Meyer later, they faced the implication that elements were complex bodies.

Apart from the disapproval of the pro-Davy group of chemists at the Royal Institution,[40] on the whole Thomson received a good English press.[41] His atomic weights became standard among British and American chemists; by the beginning of 1827 Prout was able to say that his law of integral multiples appeared to have been generally adopted by chemists.[42] One of the few exceptions he might have noted was Andrew Ure, whose 'severe animadversions' against Thomson had been the last of a tedious, abusive and continuous campaign against his work. Tedious the disputes between Thomson, Ure and Brande may have been—they are certainly arid reading for the historian—yet it is possible that they brought Thomson a good deal of sympathy. If this was the case, then they probably also hindered the serious experimental appraisal of his work.

However, the reception of the *First principles* was not confined to either fulsome praise or rhetorical abuse; far more serious for Thomson's reputation as a credited chemist was the attack made on his specific gravity determinations by a friend, the Glaswegian physician, Harry Rainy. Rainy's criticisms were similar to, and continued, those made in 1822 by the Irish physician James Apjohn;[43] and they foreshadowed the searching experimental appraisal of Thomson's gravimetric work which was published by Turner between 1828 and 1833.

In April 1822 Thomson had published an answer to a friend's private criticism (probably Rainy's) that he had not corrected for the presence of water vapour when he published an account of the determination of the specific gravity of hydrogen in 1820.[44] Thomson argued that although he had said nothing about the presence of vapour in hydrogen he had been fully aware of such 'an obvious source of inaccuracy'. In practice, he argued, the error was so small that it could be ignored; and his and Prout's value of 0·0694 for the specific gravity of hydrogen was correct.

Thomson's later account of the specific gravity of hydrogen in the *First principles*[45] attracted the attention of Rainy who hastened to report that Thomson had badly under-estimated the quantity of water vapour in his hydrogen sample.[46] Rainy had made some experiments and discovered that the Prout-Thomson value for the specific gravity of dry hydrogen was incorrect for *any* given temperature and pressure; and he proposed a vapour correction factor which had the significant effect of reducing the specific gravity of hydrogen from Prout's and Thomson's 0·0694 to 0·0673. This gave a H : O ratio of 1 : 16·54 instead of 1 : 16.

Although Rainy's H : O ratio was not correct, since it was based upon Thomson's erroneous value for the specific gravity of oxygen, his result was of importance because it led him to suggest that the truth of the integral multiple weights hypothesis was an open question whose proof was dependent upon the experimentalist's skill.

If Dr Thomson's experiment is correct (and of this we can scarcely doubt from the care and attention with which it is performed), it *disproves* the hypothesis that the specific gravities of all the gases are multiples by integer numbers of the specific gravity of hydrogen. It is true that 16·54 does not differ from 16 by more than about $\frac{1}{32}$ of the whole, and that a very slight change in the number adopted for the specific gravity of hydrogen would account for the difference; but this merely shows how difficult it is to make any experiment sufficiently accurate to decide on the truth of the hypothesis.[47]

Here Rainy hit the nail on the head, and Thomson seemed to be placed in the awkward position of either

J D—S

admitting that his experiments were at fault, or that his experiments were accurate, but that Prout's hypothesis was wrong. But Thomson was unperplexed. He replied to Rainy in a friendly fashion[48] admitting there had been an error over the vapour correction; but this error had not been in the direction claimed by Rainy. Far from under-estimating the amount of vapour in hydrogen, Thomson now believed that he had over-estimated it. He agreed with Rainy's formula for the conversion of moist to dry specific gravities, and used his own vapour pressure data to derive a new H : O ratio of 1 : 15·941. Some further experiments with thoroughly dry hydrogen[49] gave the ratio 1 : 15·87, which he claimed was still sufficiently close to the integral ratio of 1 : 16 to justify the multiples hypothesis.

Rainy thought otherwise; far from clearing away his doubts Thomson's new measurements only strengthened them. In March 1826 he replied more forcefully and critically that Thomson had made errors in his experimental routines with both moist and dry hydrogen.[50] On the basis of some of his own experiments on vapour pressure, whose results differed from the published tables of Dalton and Ure, he rejected Thomson's old, but amended H : O ratio of 1 : 15·941. As for the new determination with dry hydrogen, even on the assumption that the new ratio was correct, he questioned whether the difference between H : O : : 1 : 16 and 1 : 15·87 was immaterial.

Rainy's attitude foreshadowed that taken by Stas: atomic weights approach integral numbers, but this approach need not have any deeper significance. His attitude perhaps also reflects that of the Daltonian multi-element school that the integral weights hypothesis was compromised with a particular and simple view of Nature.

Clearly Thomson got himself into a contradictory position with Rainy. In 1822 he had denied that water vapour made any material difference to the specific gravity of hydrogen; yet in 1826 he conceded an influence, but denied that it affected the validity of the integral multiples law. Thomson made no public reply to Rainy's second paper, and Rainy himself made no further contribution to the debate, or to the science of chemistry. His achievement, however, was to demonstrate that Thomson's specific gravity measurements were open to scrutiny and doubt, and that Thomson had by no means established the correctness of the integral multiples hypothesis that he had set out to prove. 'The subject,' Rainy declared, 'requires further elucidation.'[51] Although in the event the elucidation came gravimetrically from Edward Turner, the debate between Thomson and Rainy seems to have stimulated the attentions of both Dalton and Prout.

In 1831 Charles Daubeny, Professor of Chemistry at Oxford, published his study of the atomic theory.[52] Prior to publication he sent proofsheets to both Prout and Dalton, and respectfully asked them for their comments.[53] Their replies were published by Daubeny as Appendices, and complimentary copies of his book were sent to both men. Daubeny's accompanying letter to Prout survives in the Royal Institution.[54]

Dear Sir,

I have directed my Publisher Mr Murray to send you a copy of my little Essay on the Atomic Theory. The remarks you were good enough to make upon it you will find inserted in the appendix, with some comments of Dalton's upon my exposition of his Theory, and the two together form a very valuable part of the Publication. I wish you would . . . to meet at Oxford next July, when we propose receiving the British Association lately organized at York. Dalton wants much to have the specific gravity of Hydrogen and other fundamental points in the Atomic Theory settled by a sort of chemical Committee, and as he promises to be of the party at Oxford next year it strikes me that a better time could not be chosen for such an undertaking. My Laboratory, such as it is, could be . . . at your service, though I had rather leave the decision of a point requiring such delicate manipulation to more skilful hands.

Believe me dear Sir,
Yrs very truly
Chas. Daubeny

Wm Prout
Oct 27th 1831

This letter needs no comment, for Dalton's interest obviously followed on from his remarks in the *New system* of 1827. In September 1831, at the first meeting of the British Association for the Advancement of Science at York, an *ad hoc* Chemistry Committee whose members included Dalton, Daubeny and Turner,[55] had resolved that it was of the utmost importance that:

Chemists should be enabled, by the most accurate experiments, to agree in the *relative weights of the several elements*, *Hydrogen, Oxygen, and Azote*, or, what amounts to the same thing, that the specific gravity of the three gases should be ascertained in such a way as would insure the reasonable assent of all competent and unprejudiced judges.[56]

At Oxford, the following June, besides Turner's report of his investigations of the atomic weights of lead, silver, chlorine and bromine, the Association heard Prout describe his new barometer, and his account of a very accurate measurement of the specific gravity of air.[57] This research, begun sometime in 1827,[58] was to have continued with further investigations of the specific gravities of gases in both the dry and moist states, but unfortunately the work was never published. As a result of his Oxford report, the Chemistry Committee of the Association (of which Prout was now a member[59]) urged Turner to extend his work on atomic weights. It also asked Prout, together with Dalton, to make fresh experimental studies of the specific gravities of oxygen, hydrogen and carbon dioxide, and to communicate the results to the next meeting.[60] Daubeny's letter (above) suggests that the initiative for this request came from Dalton. Next year (1833) a grant of £50 to defray the expenses of apparatus was awarded to the two men,[61] and in 1834 the Chemistry Committee reported 'that they had received statements of the progress of the experiments . . ., for which sums of money had been appropriated . . ., and recommended the continuance of these appropriations'.[62] Although this indicates that the joint studies were begun, no reports of the work were published by the Association, and neither man published anything independently. Nor is there any more information concerning the results of an award of £40 to Prout and Thomas Clark of Aberdeen for specific gravity determinations in 1839.[63]

Even if one agreed with Dalton, Berzelius, Turner and Penny upon the rejection of Thomson's atomic weights, it was of course still possible to support a multiple weights hypothesis. In his famous letter to Daubeny in 1831, Prout proposed that the physical basis of the law of multiples might be a fractional unit of the weight of hydrogen.[64] Prout's commitment to the unity of matter was strong enough to withstand any criticism of Thomson's atomic weights, and like most British chemists he probably thought at first that Thomson was right. But the fact that later he disagreed with Thomson over the latter's analysis of oxalic acid,[65] and helped Turner with the analysis of silver chloride,[66] suggests that he was willing to agree with strictures on Thomson's methods, and also to agree with Turner that the *simple* law of multiples maintained by Thomson was erroneous. This was partly the point of the speculation offered to Daubeny.

Dalton passed no comment on this new speculation, but knowing as we do his commitment to many elements, his aversion to the *protyle* hypothesis and the multiples hypothesis, and his disagreement with the 'complexities' of an Avogadro-Prout molecular theory, it is not difficult to imagine his attitude to the way Prout proposed to save the phenomena. Surely he would have agreed with Berzelius that speculations on the whole subject ought to cease, otherwise:

Elles pourraient facilement conduire à des hypothèses dont la fausseté ne se trahirait peut-être que tard. Je pense donc que, dans aucun cas, lorsque le poids atomique d'un corps simple se rapproche du multiple d'un autre corps, on ne doit rendre le nombre, donné par l'expérience, égal a ce multiple.[67]

Notes

Originally subtitled 'The Problem of the Elements'. Some of the documentation for this essay has been drawn from chapter 7 of my doctoral thesis, *The chemical career of William Prout* (Leicester, 1966).

1 E.g. Thomson, *System of chemistry* (Edinburgh, 1802) i, 386; substantially repeated in later editions.

2 The major study by D. M. Knight, *The problem of the chemical elements from Humphry Davy to Benjamin Brodie the younger*, D.Phil. thesis (Oxford, 1964) awaits publication. See W. V. Farrar, 'Nineteenth Century Speculations on the Complexity of the Chemical Elements', *British Journal for the History of Science*, ii (Dec. 1965) 297–323; D. M. Knight, 'The Atomic Theory and the Elements', *Studies in romanticism*, V (1966) 185–207; and for the story before Dalton, M. Boas Hall, 'The History of the Concept of Elements', supra.

3 On the tradition of mathematical chemistry see A. Thackray, 'Quantified Chemistry: The Newtonian Dream', supra; and Knight, op. cit. (2) 185–9.

4 W. H. Brock and D. M. Knight, 'The Atomic Debates', *Isis*, lvi (1965) 8–9, with further comments in W. H. Brock (ed.), *The atomic debates* (Leicester University Press, Leicester, 1967).

5 R. Siegfried, *Journal of Chemical Education*, xxxiii (1956) 263–266; *Chymia*, v (1959) 193–201; *Isis*, liv (1963) 247–58; *Chymia*, ix (1964) 117–24.

6 In 1809 Davy wrote to Dalton that he was pleased to hear of his views on atoms but doubted 'whether we have yet obtained any

Notes   elements', Roscoe, *John Dalton and the rise of modern chemistry* (London, 1895) 155. See Brock and Knight, op. cit., (4) 7.

7 H. E. Roscoe and A. Harden, *A new view of the origin of Dalton's atomic theory* (London, 1896) 100.

8 C. Babbage, *Reflections on the decline of science in England* (London, 1830) 178; W. Prout, *Medical Gazette*, viii (1831) 262.

9 Cf. Dalton's lecture notes for 3 February 1810, Roscoe and Harden, op. cit., (7) 118–20.

10 Ibid., 112. Ironically, in the same year Prout cited Newton in support of the unity of matter.

11 Dalton, *Annals of Philosophy*, iii (1814) 175.

12 Prout's essay of 1810 and his notes of 1814 were briefly described by me at the XIth International Congress of the History of Science, Warsaw, August 1965 (*Actes*, in press). Fuller details will be published elsewhere.

13 T. Thomson, *Ann. Phil.*, ii (1813) 32–52 et seq.; J. J. Berzelius, ibid., 443–54 et seq.; W. H. Wollaston, *Phil. Trans. Roy. Soc.*, civ (1814) 1–22; Anon. [W. Prout], *Ann. Phil.*, vi (1815) 321–30.

14 Anon. [W. Prout], *Ann. Phil.*, vii (1816) 113.

15 Note that the excitement really only began after Thomson had publicized the multiple weights hypothesis. 'It is a very remarkable circumstance', wrote Rainy in 1826, 'that though more than ten years have now elapsed since Dr Prout's paper was published . . . no chemists, except Dr Thomson, should have engaged in any experimental researches on a subject so highly important', *Ann. Phil.*, xxvii (= xi) (1826) 193. The more conventional view appears to have been due to J. F. W. Johnston: 'The simplicity of this relation drew the immediate attention of chemists', *Report of the British Association*, 2nd meeting, 1 (1832) 415–16.

16 J. R. Partington, *A history of chemistry* (London, 1962) iii, 810–11.

17 Dalton, *A new system of chemical philosophy*, Parts I and II (Manchester, 1808, 1810) 215, 237, 239, 241, 250, 254, etc.

18 T. Thomson, *The history of chemistry* (London, 1831) ii, 295.

19 J. L. G. Meinecke, [*Gilbert's*] *Annalen der Physik*, (2) xxiv (1816) 162. This has caused some confusion among historians who have sometimes thought Meinecke attributed the *protyle* hypothesis to Dalton. Since elementary atoms were indivisible for Dalton, this would have been impossible; Meinecke did not make this mistake. See editorial analysis, *Prout's Hypothesis* (Alembic Club Reprint, No. 20, Edinburgh, 1932) 7–13; O. T. Benfey, 'Prout's Hypothesis', *J. Chem. Educ.*, xxix (1952) 78–81.

20 T. Thomson, *An attempt to establish the first principles of chemistry by experiment* (2 vols, London, 1825). J. J. Berzelius, *Jahres Bericht*, vi (1827) 77, translated and publicized by R. Phillips, *Philosophical Magazine* (2) iv (1828) 450–3.

21 H. Davy, 'Advertisement' for projected 2nd edn of his *Elements of chemical philosophy*, published by J. Davy in *The collected works of Sir Humphry Davy, Bart.* (9 vols, London, 1839–40) 4, xv.

22 Berzelius commented, 'The method which they [Dalton, Davy and Young] have adopted of giving round numbers, though it facilitates the recollection and calculation, is scarcely consistent with the object of scientific researches, and ought to be rejected: for even supposing that perfect exactness could never be obtained, it is nevertheless the object towards which all our efforts should be directed', *Ann. Phil.*, ii (1813) 454.

23 Dalton, *Ann. Phil.*, ix (1817) 186–94. See p. 188. For Prout's remark see ibid., vi (1815) 321.

24 Yet in 1821 a mathematician, Charles Sylvester, claimed that 'the relation of the specific gravity to the weight of the atom I pointed out to Mr Dalton, Dr Henry, and to Dr Thomson, long before the account of it was published by Dr Prout in Thomson's *Annals*', *Ann. Phil.*, xviii (= ii) (1821) 213.

25 Thomson, *Ann. Phil.*, vii (1816) 343.

26 A. L. Smyth, *John Dalton. A bibliography* (Manchester, 1966) items *98, 279.*

27 E. Turner, *Phil. Trans. Roy. Soc.*, cxix (1829) 291–9; *Phil. Mag.*, (3) i (1832) 109–12; *Phil. Trans. Roy. Soc.*, cxxiii (1833) 523–39.

28 The manuscript is owned by the Manchester Lit. and Phil. Soc. and has been transcribed by A. Thackray in the Society's *Memoirs and Proceedings*, cviii (no. 2, 1965–6) 21–42.

29 Dalton, 'Chemical Observations', 3, my italics.

30 Thomson sent Dalton a copy of his book in April 1825, Roscoe and Harden, op. cit., (7) 179.

31 Dalton, 'Chemical Observations', 4.

32 See the remarks of Johnston, op. cit., (15) 420–1.

33 Dalton, 'Chemical Observations', 4–6. Berzelius's values are listed by Partington, op. cit., (16) iv, 166.

34 Dalton, op. cit., (17) ii (Manchester, 1827) 352.

35 Ibid., 347.

36 Ibid., 300–1.

37 J. W. Mallet, 'Stas Memorial Lecture', *Memorial Lectures Delivered Before the Chemical Society (1893–1900)* (London, 1901) 19; Partington, op. cit., (16) iii, 721.

38 E.g., Thomson, op. cit., (20) i, 160.

39 Ibid., ii, 457 ff.

40 A. Ure, *Quarterly Journal of Science*, xx (1825) 113–41.

41 E.g., Phillips, *Ann. Phil.*, xxvi (= x) (1825) 147; ibid., xxvii (= xi) (1826) 68.

42 Prout, *Phil. Trans. Roy. Soc.*, cxvii (1827) 355.

43 Apjohn, *Ann. Phil.*, xix (= iii) (1822) 385–7. The better known attack by Berzelius in 1827 (ref. 20) was concerned with gravimetric techniques, not with specific gravity measurements.

44 Thomson, *Ann. Phil.*, xvi (1820) 165–70; note also ibid., xiv (1819) 65–6.

45 Thomson, op. cit., (20) i, 67–76.

46 Rainy, *Ann. Phil.*, xxvi (= x) (1825) 135–7. Rainy (1792–1876) is noticed in the *Dictionary of national biography*.

47 Rainy, op. cit., (46) 137.

48 Thomson, ibid., 352–60. Thomson thought Rainy's paper was written with 'perspicuity, accuracy and modesty'.

49 Purified hydrogen was passed through about 37 inches of calcium chloride tubing, and the amount of water absorbed used as an additional check on the calculations.

50 Rainy, *Ann. Phil.*, xxvii (= xi) (1826) 187–94. Note especially p. 190.

51 Ibid., 194.

52 C. Daubeny, *An introduction to the atomic theory* (Oxford, 1831).

53 Dalton replied that Daubeny's integral 'numbers denoting the weights of the atoms . . . are, not at all, I fear, sufficiently correct. I do not know where we are to look for the exact sp. gr. of hydrogen gas, and if this be not correctly known, then all the atomic weights will be wrong, and the doctrine of volumes be in jeopardy.' The lists of Turner's and Berzelius's atomic weights which Daubeny also published, contained 'several errors . . .; but as this is debateable ground, I shall not enter upon it at large', ibid., 137.

54 Bound in Prout's copy of Daubeny's book in the Old Library. I am grateful to the Librarian of the Roy. Inst. for permission to publish this letter. The lacunae denote illegible words.

55 *Brit. Ass. Reports*, i (1831) 46.

56 Ibid., 53.

57 *Brit. Ass. Reports*, i (1832) 570–5.

58 Prout, op. cit., (42) 370.

59 *Brit. Ass. Reports*, i (1832) 113. Dalton was Chairman of this enlarged Committee for Chemistry, Mineralogy, Electricity and Magnetism.

60 Ibid., 116.

61 *Brit. Ass. Reports*, ii (1833) xxxvi.

62 *Brit. Ass. Reports*, iii (1834) xxxiv. In the same year Dalton and Prout were appointed to a committee on chemical symbolism.

63 *Brit. Ass. Reports*, viii (1839) xxix.

64 Daubeny, op. cit., (52) 129.

65 Mentioned by Thomson, op. cit., (20) ii, 100 and *Phil. Mag.*, (2) v (1829) 22–3. Later he admitted Prout was right, *A system of chemistry of inorganic bodies* (2 vols, 7th edn, London, 1831) ii, 15.

66 Turner, *Phil. Trans. Roy. Soc.*, cxxiii (1833) 534 and emphasized in *Phil. Mag.*, (3) iv (1834) 397.

67 Berzelius, *Traité de chimie* (6 vols, 2nd edn, Paris, 1847) iv, 512. Note also his remark quoted in ref. (22).

*Berzelius and the
Development of
the Atomic Theory*

Introduction

It is a curious fact of history that the veneration of
Dalton today is due in no small measure to the chemical
expertise and influence of a rival from whose views
Dalton detached himself with force and candour. The
ideas of the Manchester philosopher were immortalized largely by the Swedish chemist Jöns Jacob
Berzelius through whose efforts atomism became incorporated in a scheme of chemistry more comprehensive and far-reaching than any yet produced. His
differences from Dalton were not so much reflections
on the inadequacies of the latter's concepts; they were
rather extensions of them made possible by Berzelius'
exceptional powers of generalization and profound
chemical insight.

Berzelius was, of course, the dominant figure in
early nineteenth-century chemistry, and for several
decades wrote with unequalled, and often unquestioned, authority. Of his place in the history of
chemistry as a whole Sir Harold Hartley has well
written:

Chemistry was indeed fortunate that in the years when she
was becoming an independent science and the stream of
knowledge was growing so rapidly she had the encyclopaedic
mind, the judgment, the craftmanship and the watchful eye
of Berzelius to guide her career. It was that rare combination
of qualities that made possible his massive contribution that
is unique in the history of chemistry. His systematic mind
saw the need for a structure in which chemistry could grow

with the precision and the articulation of a living organism. The basic principle of his design was atomic composition.[1]

Berzelius first encountered atomism in a *chemical* context; his introduction owed little to physics or meteorology. A short extract from his own account is as follows:

> While occupied with the publication of an elementary text-book of chemistry, I was perusing (among other works which one does not generally read) Richter's *Memoirs* . . . . and was impressed by the light which I found there on the composition of salts and the precipitation of metals by each other. . . . It follows from Richter's researches that by means of good analyses of several salts, one could calculate precisely the compositions of all the others. . . . At the same time I formed the project of analysing a series of salts so as to make it unnecessary to examine the others. . . . When I heard of Dalton's ideas on multiple proportions, I found in a number of analytical results which I already had such a confirmation of this theory that I could not prevent myself from examining the said phenomena [of metallic precipitation]; and so it came about that, initially dealing with very limited chemical proportions, the plan of my work grew more and more to include proportions in their whole extent.[2]

Access to Dalton's ideas was far from easy, and for several years Berzelius suffered in a form acute even in those days from the difficulties of scientific communication. His correspondence with chemists outside Sweden contains many a *cri de cœur* for information, books and periodicals. We know[3] that he was aware of Dalton's 1807 paper on mixed gases,[4] and he observes[5] that he met English atomism first in Wollaston's ingenious essay on superacid and subacid salts the following year.[6] From then on every effort was made to acquaint himself further with the new doctrines. Thus to Berthollet he wrote in about 1810:

> I should like to have knowledge of the ideas of Mr Dalton, who, according to all appearances, is one of the most ingenious physicians of our age. Mr Davy, whom I asked if he knew something more of his system, replied that Dalton had come to London to publish it, and that he would obtain his work for me as soon as it was published. But it is over two years since I have had communication with Mr Davy.[7]

In June 1811, a letter to Davy himself proceeded:

> Pardon me, sir, if I trouble you again with a request that I have already made once, i.e., to acquaint me with some ideas on the system of Mr Dalton. Despite all my researches I have

still been able to obtain other information on his doctrines only from a supplement to Murray's *System of chemistry* that Mr Brandel brought me on his return from London. The edition of Mr Thomson's *Chemistry* where Mr Dalton's ideas ought to be mentioned, translated into French by M. Riffault, which I have requested from Count Berthollet, has not yet reached me. There is every appearance that the ideas of Mr Dalton, of whom I have a very high opinion, will help to correct my own, in addition to which he must have done many experiments which will save me the trouble of doing them for myself.[8]

Murray's book[9] would have commended itself by its stand against the anti-Berzelian views on the nature of chlorine, and Berzelius confessed to Gahn[10] that he preferred it to Thomson's work. The supplement mentioned is in fact a Note[11] at the end of Volume ii dealing (in a disapproving way) with Dalton's theory of mixed gases. But it was only a snack not likely to satisfy for long Berzelius' voracious appetite for atomism. Eventually, in 1812, a copy of Dalton's *New system* reached him from the author a few days before his departure for England. His reactions were expressed to Gaultier de Claubry in these words:

Never has a present given me such pleasure as this one did at first. I have been able only to skim through the book in haste, but I will not conceal that I was surprised to see how the author has disappointed my hopes. Incorrect even in the mathematical part (e.g., in determining the maximum density of water), in the purely chemical part he allows himself lapses from the truth at which we have the right to be astonished.[12]

He goes on to lament Dalton's bondage to his preconceptions with all the unreliability (for Berzelius) that this involves. But if this was an anti-climax to his years of searching and grouping it also marked a redefinition of his own views over against those that he now discovered to be Dalton's. His original adoption of an atomic philosophy two or three years previously had not been followed by much success in convincing others: 'I have been publishing memoirs on the subject on the continent for more than three years, without having hitherto, as far as I know, made a single proselyte.'[13] Now, however, some headway was to be made as the divergence of his ideas from those of Dalton gave rise to a series of articles in Thomson's *Annals of Philosophy* under the title 'Essay on the cause of Chemical Proportions, and on some Circumstances relating to them: together with a short and easy Method of expressing them'.[14] After three instalments of this essay had appeared, Dalton published some 'Remarks on the Essay of Dr Berzelius on the Cause of Chemical Proportions'[15] which drew forth from Berzelius a characteristically forthright rejoinder. This was in the form of a letter[16] to Thomson which the latter published[17] after toning it down and amending it in a few other ways. No further reply seems to have been made by Dalton, and the whole episode now seems rather futile and pointless. Yet the polemics did draw attention to the real issues involved and gave Berzelius his first major opportunity for a systematic, public exposition of his own brand of atomism.

The atomic philosophy which he adopted underwent some change over the years, but most of its important features emerged in the debate of 1813–14. We shall now review the main points of departure from Daltonian atomism because they provide the clues to much of later chemical history.

Dalton v. Berzelius: Emergent Atomism

1 'Figure' of the atoms

In 1813 Berzelius supposed 'that atoms are all spherical, and that they have all the same size',[18] for only in this way could regular figures be obtained. Dalton, on the other hand, refused to be committed to any relation between sizes and weights of atoms, though inclined to the opinion that atoms were not all of the same size. Moreover he could not see why sphericity was probable, and imagined that an oxygen atom might be a regular tetrahedron, the nitrogen atom a cylinder and so on. But he did concede that all would be enveloped in roughly spherical atmospheres of heat.[19]

Many years later Berzelius expounded the same doctrine of equal-sized spheres as an explanation of isomorphism (discovered by his own assistant, Mitscherlich, in 1819[20]): identical numbers of these atoms arranged in the same way always produce the same solid figure, i.e. crystalline form.[21] Further, it should be possible for the same number of such spheres to be differently arranged giving products having different chemical properties. To him, therefore, we owe the idea of isomerism—the first successful prediction from the atomic theory alone.[22]

Now it is not of course necessary to assume that all atoms are spheres of equal size in order to provide an atomistic explanation of isomorphism or isomerism. But the first does demand a similar geometrical form in the atoms being compared, and the second requires an interchangeability of atoms. Both of these conditions were fulfilled in Berzelius' spheres.

Perhaps the chief significance of Berzelius' difference from Dalton on this point was methodological. Berzelius regarded Dalton's tetrahedral atoms of nitrogen, etc., as a flight of fancy beneath his notice,[23] even though they had been advanced with far greater caution than his own confident assertions. Essentially the supposition of Dalton was unnecessary and metaphysical since no way existed of distinguishing between the atom *per se* and an atom in its spherical heat envelope.

2 *Atomic symbolism*

In the third part of his English 'Essay'[24] Berzelius devoted himself to the first full account of a new chemical symbolism, intended to replace the circular signs of John Dalton. This was, of course, the alphabetical notation from which modern symbolism is derived.

Much has been written on this already.[25] We know that Berzelius was not the first to employ an alphabetical method, that it underwent a number of changes at his own hands, that its initial popularity was small, especially in England, and that he himself made little use of it in his published writings.[26] However, there are a few points that are worth re-examination here in view of the great importance of this symbolism for the spread of the atomic concept.

Thus it is desirable to stress that Berzelius was not the first to conceive formulae as expressing quantities. Certainly he wrote, 'The object of the new signs is not that, like the old ones, they should be employed to label vessels in the laboratory; they are destined solely to facilitate the expression of chemical proportions'.[27] But Dalton's signs had the same intention. The obvious advantage of the new symbols was ease of reproduction by hand or in print, with a consequent saving of time and cost. For this reason the service rendered to atomism by his new notation is precisely that given to the theory of valency by the notation of Frankland and Crum Brown. In both cases improved techniques of communication were followed by rapid assimilation of the ideas symbolized.[28]

The formulae of Berzelius had another, less obvious advantage over those of Dalton, and this was because of what they did *not* do. In the symbolism of *A new system of chemical philosophy* there lurked a quasi-structural significance that had no right to be there. Thus Dalton wrote 'carbonic acid' as

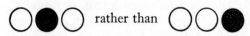 rather than

Berzelius did not commit himself to any arrangement of atoms in a molecule, and his symbols appeared to Dalton as 'horrifying':

A young student of chemistry might as soon learn Hebrew as make himself acquainted with them. They appear like a chaos of atoms. Why not put them together in some sort of order? Is not the allocation a subject of investigation as well as the weight? If one order is found more consistent than another, why not adopt it till a better is found?[29]

Dalton seems to have been guided by an aesthetic feeling for the symmetry of the system in writing down certain preferred patterns. He often spoke of the beauty and simplicity of the atomic theory, and in this respect the Berzelian notation is lacking. But Berzelius saw the dangers of submerged assumptions of this kind, and in the absence of other evidence preferred his own non-committal formulae.

To suppose that aesthetic considerations were Dalton's sole guide, however, would be manifestly unjust. Of his own formulae he wrote:

When three or more particles of elastic fluids are combined together in one, it is to be supposed that the particles of the same kind repel each other, and therefore take their stations accordingly.[30]

This was a remarkable anticipation of our own understanding of an important rule of molecular geometry. It might have found a sympathetic response in Berzelius whose devotion to the dualistic doctrine that 'like repels like' was almost unequalled. But for some reason it did not. One can only conclude that it was too speculative, and fundamentally, of course, Berzelius was right. One cannot have a theory of structure without a theory of valency.

3 *Rules of chemical combination*

Berzelius was the first of the great pioneers in the accurate determination of atomic weights. In this again he built upon the foundation laid by Dalton, and, like the English chemist, he proceeded from a set of axioms, termed in his case the 'corpuscular theory'. His early views may be generalized in the formula of a binary compound as AB_n, where A and B are elements and n is an integer up to 12. In other words, one element (A) is restricted to one atom in each molecule, so combinations of the type $2A + 3B$, $2A + 2B$ and so on were excluded. These would be 'contrary to sound logic' because 'no obstacle, either mechanical or chemical' existed 'to prevent such an atom from being divided', and because 'such a composition would almost totally destroy chemical proportions'.[31] Dalton's sceptical rejoinder to this[32] brought forth the assertion that the rule was founded upon analyses of inorganic compounds ('and I have analysed a great number of them') and the challenge to offer 'one proof that this opinion is evidently incorrect'.[33]

Now the fact that Berzelius was wrong about this matters less than the reason behind his mistake. His conclusions, because they were based upon analysis, however limited, were sounder than the more arbitrary rules of Dalton. And subsequent experimentation caused him to change his mind, so that by 1831 he was conceding that 2 atoms of one element could combine with 3, 5 or 7 of another, and wondering whether combinations with 2, 4 or 6 atoms of the other might be found.[34] His theory, based as it was upon analysis, became the starting-point for a whole series of other analyses and gradually a self-consistent picture of atomic weights began to emerge. The superb quality of this experimental work received the homage of the author of the Stas Memorial Lecture who wrote:

The high and highly deserved reputation of Berzelius for accuracy, never before surpassed in quantitative determinations, demanded extraordinary care on the part of any one who should call in question the numbers accepted on his authority. . . . With apparatus in many respects inferior to that of the present day, and with scarcely any aid from chemical manufacturers in preparing pure materials and reagents, but with unsurpassed manipulative skill, and the most honest criticism of his own work and endeavour to improve its accuracy, he produced the first fairly trustworthy list of numbers representing the proportions by weight in which the elements combine.[35]

It is well known that Berzelius supplemented the rules mentioned above with the law of isomorphism and that of atomic heats. As a result, he obtained atomic weight values for some thirty elements which, corrected from his standard of O = 100 to our own, come very near the modern values. His most important error sprang from the false assumption that all strongly basic oxides were of the form M.O, so that he obtained for the alkali metals and silver double the correct values. This had a serious effect later on analyses of organic acids whose equivalents were generally obtained from ignition of their silver salts. Dalton's frank confession could have been also made by Berzelius:

After having the atomic principles in contemplation for ten years, I find myself still at a loss, occasionally, to discriminate between the combinations which contain two atoms of a given body from those which contain only one atom.[36]

This was a difficulty that remained until Avogadro was allowed to provide the solution.

Evaluation of atomic weights was only one fruitful result of the atomic interpretation of combining quantities. The very success of these investigations prompted Berzelius to wonder whether atomism was relevant to the vast and little understood realm of organic nature.

At one time he had doubted it. An analysis of oxalic acid implied far more than twelve atoms attached to a single atom of hydrogen—a result quite at variance with the expected composition of inorganic compounds. It would appear that this was a great stumbling-block to Berzelius who felt that the atomic theory could not be applied to organic compounds.[37] Dalton disagreed with the analysis figures, and produced his own which are in fact correct.[38] It is probable that he diagnosed Berzelius' fault correctly, suggesting that the lead oxalate used had not been dried at a high enough temperature. Since the presence of a small amount of hydrogen vitiated the first result, inadequate drying was probably responsible for the error. With Dalton's figures no difficulty arises with an atomic interpretation.

It was after this experience that Berzelius resolved to examine how far organic compounds could be viewed from a corpuscular standpoint. With an improved method of analysis he obtained data for thirteen compounds within a few months, and concluded that although the law of definite proportions did not seem applicable, formulae could be given in accordance with Dalton's atomic theory.[39] From this time onwards atomism became applied to every kind of ponderable matter, and this decisive step forwards was taken by Berzelius in 1814–15.

One other rule of chemical combination presents some interesting features. This concerned the reaction between two oxides, which according to Berzelius always took place in such a way that the ratio of oxygen in each was always a whole number. Permitted combinations could include, for example, $(A + O)$ with $(B + 2O)$ but not $(A + 3O)$ with $(B + 2O)$. Dalton's atomic theory could not explain this restriction. Conversely, the 'oxide rule' allowed combinations that were absurd in Daltonian terms as $(A + 3O)$ with $(B + 1\frac{1}{2}O)$.[40]

In fact the rule is not strictly correct, but does hold for the majority of combinations (partly because most basic oxides contain only one oxygen atom). Its chief interest is the construction that Berzelius placed upon it. Dalton was quick to point out that the difficulty involving the oxide $(B + 1\frac{1}{2}O)$ may be resolved by regarding it rather as $(2B + 3O)$ by halving the atomic weight of B. On the question of the atomic theory permitting $(A + 3O) + (B + 2O)$ he observed that it was no more the business of the theory to explain the nonoccurrence of this combination 'than to show why all the metallic oxides do not mutually combine with each other'.[41] Here, surely, he was on solid ground. It was quite unreasonable for Berzelius to demand that any hypothetical scheme should *by itself* cover all phenomena, and it is now obvious that a complete explanation could not be forthcoming without the concept of

J D—T

valency. He returned to the matter in his reply to Dalton, and in a passage not printed by Thomson remarked that:

when a theory explains only half of what should follow from a theory of these phenomena, that theory is incomplete. Where the theory is deficient a difficulty exists that cannot be shrugged off by the assertion of an individual pretending that he expects from it a satisfactory explanation of only one part of the phenomena presented.[42]

It is clear that Berzelius had no criteria to offer by which the valid limits of a hypothesis could be delineated, and this methodological blind-spot is an interesting indication of one of his chief limitations. Yet as he wrote to Thomson, 'When a corpuscular theory of chemistry is involved, I have believed that this theory ought to be the fundamental theory of the science, and that it ought . . . . to embrace all'.[43]

4 *Theory of volumes*

A brief reference must be made to another topic in which Berzelius differed from Dalton, the theory of volumes. Gay-Lussac's law of combining volumes was an important generalization on the chemistry of gases. It was seen by Berzelius as an experimental basis for his corpuscular theory which was thereby placed in a stronger position than Dalton's hypothetical atomism:

What in the one theory is called an *atom* is in the other theory a *volume*. In the present state of our knowledge the theory of volumes has the advantage of being founded upon a well-constituted fact, while the other has only a supposition for its foundation.[43]

The inapplicability of volume theory to organic compounds was at that time deemed an advantage for it was not then clear that atomism was relevant to them. In 1814 Berzelius said that he regarded the theory 'as a leading-string to keep us in the way of truth'.[44] He used it to show that the ratio of oxygen to hydrogen atoms in water was 1 : 2, for example. Unfortunately he was unable to apply it to compound gases for this would have committed him to either a demi-atom of oxygen (for instance) or to a molecule of an element containing more than one atom. He deplored either possibility, polyatomic molecules of one element being a violation of dualism. He concluded that several compound gases 'diminish in volume at the moment of chemical combination, since the repulsive force of one or all of the elements is diminished by the juxtaposition of an atom of another element',[45] so the theory of volumes does not apply to them. That was as near as he got to Avogadro's position. Had he been able to take the final step he would not only have given atomism the weight of his immense authority, but would also have advanced its cause by half a century.

5 *Dualistic atomism: the electrochemical theory*

In his Essay on Chemical Proportions of 1813 Berzelius had lightly touched on the supposition of spherical atoms in contact with each other and held together by neutralization of opposite electrical charges. This was not the first reference to the idea of an electrochemical union. The view that chemical affinity and electricity were essentially the same had been put forward in 1811,[46] and the idea had been expanded the following year.[47] In 1813 Nicholson had published a lengthy Note by Berzelius in his *Journal* as a 'beautiful generalization of facts'. It included the passage:

As at the moment of union [of two reacting substances] there is a production of heat, which may vary from a very slight elevation of temperature to that of the most intense fire, we think we may conclude, that at the moment of the chemical combination there is a discharge of the opposite electric state of the bodies which, here, as in the pile, produces the phenomenon of fire, at the instant when the electricities disappear.[48]

Dalton's objection was to the imposition of these electrochemical speculations upon his own atomism. He protested that they make 'no necessary part of the atomic theory such as I maintain it'.[15] It is clear that this phrase in particular greatly offended Berzelius, for he quotes or parodies it several times in his letter to Thomson, not all of which came to be published in *Annals of Philosophy*. He contrasts Dalton's attitude with his own endeavours 'to strain towards the first principle of science' by broadening his theory as far as possible. It is true that he categorized his views as 'conjectures', but added that 'Ideas on the relation of atoms to their electrochemical properties ought in my opinion to constitute an essential part of the corpuscular theory as I have envisaged it'.[49]

From now on Berzelius committed himself to a view of matter in which atomism and electrochemical dualism were so intimately associated that they had to stand or fall together for the rest of his life. This partly explains his single-minded, dualistic philosophy even in the face of great opposition. The very success of atomism encouraged him in his devotion to its electrochemical interpretation. It also accounts for the intensity of feeling behind his long reply to Dalton's mild comments on his Essay.

I have given an account elsewhere of Berzelius' electrochemical theory,[50] and it will be sufficient to note here the main aspects of its later relation to atomism.

The first detailed exposition of it came in 1818–19, in the influential *Essai sur la théorie des proportions chimiques et sur l'influence chimique de l'électricité.*[51] From this we see that at the heart of his theory lay the concept of atomic polarization: 'we can represent each atom as having an electrical polarity'.[52] This meant that electricities were concentrated in opposite parts of the atom, rather like magnetic poles. To explain why some atoms tended to be positive and others negative, Berzelius supposed one pole might predominate—and this phenomenon he called unipolarity. Later on, he added the idea of several electrical axes in an atom in order to account for multiple combinations.[53] In several ingenious ways these ideas were developed to cover as many phenomena as possible. Thus he assumed that the intensity of polarity varied with different substances, that it depended also upon temperature, and so on. To account for the effects of environment and physical state he assumed that spatial effects operated, that reaction was facilitated when atomic poles were near each other and that certain relative orientations of the atoms were more favourable than others.

In all of these respects his scheme was irrevocably committed to a vivid, pictorial atomism. It covered all types of chemical reaction, mechanical cohesion, dissolution, electrolysis and so on. It ranged from simple binary inorganic compounds to complex organic substances. To use modern terminology, the extension of a fundamentally ionic concept to covalent carbon compounds had unfortunate consequences, though even here Berzelius' view of the unity of chemistry had profound justification.

These things need to be said because it is so easy to deride Berzelius, as he derided Dalton, for harmful extensions of his hypothesis. It cannot be denied that dualism held up the progress of the atomic theory in blinding its adherents to the rightness of Avogadro's hypothesis, but its other effects assisted that progress greatly. Yet so profound was the impact of such dualistic philosophy that as late as 1861 Kekulé needed to observe that, though atomic theories were compatible with dualism, they were not inherently dualistic themselves.[54]

Conclusion

In the foregoing account, much has been said of the differences between Berzelius and Dalton. This was inevitable in view of the importance of these divergences for the spread and growth of atomism. Yet it would not be fair to the memory of either man to leave it quite like that. Nor would it be right to categorize one or the other as the more truly scientific. Fortunately, we are not here to award prizes.

Both Berzelius and Dalton had their fair share of obstinacy and tenacity, but both had their vision of what science ought to be. It would be naïve in the extreme to imagine that either of them deliberately put forward one theoretical scheme in preference to an alternative necessitated by experimental facts. Their difference lay in matters of personal choice: how far they chose to consider certain factors as opposed to others, how widely-embracing they chose to make their theoretical schemes, even how far aesthetic considerations determined their ultimate decisions.

To Berzelius Marcet once wrote:

How you love chemical theory! Shall I tell you of the fault I find in your writings? It is that they embrace too much at a time. Theoretical discussions come too often to interrupt the facts. You have the whole of chemistry before your eyes like a tableau; each little fact reminds you of a theory; and each theoretical idea reminds you of a crowd of facts. There results a richness in your writings which dazzles the philosophers of ordinary calibre.[55]

Let the last word come from Berzelius himself:

When I endeavoured to draw the attention of chemists to the difficulties in the atomic theory it was not my intention to refute the hypothesis. I wanted to lay open all the difficulties of that hypothesis that nothing might escape our attention calculated to throw light on the subject. I wished the experiments to verify the theory, and I should have considered it as absurd if I had taken the other road.[56]

These two comments, illustrating as they do both the vision and the philosophy of Berzelius, serve briefly to remind us of the debt owed to him by John Dalton and by us all.

Notes

Responsibility for translation into English of citations from other languages is accepted by the author.

1 *Kgl. Svenska Vetenskapsakad. Årsbok* (1948) 49.
2 J. J. Berzelius, *Traité de chimie* (Paris, 1831) iv, 532–3.
3 Letter to Gahn, 28 September 1807, in *Jac. Berzelius Bref*, ed. H. G. Söderbaum (Uppsala, 1922) iv, Part 2, 23.
4 *Nicholson's Journal*, xvi (1807) 4.
5 *Philosophical Magazine*, xli (1813) 4.
6 *Nicholson's Journal*, xxi (1808) 164.
7 *Jac. Berzelius Bref* (1912) i, Part 1, 16.
8 Ibid., Part 2, 29.
9 T. Thomson, *A system of chemistry* (Edinburgh, 1806–7) 4 vols.
10 *Jac. Berzelius Bref* (1922) iv, Part 2, 69.
11 Op. cit., (1806) ii, 3–26 of 'Notes' at end of volume.
12 *Jac. Berzelius Bref* (1920) iii, Part 2, 105.
13 *Annals of Philosophy*, ii (1813) 315.
14 Ibid., ii (1813) 443; iii (1814) 51, 93, 244, 353.
15 Ibid., iii (1814) 174.
16 *Jac. Berzelius Bref* (1918) iii, Part 1, 27.
17 *Annals of Philosophy*, v (1815) 122.
18 Ibid., ii (1813) 446.
19 Ibid., iii (1814) 175.
20 *Abhandlung Akad. Berlin* (1819) 427.
21 Berzelius, *Traité de chimie* (Paris, 1831) iv, 548.
22 Ibid., 549; *Jahresbericht*, xi (1832) 44.
23 *Annals of Philosophy*, v (1815) 123.
24 Ibid., iii (1814) 51.
25 E.g. M. P. Crosland, *Historical studies in the language of chemistry* (London, 1962) 270–81.
26 J. R. Partington, *A history of chemistry* (London, 1964) iv, 158–60. In an article on 'Dalton and Berzelius' (*Monit. Sci.*, i (1921) 4), M. Delacre has decried Berzelius' symbols on the grounds that they add nothing new, 'absolutely nothing', to those of Dalton and has condemned the assertion that Berzelius invented atomic symbolism as the 'grossest error in the history of chemistry'. This unusual view takes no account of both the main points in the following discussion.
27 *Annals of Philosophy*, iii (1814) 51.
28 C. A. Russell, 'The Influence of Frankland on the Rise of the

Theory of Valency', *Actes of the Xth International Congress of the*
History of Science (Ithaca, 1962) 883.

29 Letter to Graham, 1837, in W. C. Henry, *Memoirs of the life of John Dalton* (London, 1854) 124.

30 Dalton, *A new system of chemical philosophy* (Manchester, 1808) i, Part 1, 216.

31 *Annals of Philosophy*, ii (1813) 447.

32 Ibid., iii (1814) 176.

33 Ibid., v (1815) 125.

34 Berzelius, *Traité de chimie* (Paris, 1831) iv, 542–3.

35 J. W. Mallet, in *Chemical Society Memorial Lectures* (London, 1901) Stas Lecture, 3, 12–13.

36 *Annals of Philosophy*, iii (1814) 178. The result given $(H + 27C + 18O)$, seems to be a misprint for $(H + 18C + 27O)$, as the C/O ratio must be $2/3$.

37 Ibid., ii (1813) 450. There should be no hydrogen in the 'acid' (= anhydride) and therefore no need to include such large numbers of carbon and oxygen atoms.

38 Ibid., iii (1814) 179.

39 Ibid., v (1815) 260.

40 Ibid , ii (1813) 447; iv (1814) 324.

41 Ibid., iii (1814) 177.

42 *Jac. Berzelius Bref* (1918) iii, Part 1, 31.

43 *Annals of Philosophy*, ii (1813) 450.

44 *An attempt to establish a pure scientific system of mineralogy by the application of the electro-chemical theory and the chemical proportions* (London, 1814) 114.

45 Berzelius, *Traité de chimie* (Paris, 1831) iv, 553.

46 *Journal de Physique*, lxxiii (1811) 253.

47 *Kongl. Vet. Handl.*, xxxiii (1812) 166.

48 *Nicholson's Journal*, xxxiv (1813) 145.

49 *Jac. Berzelius Bref* (1918) i, Part 1, 28.

50 London University M.Sc. Dissertation, 1958. Also in *Annals of Science*, xix (1963) 117 et seq.

51 Paris, 1819.

52 Op. cit., 55.

53 Berzelius, *Traité de chimie* (2nd edn, Paris, 1845) i, 106.

54 *Lehrbuch der organischen Chemie* (Erlangen, 1861) i, 60.

55 *Jac. Berzelius Bref* (1914), i, Part 3, 43.

56 *Annals of Philosophy*, v (1815) 127.

The First
Reception of
Dalton's Atomic
Theory in France[1]

When Dalton was in his twenties[2] French chemists led the world in their subject. When Dalton began to teach chemistry in 1794 it was the English translations of the textbooks of Lavoisier and Chaptal that he used.[3] In so far as Dalton was a chemist, therefore, the influence of the chemical revolution associated with the name of Lavoisier cannot be ignored. The repercussions of this revolution continued into the early nineteenth century. Although Lavoisier himself had been guillotined in 1794, his former associates Berthollet, Guyton de Morveau and Fourcroy as well as Chaptal continued to propagate the new chemistry in their lectures and publications. I shall be concentrating attention on Berthollet and I should begin by giving a brief justification for regarding this particular chemist as the leading representative of French chemistry, at least up to about 1815. His mantle was then inherited by a worthy successor, Gay-Lussac.

Firstly, Berthollet's *Essai de statique chimique* of 1803 was the most important original contribution to chemistry in the decade following Lavoisier's death. Another reason for regarding Berthollet as the leading French chemist at the beginning of the nineteenth century was that he and he alone had built up an important research school, of which the two most brilliant products were Gay-Lussac and Dulong. Berthollet's country house at Arcueil just outside Paris became the focus of much important work in chemistry and physics.[4] Berthollet's leading position in French science was recognized out-

side France. Dalton regarded Berthollet's views as particularly influential and even when he did not agree
with them he was at pains to discuss them in detail.
This is seen in a striking manner in the first part of
Dalton's *New system*, where fifteen pages are devoted to
criticism of Berthollet's views on the interrelation of
gases composing the atmosphere. Dalton remarks:

I should not have dwelt so long upon it, had I not appre-
hended that respectable authority was likely to give it credit,
more than any arguments in its behalf derived from physical
principles.[5]

Dalton was also interested in the publications of the
private scientific society founded by Berthollet, the
Society of Arcueil, and Berthollet was able to send him,
for example, in the summer of 1809 the second volume
of the Arcueil *Mémoires* containing the statement of
Gay-Lussac's law of combining volumes of gases and
the evidence for it.

A recent article by two Russian historians of science[6]
has put forward the view that Berthollet himself maintained an atomic theory of matter. His atomic theory,
they say, has been overlooked because it was 'incomprehensible' or at least 'defective'. In the very first
sentence of his *Essai de statique chimique* Berthollet referred to chemical attraction and this between particles
('les molécules'). In discussing crystallization, Berthollet wrote:

Crystallization is one of the remarkable effects of the force
of cohesion; the parts which crystallize assume a symmetrical
arrangement which is determined by the mutual action of the
small solids separated by their force of cohesion from a liquid;
and the qualities [i.e. properties] of a solid, which is more
easily broken in one way than in another, which is more or
less brittle, more or less elastic, more or less ductile, depend
on this arrangement.[7]

Again, Berthollet referred to heat separating the particles of a substance,[8] and even to the distance between
particles.[9] The evidence adduced by Kuznetsov and
Sheptunova, drawn entirely from the first few pages of
the *Statique chimique*, is hardly sufficient to warrant
their conclusion that Berthollet's chemistry was atomistic in conception. What we can say is that Berthollet
accepted *implicitly* the particulate structure of matter, a
not uncommon position around the year 1800. This is

very different from being the proponent of an atomic theory in the sense that Dalton was.

We may note that Berthollet never spoke of 'atoms'. In the quotations referred to, Berthollet was speaking only of particles—the terms he used were *parties* or *molécules* and it is hardly necessary to point out that 'molecule' at this time did not have its present meaning. The article under discussion emphasizes Berthollet's use of atomic theory in his description of crystallization and solution. Although Berthollet did mention particles in crystal structure, it is significant that in discussing solution he made no explicit reference at all to particles —he was just not interested in this aspect. When Berthollet introduced the term 'chemical mass', it was not the mass of the individual particles which he considered. Throughout the introductory chapter of Berthollet's book, his main concern was with *forces* and the force of cohesion in particular. If it is true, as Clerk Maxwell suggested,[10] that natural philosophers can be divided into two groups according as they think of particles of matter or the conditions existing between these particles, then we should clearly place Dalton in the first category and Berthollet in the second. Although Berthollet paid little attention to particles, he was interested in the conditions of a reaction. For Berthollet, it was simply not enough to know what elements were reacting—one had to know the complete circumstances. His greatest contribution to chemistry was perhaps to point out that a variety of factors affected the course of a reaction, not least the quantity of the reactants. Berthollet argued against the established system of chemistry with its elements and compounds each with its characteristic affinity. He announced what he called a 'law'—that 'the action of any substance is always in proportion to the quantity contained within the sphere of its activity'.[11] In succeeding pages he again considered 'la sphère d'activité' of chemical affinity.[12]

Berthollet took a dynamic—one might almost say 'fluid'—view of chemical reaction. The result of any chemical reaction depended on the interplay of forces over a period of time. There was nothing fixed about it. Any acceptance by Berthollet of discrete indivisible atoms would have been inconsistent with his own position in opposing definite proportions as a general rule of chemical composition. Definite proportions were only acceptable to Berthollet in special cases such as the combination of gases, which was often accompanied by a large contraction.[13] When Berthollet's pupil Gay-Lussac published his memoir on the combining volumes of gases, it was with an introduction explaining the special circumstances in which affinities acted in the case of gases.

Gay-Lussac's memoir, published in 1809[14] was in quite a different tradition from Dalton's work. One of the wilder historical statements made by Thomas Thomson was that Gay-Lussac's law of combining volumes of gases was based on Dalton's atomic theory.[15] In case this should be taken seriously even for a moment, it may be worth examining briefly the reaction of Gay-Lussac to Dalton's ideas.

It is well known that during the Napoleonic wars, communications continued between Britain and France. Even so it may come as a surprise to learn that Berthollet received a copy of the first part of Dalton's *New system* in August 1808[16] i.e. within two months of its publication. This interval may be contrasted with the period of nearly four years before Berzelius in Sweden received a copy of Dalton's book. As at the end of August 1808 a copy of Dalton's *New system* was in the hands of Berthollet, who was Gay-Lussac's friend and patron, and four months later Gay-Lussac announced his law of combining volumes of gases, it would be easy to argue *post hoc ergo propter hoc*. Certainly Gay-Lussac mentioned, both at the beginning and at the end of his memoir read in Paris on 31 December 1808 'Dalton's ingenious idea, that combinations are formed from atom to atom. . . .' Whereas Dalton's theory explained fixed proportions, Gay-Lussac gave at least equal emphasis to Berthollet's view that fixed proportions were the exception rather than the rule. I have discussed elsewhere[17] the sequence of events which led to Gay-Lussac's announcement of the law of combining volumes of gases. The crucial point, however, is that Gay-Lussac, in his search for regularities in chemical reactions, had already investigated weights but it was only with volumes that he found a simple natural relationship:

It is very important to observe that in considering weights there is no simple and finite relation between the elements of any one compound.[18]

Again in 1814, Gay-Lussac insisted that *volumes* as opposed to *weights* gave the true relation between chemical compounds.[19] Gay-Lussac therefore thought of chemical reactions in volumetric rather than in gravimetric terms. The point here is not that the graduated tube gives more reliable results than the balance. It is rather that Gay-Lussac had observed directly the volumes of his gases and vapours. Atomic weights were not immediately accessible to experience. This of course was the reason for Berzelius' curious amalgamation of the work of Dalton and Gay-Lussac. The Swedish chemist too preferred to use the language of volumes.

In 1807, Gay-Lussac had tried to find some gravimetric relationship between the combining weights of acids and alkalis.[20] He then discovered that in those cases where the acid and alkali could be obtained in the gaseous state, there was a simple volumetric relationship. A study of volumes therefore revealed regularities of nature hidden by the gravimetric approach.[21] Dalton, in the Newtonian tradition, considered that matter consisted of atoms characterized by weight. For Gay-Lussac, in the Cartesian tradition, weight or mass was not so fundamental a property as extension or volume. To quote Clerk Maxwell, 'To those who identify matter with extension, the volume or space occupied by a body is the only measure of the quantity of matter in it'.[22]

It is now time to examine in detail what Berthollet thought of Dalton's work and in particular of the atomic theory. At the time of publication of the first part of the *New system*, Berthollet's attitude was crucial to its reception by the French chemists. Berthollet, having received Dalton's book so shortly after publication, was soon to have an opportunity of publicly commenting on Dalton's atomic theory. The supremacy of French textbooks of chemistry at the end of the eighteenth century had been seriously challenged by Thomas Thomson's *System of chemistry*, the first edition of which appeared in 1802. The value of this book was fully appreciated by Berthollet and he gave all his support to a translation of the third edition. He wrote a long introduction to the French edition and as the original third English edition of Thomson's book is notable for containing the first published account of Dalton's atomic theory, it is not surprising that Berthollet should have taken the opportunity of commenting on the theory. The French edition of Thomson's book was an important source of knowledge on the Continent of the atomic theory. It was, for example, on the basis of the account given in this book that Avogadro in 1811 discussed Dalton's ideas.[23]

The French translation of Thomson's book was begun in 1807 and continued in 1808. Berthollet did not have to hand his introduction over to the printers before November 1808 and therefore his comments on the atomic theory were not dependent on Thomson's version but were based on the primary source of Dalton himself.

Berthollet refers to Dalton's atomic theory as:

an ingenious hypothesis by which he explains the constant proportions to be found in some compounds . . . This hypothesis explains a phenomenon the cause of which has hitherto been very obscure but the more seductive the hypothesis is, the more necessary it becomes to examine it closely. [24]

Berthollet knew of the evidence of Thomson and Wollaston for multiple proportions in certain salts presented in papers read to the Royal Society in January 1808,[25] but he was not prepared to accept all similar experimental results without careful checking. For Berthollet, chemical combination in fixed proportions was the exception rather than the rule. Berthollet's conclusion was that Dalton's theory merited a more thorough examination. As regards possible arrangements of atoms, Berthollet said sharply that it was better that chemists should repeat and extend experiments relating to constant and multiple proportions 'than that they should devote themselves to hypothetical speculations on the number, arrangement and figure of atoms which escape all experience'.[26]

Berthollet's objections to the atomic theory were therefore chiefly of two kinds. In the tradition of Lavoisier, he was suspicious of accepting as a fundamental unit of chemical reactions entities which were not accessible to experience.[27] At the same time, the strongest experimental confirmation of the atomic theory—constant and multiple proportions—was itself independently disputed by Berthollet.

Further documentation on Berthollet's views on Dalton's theory is provided by a recently discovered manuscript in Berthollet's handwriting of a draft second edition of the *Statique chimique*. The manuscript notes for this revision are being edited by Madame Sadoun-Goupil, who has been kind enough to transcribe for me certain passages with a bearing on Berthollet's opinion of Dalton. I have found letters[28] which show that this manuscript dates from 1815. Berthollet now criticized Dalton's rather vulnerable rule of simplicity:

> We have no means of determining the number of atoms which combine in this manner in each compound; we must therefore have recourse to conjectures.

If only a surer method were available of determining the number of atoms in a compound, then the atomic weights need not be in dispute. Speaking of Dalton's method of deducing atomic weights, Berthollet inquired:

> Can such presumptions serve as the basis for the determination of the elements of chemical combinations? Are we not accepting the vaguest speculations of metaphysics by reducing elements to atoms which are indivisible but different in size and combined together in certain numbers by an indeterminate force? We know bodies only by the effects which they produce by their action but nothing in this action can inform us of the distinct properties of their ultimate atoms. . . .

Further criticisms by Berthollet were directed against Dalton's assumptions about the shape of atoms and their arrangements in different compounds. Although Berthollet distrusted the theory, he was prepared to discuss it at length and now even to accept its use to a very limited extent. He came nearest to this in 1815 in a favourable reference to Thomas Thomson's use of the theory.[29]

Although these notes by Berthollet of 1815 were read by Gay-Lussac, they never reached the public domain. After the translation of Thomson's book, the second occasion on which Dalton's atomic theory was discussed in a book published in France was in 1812 when the translation of the sixth English edition of William

Henry's *Elements of experimental chemistry* appeared.[30]
A copy of the book had been sent to Berthollet but the
translation was carried out by Henry François Gaultier
de Claubry, a name which to many will be completely
unknown, yet one that cannot be excluded from the
Dalton story. His entry to science had been through
pharmacy and he had subsequently been a junior
assistant to Gay-Lussac at the École Polytechnique and
to Thenard at the Faculté des Sciences in Paris.[31]
Gaultier de Claubry was significantly a very junior
member of the French scientific community. He had
undertaken the translation of Henry's *Elements* in his
late teens and was only twenty in 1812 when it was
published. He could not have undertaken this task and
secured publication on his own and in his preface,
Gaultier de Claubry acknowledged his indebtedness
not only to his teachers[32] but most significantly to
Berthollet. Just as Berthollet had been responsible for
getting Thomson's textbook translated into French, so
again Berthollet had considered it desirable to have a
French edition of Henry and had asked young Gaultier
de Claubry to undertake it. According to the translator,
without the constant support and encouragement of
Berthollet he would never have undertaken the work
and it was only under his patronage that he presumed
to have it published. Thus for the second time, Berthollet was indirectly responsible for the propagation of
Dalton's atomic theory in France despite his own rejection of it.

The connection of Henry's book with Dalton is in the
first place the fact that displayed prominently on the
title page of the French translation was the dedication
to Dalton. More important of course, are the contents
of the book. In the sixth English edition of his textbook, Henry gave a brief but sympathetic account of
Dalton's atomic theory as an integral part of his
discussion of chemical affinity.[33] He considered that
Dalton's theory 'appears more consonant to the general
simplicity of nature than the theory of indefinite proportions favoured by Berthollet'. Yet Henry warned the
reader that Dalton's theory 'cannot at present be regarded in any other light than that of an hypothesis'.
At the end of the second volume of this edition, however, Henry added an appendix describing 'recent

discoveries in chemistry' and in this he devoted four pages to a further discussion.[34] In particular, he gave a table of atomic weights taken from Part 1 of Dalton's *New system* with an explanation of how they had been obtained. Henry agreed that Dalton's rule of simplicity was 'a gratuitous assumption' but affirmed that no experimental fact had yet been found which contradicted it. Henry's book, therefore made a major contribution to the knowledge of Dalton's atomic theory in France.

Brief investigation of the correspondence of Gaultier de Claubry reveals that he had actually undertaken a translation of Dalton's *New system* as well as of Henry's book. Writing to Berzelius on 8 August 1811, Gaultier de Claubry stated that both were shortly to be printed,[35] and he offered the Swedish chemist a copy of his translation of Dalton.[36] Berzelius was all the more grateful for this offer as, despite his interest in Dalton's work, he had so far failed to procure a copy of the work published in England three years previously. With this interesting example of the possible indirect transmission of Dalton's ideas to the greatest chemist of the next generation, the story ends rather disappointingly. The French translation of Dalton never appeared and in April 1812, Berzelius at last received a copy of the *New system* from the author himself. Berzelius' frank comments on Dalton's book in a letter to Gaultier de Claubry[37] are interesting, but must be passed over as outside the subject-matter of this paper.

Why the French translation never appeared must remain a matter of conjecture. It is possible that Berthollet's expected support did not materialize. Even Gaultier de Claubry himself, after hearing the reservations of Berzelius, became less convinced of the merits of Dalton's theory and in February 1813, he wrote to say how shocked he was that a man of Dalton's ability should have been so carried away by his own theory that he had tried to make experience fit his theory, rather than modify his theory in the light of experimental evidence.[38] The non-appearance of the French translation of Dalton may be related to external as much as to internal factors. 1812 was, of course, the year of Napoleon's retreat from Moscow and the years 1813–14 saw the collapse of the Empire. As far as the publication of scientific bodies in Paris is concerned, there was a significant delay of two years after the publication in 1812 of the first part of the *Mémoires* of the First Class of the Institute for the year 1811. The second part was not published until 1814. If the official body of French science could do no better than this, lesser publications may understandably have sunk without trace.[39]

We have thus arrived at the end of the First Empire in France. There was one more occasion on which Berthollet pronounced on the merits of Dalton's atomic theory. This was in 1816, when he and Thenard were appointed by the Académie des Sciences to report on a memoir by Dulong on the acids of phosphorus. In the course of this memoir, Dulong gave a re-evaluation of the atomic weight of phosphorus. This provoked from Berthollet the following remarks:

> The atomic doctrine and that of the proportions in which the elements of compounds combine or pass from one state of combination to another have become particularly prominent in chemical speculations. They throw considerable light on the theory of combination but at the same time they cause obscurity in current work and in chemical language and we have therefore thought it would be useful to provide a sketch of the present state of chemical science. . . .[40]

Because this survey was not strictly relevant to the report on Dulong's work, it was presented separately. Berthollet's essay entitled 'Esquisse de l'état actuel de la doctrine atomistique' was read at the meeting of the Académie des Sciences on 21 October 1816.[41] It would have been of great interest to have had the text of this document, but unfortunately it is missing from the archives of the Académie des Sciences. It might not be unreasonable, however, to suppose that it consisted largely of a warning by the veteran Berthollet about the unproven character of the atomic theory, which was beginning to appeal to some of the younger generation of French scientists, including his own pupil, Dulong.

If Arcueil had been one of the centres of resistance to the atomic theory, the irony is all the greater that it was there in March 1819 in Berthollet's country house that Dulong collaborated with Berzelius in the determination of a series of atomic weights.[42] Berzelius was staying in Paris from August 1818 to June 1819 and, although he himself learned much from his contact with the galaxy of talent concentrated in the French capital, the contact was not entirely onesided and the Swedish chemist was able to communicate to the French men of science some ideas of his own, including his version of Dalton's atomic theory. Among those who came into closest contact with Berzelius and would have been most receptive to these ideas was Dulong, then in his early thirties.

On 12 April 1819 (i.e. a few weeks after Dulong's collaboration with Berzelius), Dulong and Petit announced to the Académie des Sciences the law which bears their name. Their law of atomic heat took atomic weights as a basic property of each element. Dulong and Petit, in a cautious introductory sentence to their memoir noticeable for its circumlocution, hazard the possible use of the atomic theory in chemistry. In their own words, they had 'attempted to introduce the best established results of the atomic theory'.[43] The following year, Dulong wrote:

> I am convinced, notwithstanding the objection of M. de Laplace and of some others that this [atomic] theory is the most important idea of the century. . . .[44]

Thus, by 1820 Dulong was one of the leading protagonists in France[45] of the atomic theory, consciously dissociating himself from the scepticism of his mentors, Berthollet and Laplace. When, however, Sir Humphry Davy conversed with Laplace in 1820, he recorded that the French mathematician 'allowed all the merit of John Dalton',[46] which was a position in marked contrast to Davy's impression of Laplace seven years earlier. It is true that what Davy was noting was principally the change in Laplace's personal relations with him, but this remark is also indicative of the progress made by the atomic theory in France. Other members of the Arcueil group such as Biot[47] had expressed their reservations about the atomic theory but the validity of the generalization established by Dulong and Petit could not be disputed and this law did much to make the atomic theory acceptable. By 1830, Gay-Lussac had agreed in principle to the usefulness of an atomic theory in chemistry[48] but Thenard, who had introduced a general discussion of chemical theory into the later editions of his textbook, maintained the traditional caution.[49] Later in the nineteenth century hostility to the atomic theory was shown by a number of chemists of whom the most influential were J. B. Dumas and Marcellin Berthelot. In 1836, Dumas wished the word 'atom' could be removed from the language of chemistry as going beyond experience.[50] In the same tradition, Berthelot attacked atoms as metaphysical entities.[51] It was largely the successive influence of Dumas and Berthelot that was responsible for the exclusion of atomic theory from the official syllabus of French secondary education until 1893.[52]

Before closing, let us return to Dalton. Although Dalton's atomic theory was viewed with some suspicion in France for a considerable time after its publication, Dalton himself was held in general esteem in scientific circles. In 1816, when there were three vacancies in the Académie des Sciences for the place of correspondent in the chemistry section, the three successful candidates were Wollaston, Dalton and Berzelius, in that order.[53] As Davy had been elected a correspondent of the Académie in 1813, this would imply that in the opinion of the official body of French science, Dalton was the third most eminent British chemist. In England in 1816, the assessment of Dalton's eminence would not have been very different. In October 1817 Biot, then on a scientific expedition to the British Isles, visited Dalton in Manchester and presented him with the certificate of his election as correspondent of the Académie des Sciences. In the summer of 1822, Dalton was able to pay a visit to Paris, where he met all the leading French men of science. We may take our leave of Dalton on a fine Sunday afternoon in July when he was entertained by Laplace and Berthollet at Arcueil.[54]

Notes

1 This paper, which is concerned with the French reaction to Dalton's theory, should ideally be presented in conjunction with a second paper, in which the reaction in Britain to Dalton's atomic theory is discussed. My terms of reference preclude discussion of objections raised to Dalton's theory by Davy, Wollaston and other British men of science. When, however, I refer to criticisms in France of Dalton's theory, it should be remembered that parallel criticisms were made in Britain. A summary of some of the objections levelled at Dalton's atomic theory in Britain, is given in the introduction to a recently-published paper (W. H. Brock

and D. M. Knight, 'The Atomic Debates: "Memorable and interesting evenings in the life of the Chemical Society" ', *Isis*, lvi (1965) 5–25).

2 i.e. the period 1786–96.

3 R. A. Smith, *Memoir of John Dalton* (Manchester, 1856) 18.

4 See M. P. Crosland, *The Society of Arcueil: a view of French science at the time of Napoleon I* (London, 1967).

5 *New system of chemistry*, Vol. i, Part 1 (Manchester, 1808) 172.

6 V. I. Kuznetsov and Z. I. Sheptunova, 'Atomistic and chemical individualities in the doctrine of Berthollet' (in Russian), Voprosy istorii estestvoznania i tekhniki, xix (1965) 79–87. I should like to thank my wife for translating this article.

7 *Essai de statique chimique* (Paris, 1803), Vol. i. Introduction, 12–13, trans. *An essay on chemical statics*, Vol. i (London, 1804) xx–xxi.

8 *Essai*, 18, transl. xxvii.

9 *Essai*, 24, transl. 2.

10 Art. 'Atom', *Encyclopaedia Britannica*, Vol. iii, 9th edn (Edinburgh, 1875) 37.

11 *Essai*, 13, transl. xxi.

12 *Essai*, 18, 35.

13 Ibid., 366–7.

14 *Mémoires de physique et de chimie de la Société d'Arcueil*, ii (1809) 207–34, transl. Alembic Club Reprint No. 4 (Edinburgh, 1950) 8–24.

15 Thomson actually wrote: 'The object of Gay-Lussac's paper was to confirm and establish the new atomic theory by exhibiting it from a new point of view' (*History of chemistry*, Vol. ii (London, 1830–31) 299).

16 Royal Society, *Blagden Letters*, B. 133 (31 August 1808). In this letter Berthollet acknowledged receipt of Dalton's book.

17 M. P. Crosland, 'The Origins of Gay-Lussac's Law of Combining Volumes of Gases', *Annals of Science*, xvii (1961) 1–26.

18 A.C.R. No. 4, p. 15.

19 *Ann. chim.*, xci (1814) 132–3.

20 *Mémoires de la Société d'Arcueil*, i (1807) 379–80.

21 Gay-Lussac suggested that 'the capacity of saturation of acids and alkalis measured by volume . . . might perhaps be the true manner of determining it'. A.C.R. No. 4, p. 24.

22 See note 10.

23 *Journal de physique*, lxxiii (1811) 62 n.

24 T. Thomson, *Système de chimie*, Vol. i (Paris, 1809) Introduction, 21.

25 *Phil. Trans. Roy. Soc.* (1808) 63–95 (Thomson); 96–102 (Wollaston).

26 Thomson, op. cit., 27.

27 For the emphasis which Berthollet had already placed on knowledge based directly on sense experience, see *Essai de statique chimique*, Vol. i (Paris, 1803) 8.

28 E.g., Royal Society, *Blagden letters*, B. 140 (23 March 1815).

29 'M. Thomson . . . a donné un système complet et plus conforme à l'analyse des combinaisons chimiques déterminées par les atômes qui les forment.'

30 *Élémens de chimie expérimentale par M. William Henry . . . traduit de l'Anglois sur la sixième Edition, dédiée à M. Dalton*. Par H. F. Gaultier-Claubry, Bachelier ès lettres, ex élève des hôpitaux civils de Paris, 2 vols (Paris, 1812).

31 [Anon.] *Notice sur les travaux de M. H. F. Gaultier de Claubry*, 1841.

32 i.e. Deyeux and also d'Arcet, whose work he had used.

33 The English edition is referred to in this paragraph to avoid any difficulty of double translation: *Elements of experimental Chemistry*, Vol. i, 6th edn (London, 1810) 81–2. There was a significant increase in the attention paid to the atomic theory in the next edition of Henry's book (op. cit., Vol. i, 7th edn (London, 1815) 29–38).

34 *Elements*, Vol. ii, 6th edn, 475–8.

35 Berzelius, *Bref* (Uppsala, 1912–25) Vol. 3, Part vii, 101.

36 Letter from Berzelius to Gaultier de Claubry [Autumn 1811]: 'Votre offre de me faire cadeau d'un exemplaire de votre traduction de l'ouvrage de M. Dalton m'est fort agréable et je l'accepte avec reconnaissance', ibid., 102.

37 E.g., Berzelius says that Dalton 'cherche partout à modeler la nature d'après son hypothèse', ibid., 105.

38 Ibid., 107.

39 For the vicissitudes of the publication of the third volume of the *Mémoires* of the Society of Arcueil, due to be published in 1811 but which only achieved publication in 1817, see M. P. Crosland, *The society of Arcueil*, etc., (1967), 337–8.

40 *Procès-verbaux des Séances de l'Académie des Sciences*, Hendaye, (1910–22), Vol. vi, 103.

41 *Ann. chim. phys.*, iii (1816) 201.

42 *Ann. chim. phys.*, xv (1820) 386–95.

43 *Ann. chim. phys.*, x (1819) 395.

44 Berzelius, *Bref* (Uppsala, 1912–25), Vol. 2, Part iv, p. 12.

45 Petit died on 21 June 1820 at the age of 29.

46 John Davy, *Memoirs of the life of Sir Humphry Davy*, Vol. i (London, 1836) 470.

47 *Traité de physique*, Vol. i (Paris, 1816) 4–5.

48 E.g., Gay-Lussac, *Cours de chimie*, Vol. 1 (Bruxelles, 1828) 12.

49 E.g., Thenard, *Traité de chimie élémentaire*, 6th edn (Paris, 1834), Vol. v, 'Essai de philosophie chimique', especially pp. 415–17. Nevertheless, A. Baudrimont's *Introduction à l'étude de la chimie par la théorie atomique* (Paris, 1833) was dedicated to Thenard.

50 J. B. Dumas, *Leçons sur la philosophie chimique* (Paris, 1837) 290. For a discussion of Dumas' attitude to the atomic theory, see Gerd Buchdahl 'Sources of Scepticism in Atomic Theory', *British Journal for the Philosophy of Science*, x (1959–60) 120–34.

51 E.g., *Comptes Rendues de l'Académie des Sciences*, lxxxiv (1877) 1194.

52 R. Massain, *Chimie et chimistes*, 3rd edn (Paris, n.d.) 215. Massain emphasizes the antagonism of Sainte Claire Deville to the atomic theory.

53 *Procès-verbaux*, Vol. vi, 117 (2 December 1816).

54 A full account of Dalton's visits to Arcueil is given in W. C. Henry, *Memoirs of . . . John Dalton*, 1854, 164–8.

The great activity in chemistry, which was so characteristic of England in Dalton's time, had no counterpart in Austria. There had been, however, good teachers in this subject in the Universities of both Vienna and Prague since the introduction of chemical education by G. van Swieten in 1749. The textbooks of Nikolaus von Jacquin and his son, Joseph, were known beyond the borders

W Oberhummer

of Austria; that of Joseph von Jacquin was even translated into English, and in a short time (1799–1803) ran into three editions, under the title *Elements of chemistry*.

According to the regulations of the time, university instruction in Austria had to be given through approved textbooks; so such books offer us valuable insight into the content and treatment of of the material taught. The publication of the first volume of the fourth and last edition of Joseph von Jacquin's book (he was Professor of Chemistry and Botany in Vienna 1797–1838) came too near that of the *New system* (Part I) to contain any mention of Dalton.

But a few years later we find Joseph von Jacquin testifying to the high opinion in which he held Dalton. At Jacquin's wish, his former pupil and friend, Benjamin Scholz (later Professor of Chemistry in the Vienna Polytechnic) had written a textbook *Anfangsgrunde der Physik* specially for the chemistry school of the University of Vienna. Jacquin wrote a preface for this book, claiming that it had special value because it contained 'a comparison, not yet found in many books, of the doctrines of our famous contemporaries Berzelius and Dalton, regarding the quantitative relations in which bodies enter into chemical combination'. In the first edition (1816) of this book, Dalton is called 'the most important of present-day atomists', his theory praised as 'ingenious' but finally rejected because of its 'far too insecure basis'. Even in later editions (5th, revised by Anton Schrötter 1837) the 'dynamic' theory is preferred to the atomic theory. Accordingly, the law of multiple proportions is so treated in this book that the concept of atom is not used: the term 'atomic weight' ('called for brevity an atom') is merely given as a synonym, without further explanation, for the concept of 'combining weight', 'stoichiometric number', 'equivalent weight' etc.

The student of chemistry or physics of 1820, however, did not learn Dalton's name only in connection with the structure of matter, or the interpretation of chemical reactions. In the section on the atmosphere, extended notice was taken of Dalton's investigations, views and measurements. Dalton's law of partial pressures is mentioned, his grounds for the view that oxygen and nitrogen in the atmosphere are mixed and not in chemical combination are thoroughly treated. Even Dalton's measurements of the annual precipitation in Manchester and his estimate of the average annual rainfall in England, together with his copious table of the expansive force of water-vapour at all temperatures are given as illustrative examples in the first edition (1816) of Scholz's book.

The last edition of *Anfangsgrunde der Physik als Vorbereitung zum Studium der Chemie* appeared in 1837 after the death of Scholz, edited by Anton Schrötter (Professor of technical chemistry in the Vienna Polytechnic 1843–68; later well known for his studies of red phosphorus).

Joseph von Jacquin's textbook of general and practical chemistry was replaced in university teaching after 1836 by Ignaz Gruber's *Grundzugen der allgemeinen und medizinischen Chemie*. In this book, which was lectured from until 1848, Dalton already appears as an historical figure. In the introductory historical account of the development of chemistry Dalton is named together with Wenzel and Richter as a founder of stoichiometry.

We can say broadly, that Dalton's work was quite early appreciated in Austria, and by a large number of people, as may be seen from numerous articles in Gilbert's *Annalen der Physik*.

Nikolaus von Jacquin, to whom Dr Oberhummer has referred, Dr J Zemplen
played an important part in the development of chemistry teaching
at the famous mining school of Banska Stavnica (Selmecbánya, or
Schemnitz as it was called by most eighteenth-century French and
English writers). von Jacquin was of Dutch origin and worked
first as a physician in Vienna. He was appointed first professor at
Selmec (1766–9) before he got the chair of chemistry at Vienna.
He organized the teaching of chemistry very well indeed and
founded the world's first chemical laboratory for the use of students. Fourcroy, speaking at the foundation of the Ecole Polytechnique (1794), referred to Selmec as an outstanding example to
follow.

von Jacquin's successors at Selmec, together with Professor J.
Winterl at the University of Hungary, were more interested in
theoretical problems. von Jacquin, A. Ruprecht and Winterl had
their own, rather personal, versions of the atomic theory. Dalton's
original teachings were only really known and accepted in Hungary
from about 1830 onwards; in the first place through the works of
Berzelius.

Dalton and
Structural
Chemistry

John Dalton had a pictorial imagination. There was never anything shadowy or metaphysical about his atoms; they were (in Newton's phrase, which he often quoted) 'solid, massy and hard'; too small to see, but very real. This concreteness of the imagination proved to be Dalton's great strength as a chemist; for it so happened that chemistry in the nineteenth century thrived when it was naïve and pictorial, and languished when it tried to be abstract and subtle.

Already by about 1804 Dalton, in his notebooks (now lost) was trying to represent his theory to himself with the familiar pictures of compound atoms as collections of circles (standing for simple atoms) arranged in various patterns. By about 1810 this had gone so far as the construction of three-dimensional models of balls and sticks:

My friend Mr Ewart, at my suggestion, made me a number of equal balls, about an inch in diameter, about 30 years ago; they have been in use ever since, I occasionally showing them to my pupils. One ball had 12 holes in it, equidistant; and 12 pins were stuck in the other balls, so as to arrange the 12 around the one and be in contact with it. . . .[1]

Some of these models are preserved in the Science Museum, South Kensington. As the quotation shows, he used them for teaching purposes; certainly he never referred to them in print until his very late group of privately published papers in 1840. We shall examine later the use he made of them during his later years.

This primitive structural aspect of Dalton's atomic

theory was also recognized as early as 1808 by W. H. Wollaston. In his paper of that year. 'On super-acid and sub-acid salts' Wollaston could only foresee an explanation of some of his analytical results in terms of some future 'chemistry in space':

> I am further inclined to think, that when our views are sufficiently extended, to enable us to reason with precision concerning the proportions of elementary atoms, we shall find the arithmetical relation alone will not be sufficient to explain their mutual action, and that we shall be obliged to acquire a geometrical conception of their relative arrangement in all the three dimensions of solid extension.[2]

And he went on to speculate about some simple symmetrical arrangements, and to wonder whether the structure of an isolated molecule would be altered by packing in among others of the same type.

Thus at a very early stage, in the minds of Dalton and at least one of his contemporaries, there seems to have arisen the idea that molecules were structured entities, rather than mere collections of the requisite number of atoms. Neither Dalton nor Wollaston, of course, had any criteria for assigning one structure rather than another; and, in fact, from the time of the *New system* until his old age, Dalton did nothing to advance his pictorial ideas of molecules. Wollaston too, as we know, soon lost most of his faith in the atomic theory, and retreated into agnosticism and 'equivalents'. Given the state of the art at that time, and their relative lack of interest in organic chemistry, there was perhaps little that either could do; but chemists elsewhere were beginning to come to grips with the problem of *isomerism*.

Almost as soon as elementary analyses of fair accuracy became possible (say after 1800), chemists were faced with the paradox of two obviously different substances giving the same analytical results. Some of them did not hesitate to ascribe this to different arrangements of the atoms in space. Very often, however, their explanations were ill-founded and later abandoned, since their facts were wrong. Gay-Lussac, for example, who in 1814 was probably the first to invoke the 'structural' explanation, was using it to explain why acetic acid and cellulose had the same composition; the real answer is that they do not; his analyses were incorrect.[3] Another case, that of the two forms of hydrated stannic oxide (1816) has a more difficult explanation, involving polymorphism and slight differences of water content.[4] (The difficulty seems to have been dimly realized, for it was never allowed to become a crucial case). Chevreul in 1823 was nearer the mark in his studies of fats and long-chain fatty acids, for substances like these (even if not actually isomeric) give analytical figures which are very close together; he also used the 'structural' explanation.[5]

It was believed by Roscoe[6] that Dalton was also of this opinion regarding isomerism, and that he was indeed the first to express it, though only in a semi-public fashion. This belief was based on Roscoe's study of the Dalton notebooks; these are now lost to us, but judging from what little evidence remains, the verdict can only be one of Not Proven. A photograph of one of Dalton's lecture demonstration sheets (probably dating from 1811), has been published[7] in which the two proteins albumen and gelatin are pictured as different arrangements of C_2H_2NO:

albumen   gelatin

But the analyses (by Gay-Lussac) of albumen and gelatin are also given, and even by the most reckless standards of the time, these analyses are not identical; and indeed we are told that (in Dalton's notebook for October 1811) these two diagrams are reproduced, together with the analytical figures, but that albumen (C_3H_2NO) now has one carbon atom more than gelatin. This gives a better fit to the analyses, and makes one wonder (to say the least) whether the 'isomers' of the demonstration sheet were simply a careless error, either of Dalton or his draughtsman.

In 1826 the first genuine, well-founded case of isomerism was published by Liebig;[8] the facts were only established after several years of muddle and controversy. This was the isomerism of silver cyanate and silver fulminate (AgCNO). It was soon followed by the study of tartaric and racemic acids by Berzelius,[9] and perhaps most important of all, by Wöhler's discovery[10] that ammonium cyanate can readily be transformed into the isomeric urea. Berzelius indeed in 1830 introduced the word 'isomerism' to denominate this increasingly common event of different compounds having the same composition. We now encounter the paradox, however, that just as isomerism was being established as a fact, naïve atomism was entering on its mid-century decline, and the 'structural' explanation was falling out of favour.

The situation was complicated by the possibility that two compounds having the same analysis might be of the type $(ABC . . .)_n$, where n could have different integral values. These are not isomers in the modern sense, since their molecular weights are different. 'Polymerism' as Berzelius called it, is a perfectly valid explanation in many cases, and was generally accepted as being so for ethylene and isobutylene, which are $(CH_2)_2$ and $(CH_2)_4$ respectively. For the chemists of 1830 the great difficulty was that of the determination of molecular weights. For gases, it was agreed that molecular weight and vapour density stood in some kind of relationship, but since Avogadro's hypothesis was not generally accepted, it was not clear what the relationship was. For liquids and solids (the vast majority of chemical compounds) assignment of molecular weight was a matter of pure assumption. In face of this difficulty, it would have been possible to hold that polymerism was the universal explanation of isomerism; but few chemists did believe this. They felt that if $(ABC . . .)$ were a stable molecule, then $(ABC . . .)_n$ should spontaneously fall apart into n molecules of $(ABC . . .)$.

To a modern chemist it seems almost impossible to think of an explanation of isomerism which does not involve spatial arrangement of entities of some sort. Polymerism apart, the ingenuity of the 1830's devised two main non-structural explanations. The first was 'metamerism' in Berzelius' original meaning of the word. Atoms are assumed to combine in pairs, of opposite but not necessarily equal electric charge; these pairs can again combine in pairs of opposite charge, and so on, until the final molecule is electrically neutral.

In this way, complex molecules can be envisaged, having a kind of hierarchical structure, and one can imagine this hierarchy built up in different ways; thus in the simplest case ABCD:

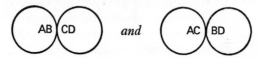

The second method of explaining isomerism was by the presence or absence of impurities. It was urged that certain impurities could have an almost magical effect on both the chemical and physical properties of a compound; the favourite analogy was that of the effect of traces of carbon in steel. Since the impurities could be imagined to be present in such small amounts as to defy the most sensitive analysis, this theory was difficult to confirm or refute experimentally.[11]

Despite the obvious (and frequently admitted) inadequacy of both these explanations, the naïve structural ideas of the early days of the atomic theory seem to have lingered on only in Scotland. The most striking example is the table of formulae used by Thomas Clark in his lectures to the Glasgow Mechanics' Institute in 1826–7; these have been preserved, quite by chance, in a book written much later by his friend J. J. Griffin.[12] Clark unfortunately gave no example of his treatment of isomers (it must be remembered that isomerism was hardly established fact in 1826); but formulae such as:

CH,H,H;CO,O;H   acetic acid
HO;CH,H;C,H,H,H   ethanol
Ch(CH,H,H,H;C)Ch   1,2 dichloroethane

can hardly be other than structural, in the sense of being attempts to draw a map of the molecule; although we do not know what kinds of combination were intended to be signified by the comma, the semicolon and the bracket. We do not know the origin of Clark's ideas, nor even how he was educated in chemistry at all. The two most prominent Scottish chemists of the 1820's were Andrew Ure and Thomas Thomson. Ure, an admirer of Davy, concerned himself very little with the atomic theory. Thomson's involvement with atomism needs no stressing, but his views on structure as expressed in his *History of chemistry* (1831) are much cruder than Clark's.[13] In this book he explained the supposed isomerism of acetic and succinic acids as due to differing arrangements of the atoms in the molecule, which might be pictured as:

acetic acid   succinic acid

(actually the two acids are not isomers at all, as Clark knew very well five years earlier!) Nevertheless, the crudity of Thomson and the strange sophistication of Clark give us tantalizing glimpses of what we must suppose to have been a climate of thought in Scotland favourable to naïve structuralism. It bore fruit in the next generation with the brilliant structure-theory paper of the unfortunate Couper, and with the distinguished work of Crum Brown; and, almost as interesting in their way, with the unorthodox structural fantasies of Macvicar and of Goodsir.

It may have been the influence of this Scottish school of thought, transmitted through his friend Thomson, that stirred Dalton's interest in structure again towards the end of his life. We are told of a three-dimensional formula for oxamide in a notebook of 1834; one atom each of carbon, hydrogen, nitrogen and oxygen arranged at the apices of a tetrahedron.[14] It is from this period that we have Dalton's well-known letter to Thomas Graham,[15] objecting to the new symbols of Berzelius; 'Berzelius's symbols are horrifying: a young student in chemistry might as soon learn Hebrew as make himself acquainted with them. They appear like a chaos of atoms. Why not put them together in some sort of order? Is not the *allocation* a subject of investigation as well as the weight? If one order is found more consistent than another, why not adopt it till a better is found?' This is certainly the programme for a structural organic chemistry, but the trouble was, of course, that no criteria had yet emerged for declaring one arrangement more 'consistent' than another; all Dalton could fall back on was a vague feeling that symmetry was important.

In the notebooks of the 1830's also, we find Dalton

toying with the idea of a 'vegetable atom' consisting of one atom each of carbon, hydrogen and oxygen (CHO), which he thought might be the fundamental 'building block' for biochemical synthesis.[16] But it is not until 1840 that we find him really coming to grips with structural concepts; twenty years ahead of his contemporaries in some respects, but twenty years too late to give them an authoritative lead. In the group of pathetic, rambling papers privately published in that year, we read of him actually using his ball and stick models, made so long ago, to solve chemical problems. In his paper on the phosphates[17] he uses them to eliminate possible formulae for hydrated salts; 'I do not believe that ever 23 or 24 atoms of water are around any other atom, either simple or compound. It is limited to 12 or 16 atoms in a crystal, at the most. I can collect 12 balls around one ball of the same magnitude, but no more'. It does not matter for the moment that this particular argument is wildly wrong; it is this *sort* of argument which has proved so fruitful in organic chemistry up to the present day, and is being used, at this moment, on countless laboratory benches.

Finally, in what was probably the last paper he ever wrote, 'On a new and easy method of analysing sugar', Dalton really thought he had found the key to the whole of organic chemistry. It was, of course, only the delusion of a sick old man, whose mental powers were waning; but an intellect like Dalton's is worth study even in its decline. In brief, he seems to have carried his speculations about the 'vegetable atom' (CHO) so far, that he was now thinking that *all* organic compounds were compounds of carbon and water in various proportions (the rôle of nitrogen and other elements was tacitly ignored). Furthermore, on dissolving an organic compound in water, Dalton thought he had discovered that the combined carbon would fit itself in between the particles of solvent, without adding to the volume; the only increase in volume would be due to the combined water. Thus the empirical formula of any organic compound could be found in the form $C_x'(HO)_y$. 'It is the greatest *discovery* that I know of next to the atomic theory' he wrote; and a little later; 'Now that I have found the *clue* to the theory of this kind of atoms, I have only to follow on the clue methodically.'

He went on to end the paper, and indeed his life's work, by giving an account of what he imagined to be the structural formulae of six organic compounds; sugar (sucrose), tartaric acid, acetic acid, oxalic acid, 'vinic acid' (i.e. racemic acid) and citric acid. It will suffice to repeat one of these.[18]

TARTARIC ACID

1 is the central atom of *charcoal*;
6 surrounding it of *oxygen, apart* from each other;
12 of *charcoal* and *hydrogen* in contact with each other;
in all 19 atoms to form an atom of *Tartaric* Acid

Clearly, if more chemists had been playing with balls and sticks in the same way as Dalton, the world would not have had to wait so long for the theory of structure. On the other hand, Dalton's imaginary formulae for tartaric acid and the rest illustrate very neatly two of the mental blocks which had to be removed before a viable structure theory could be conceived. First, the explicit care with which he separates atoms of the same element; as he wrote, 'No *contact* between oxygen and oxygen, charcoal and charcoal, and hydrogen and hydrogen, whatever; they having a *repulsion* to each other'. This fixed idea of the essential repulsion of like atoms was preventing, not only acceptance of Avogadro's hypothesis, but also of the concept of carbon atoms linked together in chains and rings, which is fundamental to the structure theory.

Secondly, when unlike atoms attract one another chemically, it is tacitly assumed that the attraction is exerted uniformly in all directions around the atoms. Now the great exemplar of a multiple system of bodies in stable equilibrium under an attraction of this kind is, of course, the solar system. So we find not only Dalton, but many other speculators about chemical structure, right up to the 1870's, feeling obscurely (rather than stating explicitly) that chemical compounds must be built according to a sun-and-planets model. One atom, like Dalton's atom of charcoal in all the examples he gives, must be a 'nucleus' about which all the other atoms are disposed. Couper is free from this prejudice; but it is implicit in Laurent's 'nucleus' ideas; it is implicit in Kekulé, with the central carbon atom of his 'marsh gas type'. It was perhaps no accident that Williamson in 1851, looking for a telling phrase to drive home his own concept of chemical structure, used the simile of the *orrery*:

[Formulae] may be used as an actual image of what we rationally suppose to be the arrangement of the constituent atoms in a compound, as an orrery is an image of what we conclude to be the arrangement of our planetary system.[19]

Dalton's paper on the analysis of sugar was so clearly the work of a failing man that it was tactfully ignored by his contemporaries; his structural conjectures started nothing. As we know, the structure theory was not achieved in Dalton's lifetime. When he died, and for many years after, the most influential chemists believed that knowledge of molecular structure would be for ever impossible. This belief rested on the positivist notion that all we could know of molecules was the products of their chemical reactions; and that during these reactions the structures of the reacting molecules would be disturbed in an unpredictable and random manner. But when this agnostic view faded, as it did after Kekulé and Couper had published their papers (1858), one important consequence was that agnosticism about Dalton's atoms faded with it. The triumph of structure theory (and it soon had its triumphs, not only scientific but industrial) was also the triumph of naïve Daltonian atomism among chemists. If you believe that a compound has a determinate structure, then you must admit some kind of reality to the units out of which that structure is built. To hide the atomic theory behind the word 'equivalents' is no longer enough.

Structure theory, as it turned out, required that the forces between chemically combining atoms should be directional, rather than simply generalized attraction. This, I think, implies that atoms themselves must be more complex than Peter Ewart's round wooden balls; but that is another story.

1 J. Dalton, *On a new and easy method of analysing sugar* (Manchester, 1840) 3. A photograph of these models is given by F. Greenaway (*Manchester Memoirs*, c. (1958/9) 1). A cruder model (if such it is) is illustrated by F. Jones (ibid., xlviii, No. 22 (1903/4) Plate IX).

2 W. H. Wollaston, *Phil. Trans. Roy. Soc.*, xcviii (1808) 96. Wollaston had some more elaborate 'atomic models' which are also in the Science Museum. The purpose of these was to illustrate *crystal* structure rather than *chemical* structure.

3 J. Gay-Lussac, *Annales de Chimie et de Physique*, xci (1814) 149.

4 Idem., ibid., i (1816) 32; J. J. Berzelius, ibid., v (1817) 149.

5 M. E. Chevreul, *Recherches chimiques sur les corps gras d'origine animale* (Paris, 1823) 3.

6 Sir H. E. Roscoe, *Report of the British Association* (1887) 17. The claim is reasserted by J. R. Partington, *A history of chemistry*, iii, 820; iv, 751.

7 H. F. Coward and A. Harden, *Manchester Memoirs*, lix (1914/15) No. 12, 42, 56 and Plate VII.

8 J. von Liebig, *Ann. Chim.*, xxxiii (1826), 207.

9 J. J. Berzelius, *Ann. Phys.*, xix (1830) 305.

10 F. Wöhler, ibid., xii (1828) 253.

11 There was a third explanation; it could be assumed that (in the simplest case) in the molecule AB there might be more than one interatomic distance for which AB would be stable. This clearly derives from the atomic theory of Boscovich.

12 J. J. Griffin, *The Radical theory in chemistry* (London, 1858) 5–8. Griffin used Clark's table as ammunition in a polemic of his own against Gerhardt.

13 T. Thomson, *The history of chemistry* (London, 1830–1) ii, 304–5.

14 Ref. 7, 43.

15 W. C. Henry, *Memoir of the life and scientific researches of John Dalton* (London, 1854) 124.

16 Ref. 7, 57.

17 J. Dalton, *On the phosphates* (Manchester, 1840) 6.

18 Some of these structures are depicted (in planar form) on lecture sheets of uncertain date (Ref. 7, Plate VII).

19 A. W. Williamson, *Quart. J. Chem. Soc.*, iv (1851) 351.

Yu I Solov'ev
and L P Petrov

*Russian Scientists
on Dalton's
Atomic Theory*

In the history of chemistry one is unlikely to find many examples of the prompt recognition of a new theory by a wide circle of scientists. The atomic theory of John Dalton is an unusual example of a new theory which overcame a certain silent resistance soon after its appearance, then found authoritative supporters who accepted it as the guiding principle in their experimental research. As Berzelius later wrote:[1]

I came to think that Dalton's numbers lacked that accuracy which is necessary for the practical application of his theory. I realized that above all it is necessary to determine with maximum accuracy atomic weights of the majority of elements; otherwise it can hardly be expected that the dawn of chemical theory will develop into long-awaited day. At that time this was the most important task of chemical research, and I devoted myself to this entirely.

In Mendeleev's opinion:[2]

the trend of the whole of modern chemistry was predetermined solely by the discoveries of Lavoisier and Dalton. In fact Lavoisier and Dalton may be put on the same footing as Copernicus and Kepler with respect to the chemical mechanics of the molecular world.

A number of favourable circumstances have already been mentioned in the literature of the history of chemistry[3] which contributed to the swift recognition of the new theory of Dalton. The roots of atomism go back to antiquity, and the fruit of this tree became ripe only in the atmosphere of quantitative research and the search for stoichiometric laws in chemistry. The atomic theory which was to explain these laws theoretically was taken up by all those who were on the main road of chemical development at that time. Therefore Dalton's theory fortunately escaped any prolonged period of intellectual digestion, and in 1808–12 it began at once to have an effect in chemistry, attracting the attention of scientists all over the world.

Yu I Solov'ev and L P Petrov

Russian Scientists on Dalton's Atomic Theory

The first reaction to the atomic theory of Dalton in Russia appeared in 1813; even at that early date it is referred to in Russian textbooks. For example F. Gise in his *General chemistry for teachers and students* (1813–1817) expounds the basic tenets of Dalton's theory. Gise was the first Russian scientist to apply the law of definite proportions in chemical research; this is clearly seen in his paper,[4] 'On chemical nomenclature and some other chemical and physical questions'.

In 1827, Professor A. A. Iovskiĭ of Moscow University published a book which is the first Russian treatise based on the atomic theory. Referring to practical applications of Dalton's doctrine, Iovskiĭ wrote:[5]

In outlining details of the atomic system it would be useful to illustrate by some examples the benefits which can be obtained if analysis is carried out on the basis of this theory and what advantage it has compared with the routine way of analysing by weight. In fact, carrying out an analysis according to the above system we reach a better understanding of the properties of substances and especially of the differences which are inherent in compounds formed from the same elements but in different proportions.

In this book chemical formulae are given of compounds known by that time, with their Latin names as well.

The significance of Dalton's theory for the progress of chemistry is also stressed by Iovskiĭ in other papers. In 1829 he wrote:[6] 'Chemistry, by discovering the correlation of invisible particles, developing new ideas and promoting applied research of various kinds, renders incalculable service to mankind.' In 1835 he published an article[7] in which a detailed description of Dalton's chemical theory was given. In it he pointed out that the introduction of this theory led to mathematical accuracy in chemical research. 'As a result, analysis by proportion and weight became possible, and the proportions are now so simple that any composition of matter can be described by this theory.'

**Yu I Solov'ev
and L P Petrov**

*Russian Scientists
on Dalton's
Atomic Theory*

In the western literature of the history of chemistry there are few references to the fact that Russian chemists were among the first who used atomic chemical equations in their textbooks.[8] Professor G. W. Osann of Dorpat University, in his textbook of theoretical chemistry (1827)[9] expressed the isolation of oxygen from mercuric oxide as

$$\overset{..}{Hg} = Hg + 2O$$

(in modern notation: $HgO_2 = Hg + 2O$).

In 1805–18 appeared the work of the outstanding Baltic physical chemist Theodor Grotthuss (1785–1822), in which it was clearly shown for the first time that atoms are electrical in nature:

Elementary atoms of water themselves acquire opposite electrical states (namely, oxygen − E, hydrogen + E). The idea of electrical states of elementary bodies interacting chemically is the main idea of all electro-chemistry. This fundamental idea was advanced by me in 1805,[10] which was a whole year before Sir Humphry Davy.[11]

Being a supporter of the atomic theory, Grotthuss considered electricity as one of the qualities inherent in matter. He was the first to apply the idea of opposite charges to separate micro-particles. As a result of his work, the concept of the motion of electrically charged particles through an electrolyte became generally accepted. Physico-chemical processes Grotthuss explained as electro-molecular exchange between different particles:

In my earlier works (1805 and 1807) which I first contributed to the literature, I demonstrated for the first time, and developed in later papers, the idea that all chemical phenomena may be described by polar electricity (galvanism of atoms).[12]

Thus Grotthuss enriched atomic theory with a new concept of fundamental importance.

In 1831 appeared the first edition of the *Fundamentals of pure chemistry* by G. H. Hess (G. I. Gess) of the St Petersburg Academy of Sciences, who enunciated the well-known thermochemical laws.[13] The whole book is based on Dalton's theory. As Hess wrote: 'Despite the fact that the atomic theory has not come into wide use, this is the language every chemist should speak'.[14] Hess made great use of chemical equations, which at that time were an innovation; most of his chemical reactions were expressed by atomic equations. The formation of ammonia from ammonium chloride and calcium oxide may be quoted as an example:

$$\overline{NH_4Cl} + \dot{Ca} \longrightarrow Ca\overline{Cl} + \overline{H} + \overline{NH}_3$$

The formation of hydrogen was expressed as follows:

$$\overline{H} + Fe \longrightarrow \dot{Fe} + \overline{H}$$

and the synthesis of urea:

$$\overline{NH}_3 + \dot{NCH} \longrightarrow C_2N_4H_8O_2$$

(Barred letters correspond to double atoms; the points represent oxygen atoms).

This textbook by Hess was adopted by educational institutions all over Russia as the main vehicle of instruction in chemistry. It was of no small significance in shaping the views of A. M. Butlerov and D. I. Mendeleev.

In 1840, in a ceremony at St Petersburg University, the 'grandfather of Russian chemists', A. A. Voskresenskiĭ made a speech 'On the progress of chemistry in modern times' in which he praised Dalton's theory:[15]

Dalton, an Englishman, was the first to assert that all the results obtained by Wenzel, Richter, Berzelius and himself could be summarized and expressed in a very simple and general way if the suggestion is accepted that matter consists of very small and indivisible particles. It should only be assumed that every type of matter has its own atoms, different for every type by weight, and possibly, shape. Then it would not be difficult to explain the observable differences between different bodies. It is not difficult to understand why the progress of chemistry was greatly influenced by this doctrine, and to what extent it made easier the tedious and often purely mechanical work necessary for analysis.

Between 1830 and 1840 there were several investigations by Russian chemists on the determination of atomic weights of various elements, and the establishment of the correct formulae of their compounds. Thus in 1842, the mining engineer I. V. Avdeev established the correct atomic weight of beryllium as 9·308 (H = 1) or 9·34 (o = 16) (present value Be = 9·013). Avdeev based his value on the assumption that beryllium oxide was BeO rather than Be_2O_3 as was generally supposed at the time.[16]

Intense propaganda and the popularization of Dalton's theory in Russia brought its results; the new generation of Russian chemists devoted itself to creative work aimed at the development and enrichment of the atomic theory. They came to the Congress of 1860 in Karlsruhe (Mendeleev, Zinin, Shishkov, Borodin, Lesinskiĭ, Natanson, Savich) as convinced and consistent partisans of the atomic-molecular theory of Dalton and Avogadro.[17] Mendeleev wrote with a feeling of pride that 'at the Congress it was pleasant to make sure that the new ideas which all young Russian chemists have long accepted got the upper hand over the old-fashioned concepts which were still strong among the chemists'.[18]

The theory of atomic-molecular 'mechanics' runs through the entire work of Mendeleev and Butlerov. It is impossible to understand chemical and physical processes without studying the motion and interaction of atoms in molecules. The periodic law of Mendeleev (1869) and the development of the theory of chemical structure by Butlerov from 1861 may be regarded as a climax of Dalton's theory. The whole formulation of the periodic law is based on Dalton's ideas:

> The periodic variation in the properties of elements depending on mass (or atomic weight) is different from other types of periodic function in that atomic weight does not increase continuously, but by leaps, i.e. between two neighbouring elements there can be no intermediate transitional elements (for example, $K = 39$, $Ca = 40$ or $Al = 27$, $Si = 28$, $C = 12$, $N = 14$ and so on). This means that the Periodic Law cannot be expressed by any algebraic continuous function. The Periodic Law has clearly shown that atomic mass does not rise continuously but by leaps, evidently directly connected with those leaps which Dalton revealed with the Law of Multiple Proportions.[19]

Outlining the origin of the concepts of atomic weight and valency, Mendeleev also refers to Dalton:

> Dalton's Law of Multiple Proportions (or the simplicity and integral nature of the number of atoms which make up the molecule) left us with only small numbers to deal with, of which it was much easier to gain an understanding.

In Mendeleev's opinion there were always inherent leaps, crisis points and limits in chemical phenomena.

The periodic law opened up a new field for thinking in natural philosophy, for in Mendeleev's view the concept of chemical elements was linked by new ties with Dalton's theory. From 1865 to 1887 he was developing a chemical theory of solutions, attempting to introduce atomic theory into this complicated subject. 'The great doctrine of Dalton of the atomic structure of matter has not yet been applied to explain the phenomena of solubility.' In such an application, Mendeleev hoped not only to achieve a harmonious chemical theory, but to find 'new stimuli for research'.[20] He thought it possible to relate solutions to atomic theory if only by introducing the concepts of association and dissociation, which in his opinion could determine the nature of solutions.

Yu I Solov'ev
and L P Petrov

*Russian Scientists
on Dalton's
Atomic Theory*

He wrote:[21]

In my mind solutions are not a field alien to atomic concepts. Just like familiar definite compounds, solutions can be characterized and explained by the same concepts as are widely used in the theory of mass interaction, of dissociation and of gases. At the same time, solutions are for me the most general example of chemical action caused by comparatively weak affinities, and therefore they are a most fruitful field for the further progress of chemical theory.

It is interesting to remember that almost eighty years ago (September 1887), Mendeleev came to Manchester, where he spoke to the British Association about his work on solutions.[22] See Plate IVb (facing p. 170).

When Ostwald's anti-atomic teaching began to be popular in the 1890's, it is not surprising that it was sharply criticized by Mendeleev and other leading Russian chemists and physicists (Stoletov, Beketov, Konovalov, Umov, Kablukov, Kurnakov and others). Mendeleev wrote:[23]

The last few years have seen a reaction against atomic-molecular teaching. Some scientists deny matter and say we know only energy. This (to my mind) scholastic view reminds me of that philosophy according to which nothing exists except 'I' because everything comes through my consciousness. Such notions are unlikely to be retained in healthy minds.

And later.[24]

If you take away from modern chemistry atomic concepts of the structure of matter, there will be no understanding of the multitude of firmly established facts, and a rough empiricism will follow.

A way out from the mechanical system peculiar to Dalton's atomism was sought by many scientists of the nineteenth century, Mendeleev among them. However, in the new discoveries (radio-activity, the electron) he failed to resolve the problems arising from the concept of the restricted divisibility of matter. He remained convinced that the atom was indivisible, and that chemical elements do not transform one into the other. Such ideas had soon to be abandoned under pressure of the discoveries of 1895–1913.

At the beginning of the present century, N. S. Kurnakov developed the idea of the unity of continuity and discontinuity as the two forms of organization of matter; in 1912–14 he introduced the concepts of 'daltonides' and 'berthollides'. If in chemical reactions the various components of a system produce compounds of invariable composition, this (as Kurnakov showed) will appear in the composition-property diagram as a singular or Dalton point. Compounds produced in this way are subject to the laws of constant composition and multiple proportions; he named them daltonides in honour of Dalton. Compounds of indefinite composition were named berthollides in honour of Berthollet. These compounds (such as the γ-phase in the system Tl–Bi) cannot be characterized by singular points, as their composition changes with change in the equilibrium factors of the system.[25]

As Kurnakov wrote, 'Existence of individuals of variable composition widens the horizon of the concept of the chemical compound'. The study of composition-property diagrams proved to be essential to working out the basic concepts of physico-chemical analysis.

The period covered by this paper relates almost entirely to pre-Revolutionary Russia; Kurnakov, indeed, was one of the first Soviet Academicians. Soon after the October Revolution, science was given first priority in Russia, and began to develop very quickly; this resulted later in our achievements in space, in atomic energy, and other fields. But history of science also enjoys popularity, and the leading Soviet organization in this domain is the Institute of History of Natural

Sciences and Technology. It is interesting to remember that the head of this Institute (Professor Kedrov, corresponding member of the Soviet Academy of Sciences) is the leading Soviet expert on John Dalton.

Thus in Russia from 1813 onwards the theory of Dalton found numerous supporters. The scientific atmosphere imbued with materialistic teaching on atoms gave birth to important discoveries. In the works of Butlerov, Mendeleev and Kurnakov, Dalton's theory is enriched with fundamental new propositions. The theory of chemical structure and the periodic law set the seal on the age of Daltonian atomism, and prepared the ground for the majestic edifice of modern chemistry.

May we end with another quotation from Mendeleev? In 1889 the London Chemical Society invited him to deliver the Faraday Lecture, an invitation which he regarded as a mark of friendship and of high esteem.

If from me, the Russian [he said][26] they wish to hear a scientific lecture, that means they wish for a direct *rapprochement* in the field which alas! remains the only public one following the path of world-wide peaceful development. It is my personal conviction that any *rapprochement* between Englishmen and Russians should promote world progress, as both nations become strong, one on the Continent, the other on the sea, with nothing to divide them.

Notes

1 J. J. Berzelius, *Lehrbuch der Chemie* (Dresden and Leipzig, 1845) iii, 1161.

2 D. I. Mendeleev, *Principles of chemistry* (St Petersburg, 5th edn, 1889) 163, 23.

3 H. E. Roscoe and A. Harden, *A new view of the origin of Dalton's atomic theory* (London, 1896); J. Dalton, *Sbornik rabot po atomistike* (Leningrad, 1940); L. K. Nash, *Isis*, xlvii, 101 (1956).

4 F. Gise, *Ann. de physique*, 1, 95 (1815).

5 A. A. Iovskiĭ, *Khimicheskie uravnenia s opisaniem raslichnykh sposobov opredelat' kolichestvennoe soderzhanie khimicheskikh veshchestv* (Moscow, 1827) 101–2.

6 Idem., *Khozhaistvennaya Khimia* (Moscow, 1829) 3.

7 Idem., *Uchenie zapiski Moskovskogo Universiteta*, iv, 60–4 (1835).

8 G. V. Bykov and V. I. Kurennoĭ, *Voprosy istorii estestvoznania i tekhniki* (Moscow, 1957) 172; V. I. Kurennoĭ, *Ocherk razvitia khimicheskoĭ atomistiki* (Moscow, 1960).

9 G. W. Osann, *Handbuch der theoretischen Chemie* (Dorpat, 1827).

10 T. Grotthuss, *Phil. Mag.*, xxiv, 330 (1806).

11 Idem., *Physische-chemische Forschungen*, i, 113–15 (Nuremberg, 1820).

12 Idem., *Schweigger's J.*, xxxi, 492 (1821).

13 Yu. I. Solov'ev, *German Ivanovich Gess* (Moscow, 1962).

14 G. I. Gess, *Osnovania chistoĭ khimii*, 9 (St Petersburg, 1831).

Notes   **15** A. A. Voskresenskiĭ, *Zhurnal Ministerstva narodnogo prosvechenia*, vi, 148 (1840).

16 I. V. Avdeev, *Pogg. Ann.*, lvi, 101 (1842); S. A. Pogodin, *Trudy Instituta istorii estestvoznania i tekhniki*, vi, 125 (1955).

17 M. G. Faershtein, *Istoria uchenia o molekule v khimii* (Moscow, 1961).

18 D. I. Mendeleev, *Nauchnoe nasledstvo*, ii, 87 (Moscow, 1951).

19 Idem., *Izbrannye sochinenia*, iii, 202 (Moscow, 1934).

20 Ref. 2, 82.

21 Ref. 19, 211.

22 *J. Chem. Soc.*, 778 (1887).

23 Ref. 2 (9th edn, Moscow, 1927) i, 315.

24 D. I. Mendeleev, *Periodicheskiĭ zakon* (Seria 'Klassiki nauki' Moscow, 1958) 577.

25 N. S. Kurnakov, *Vvedenie v fiziko-khimicheskiĭ analiz* (4th edn, Moscow, 1940).

26 D. I. Mendeleev, *Dva Londonskikh chtenia* (St Petersburg, 1895).

The Unsolved Problem of 'Daltonism'

The first communication which Dalton ever made to the Literary and Philosophical Society of Manchester was a paper read on 31 October 1794, entitled, 'Extraordinary Facts relating to the Vision of Colours: with Observations by Mr John Dalton'.[1] Dalton had discovered that he saw colours differently from other people and his paper was the first serious study on colour deficiency to be published. So great was the stir produced by Dalton's defect that for a long time this visual infirmity was known, to his amusement, as 'Daltonism'. I trust my use of the term on this occasion will not be regarded as a mark of disrespect for the great man.

What is Daltonism? Rather than give a textbook answer in terms of wavelength discrimination and colour mixture curves, I would prefer to approach the problem as Dalton had to do, unaware at first that his colour vision differed from that of most other people and knowing very much less than we now know about the visual processes. This may, indeed, be of some help to others who are colour defective, for it must be a strange experience when you discover for the first time that your world of colour is very different from your neighbour's.

Dalton first became convinced of the peculiarity of his vision at the age of twenty-six and as a result of observations on a pink geranium. This is what he reported:

The flower was pink, but it appeared to me almost an exact

sky-blue by day; in candle-light, however, it was astonishingly changed, not having then any blue in it, but being what I called red, a colour which forms a striking contrast to blue. Not then doubting but that the change of colour would be equal to all, I requested some of my friends to observe the phenomenon; when I was surprised to find that they all agreed, that the colour was not materially different from what it was by day-light, except my brother, who saw it in the same light as myself. This observation clearly proved, that my vision was not like that of other persons; and, at the same time, that the difference between day-light and candle-light, on some colours, was indefinitely more perceptible to me than to others.

This passage could serve as a text for the remainder of my paper and I certainly want to comment on it in some detail. First, we have to remind ourselves that Dalton had to use the same vocabulary of colour names as everyone else; he had no other. Yet the range of colours that he could see was much restricted and he was almost certainly quite unaware of what redness really looked like. We can only speculate on why he chose to describe the appearance of the geranium in candlelight as red. Perhaps it appeared dark brown to him and since he was very insensitive to red wavelengths, he would tend to regard redness and darkness as synonymous.

Next, I think we have to look at Dalton's observation in the context of modern studies on the colour-rendering properties of light sources. You will know that lighting engineers have paid much attention during the last ten or twenty years to the development of fluorescent lamps. In the early days these lamps tended to make our faces and our food look too green, partly because of the mercury lines and partly owing to the lack of a good red phosphor. Now the lamps have been improved and their colour rendering performance in comparison with daylight can be rated in terms of a colour-rendering index.

Yet the fluorescent lamp is not the only light source whose spectral distribution differs from daylight. The candle is another, as shown in Fig. 24. Yet the candle has rarely given rise to criticism and is, indeed, the 'housewife's choice' as the light source for a dinner party. We like the warm colour of the light, while the main colour distortions tend to be corrected in the eye. Visual adaptation produces a measure of colour constancy.

But not always. Fig. 25 shows the spectral reflection curve of a cloth which looks quite green to me in daylight, yet very brown by candlelight. The high red content of the candlelight and the high red reflection of the cloth combine to produce a total red component which outweighs the reflection in the green part of the spectrum, even though the sensitivity of my eye, which is reasonably normal, is quite low at the far red end of the spectrum (Fig. 26). Should not a similar change occur when I look at a pink geranium by candlelight? The geranium also has two main reflection bands, one

W D Wright

The Unsolved Problem of 'Daltonism'

Spectral distribution of candlelight and a typical phase of daylight.   **Figure 24**

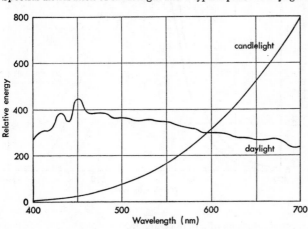

Spectral reflection of a cloth which appears green in daylight and brown in candlelight.   **Figure 25**

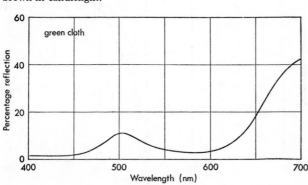

at the blue and one at the red end of the spectrum, as shown in Fig. 27. However, the breadth of the red reflection band ensures that there is sufficient red reflection at wavelengths to which my eye is still sensitive for the redness not to be swamped by the blue, even in daylight. Conversely, while the geranium will admittedly look redder in candlelight, the height and breadth of the blue reflection band ensures that sufficient of the

Figure 26   Spectral sensitivity curves for a normal subject and a protanope.

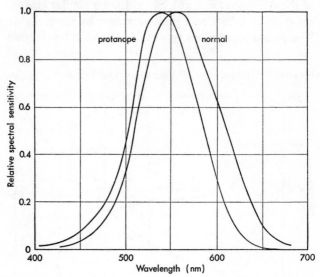

Figure 27   Spectral reflection of a pink geranium.

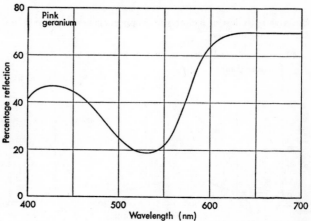

small amount of blue radiation from the candle is reflected to retain the pink hue of the geranium.

For Dalton, however, the situation was different. From the account he gave of his vision he was certainly what we would classify now as a protanope. Fig. 26 also shows the spectral sensitivity of this type of observer and the main difference from the normal is a reduced sensitivity at the red end of the spectrum. It follows that the red reflection of the geranium can make very little impact on the eye of a protanope when seen in daylight, hence the blue reflection becomes the dominant component. Yet when seen by the light of the candle, with its deficiency of blue energy and excess of red, the relative contributions are reversed and the protanope sees the geranium as 'red' (in inverted commas!). In a sense, the sharper sensitivity of the protanope makes him more critical of the proportion of red light in the mixture.

Conversely, if Dalton had had the piece of green cloth of Fig. 25 available for his experiments, I think he himself would have seen no change in its colour in going from daylight to candlelight, since the high reflection in the far red would in this case have fallen outside his sensitivity range.

It is an interesting commentary on Dalton's scientific caution that he only became convinced of his peculiarity of vision after he had made this experiment with the geranium. He had previously been aware of confusion in the naming of colours, but it required this positive demonstration of an effect which he could see and other people could not, to persuade him that here was a problem worthy of investigation.

Two further comments can be made on this initial quotation from Dalton's paper. His discovery that his brother's vision was the same as his own made it highly probable that their peculiarity of vision was hereditary. This he subsequently confirmed when he extended the range of his inquiries and found other families with brothers who were similarly affected. The other comment to be made is that there is nothing in these first observations to suggest that his vision was deficient relative to normal vision and not merely different. Rather the reverse, in fact, as he was more critical of illuminant changes than the normal.

His deficiency was revealed, however, in his description of the spectrum. He lists the six main hues seen by the normal as red, orange, yellow, green, blue and purple, whereas he saw only two distinct hues, yellow, and blue, with purple as a possible third. Curiously enough, he makes no reference to the presence of a white or neutral point in his spectrum although it must have been there. He had very little sensitivity to the red wavelengths, but what little he could see of them, together with the orange, yellow and green wavelengths, all fell within that part of the spectrum which he labelled 'yellow'. This clearly represented a major loss of colour perception. Other examples of colour confusion which he quotes are the similarity of a green laurel leaf and a stick of red sealing-wax, a dark brown woollen cloth which looked black, and blood which looked like the colour called bottle-green.

All these and other observations which he records make it clear, as I have said, that he was a protanope. Fig. 26 has illustrated one of the characteristics of this type of observer. Another characteristic is that with a trichromatic colorimeter, a protanope can do all his colour matching with two controls instead of three. This is why he is classified as a dichromat. We can also, with modern optical equipment, specify his colour confusions in precise colorimetric terms.[2]

Yet I would judge that given the knowledge of optics and vision at the end of the eighteenth century, and the apparatus available at that time, Dalton made an extremely penetrating and accurate study of his colour vision. Indeed, it is certain that many colour defectives of the twentieth century know far less about their colour vision than Dalton did in the eighteenth.

Dalton was, however, less successful in producing an explanation of his defect, since he had the idea that it was due to a blue coloration in the vitreous humour of his eye. Admittedly such a coloration would have turned a pink geranium blue in daylight, but it would have had no effect on the red, orange, yellow and green colours in the spectrum other than to reduce their intensity. Here Dalton was less critical than he should have been. Post-mortem examination of his eyes finally disproved this theory.

In the meantime, Thomas Young came nearer to the

truth. In 1802 he put forward the suggestion[3] that the retina contains three vibrating systems which respond to the principal colours in the spectrum. In 1807[4] in a reference to Dalton's colour defect, he wrote that Dalton 'thinks it probable that the vitreous humour is of a deep blue tinge . . . it is much more simple to suppose the absence or paralysis of those fibres of the retina, which are calculated to perceive red'. Red, incidentally, was one of the principal colours postulated by Young, the other two were green and violet. Little notice, however, was taken of Young's suggestion for nearly fifty years. Then it was resuscitated by Helmholtz[5] who, together with Maxwell[6] and Grassman,[7] put it on a more formal and quantitative basis. In this form it became known as the Young-Helmholtz three-components theory.

I need hardly remind you, I think, that theories of colour vision have been a hot-bed of controversy for very many years. When so little is known about so much, this is hardly surprising. I would have liked to avoid getting caught up in this controversy in this paper, yet at the same time I feel impelled to show how neatly Dalton's type of defect came to be explained on the Young-Helmholtz theory. To do this, I must first summarize as briefly as I can some of the basic facts of colour mixture and matching.

With most observers colours can be matched by an additive mixture of red, green and blue radiations. If the colours in the spectrum are matched with a suitable form of trichromatic colorimeter,[8] it is possible to derive spectral mixture curves showing the amounts of red, green and blue stimuli required to match each wavelength in the equal-energy spectrum. If the Young-Helmholtz theory were correct, it should be possible to derive from such measurements a set of curves which correspond to the spectral sensitivities of Young's three vibrating systems. One set that has been proposed[9] is shown in Fig. 28.

These curves, of course, refer to a person with good colour vision, whom we describe as a normal trichromat. Observers like Dalton, on the other hand, can do all their colour matching using only two knobs on a colorimeter instead of the usual three. They then produce a set of dichromatic mixture curves[10] which

J D—Y

consist, in the case of the protanope, simply of the blue
and green curves of Fig. 28. The red curve is missing,
as anticipated by Young. This explains also why the
overall sensitivity curve of the protanope is lower at the
red end of the spectrum in comparison with the normal,
as we saw in Fig. 26.

These are basic experimental facts from which we
can also deduce which colours are confused by the
protanope. One way to define a colour is on the Maxwell colour triangle. This consists of an equilateral
triangle in which the red process is located at one
corner, the green at another and the blue at the third.
Any point within the triangle will then correspond to a
colour which stimulates the three processes in proportion to the distances of the point from the three sides
of the triangle. The triangle thus represents a kind of
colour chart for the normal trichromat. Suppose, however, we have an observer such as a protanope whose
red process is missing. The colours he sees are the
result of the stimulation of the green and blue processes
alone. Now for colours which lie on a straight line
passing through the red corner of the triangle, the
proportion of green to blue stimulation will be the

Figure 28   A possible set of spectral sensitivity curves for the three receptor
processes of the Young-Helmholtz theory. (Thomson & Wright.)

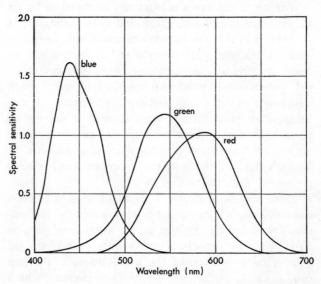

same. Hence all the colours lying on such a line will appear the same to a protanope and therefore be confused by him. In fact, there will be a family of lines radiating from the red corner of the triangle which are the loci of confusion colours for the protanope.

This deduction was first made by Helmholtz in 1867,[11] but it was some seventy years later before Pitt[10, 12] in 1935 first measured the loci for the protanope and confirmed their convergence on the red corner of the diagram. The loci as plotted in the C.I.E. chromaticity chart,[13] a modern version of the colour triangle based on rectangular co-ordinates, are shown in Fig. 29.

This diagram does two things. It summarizes the kind of mistakes to which the protanope is liable and which Dalton had to describe in words or by reference to particular objects such as sealing wax and laurel leaves. It also provides convincing evidence that protanopia is

W D Wright

The Unsolved Problem of 'Daltonism'

The loci of colours that are confused by the protanope.

Figure 29

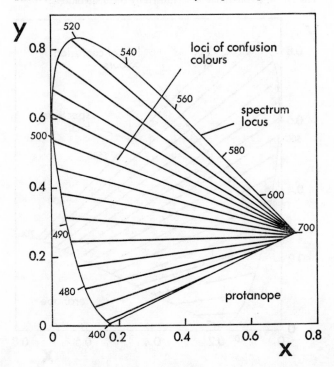

indeed due to the absence of the red process, the point of convergence of the loci defining indirectly the colour sensitivity of the missing process.

It may be useful at this stage to summarize what we know about the two other types of dichromat, the deuteranope and the tritanope. The tritanope is very rare but I was able some years ago to study a number of cases.[14] Their colour confusions are quite different from the protanope, as can be seen from Fig. 31. In this case the confusion loci converge to the blue corner of the chromaticity chart, which is again a compelling indication that the defect is due to the absence of the blue process. The cause of deuteranopia is more ambiguous. The confusion loci for this defect as measured by Pitt[12] are shown in Fig. 30. Their convergence to a more remote point of the chromaticity chart could be explained as due to the fusion of the red and green processes and this would seem to me a quite tenable hypothesis.

Figure 30 The loci of colours that are confused by the deuteranope.

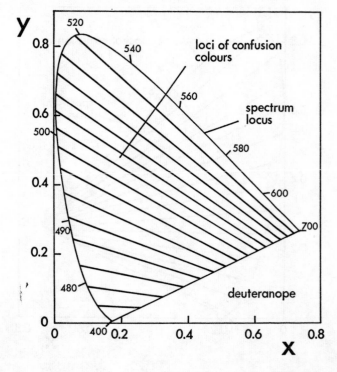

It might seem, then, as if we have nearly solved the problem of dichromatism, but this is very far from the truth. These visual observations may give us a clue to what is happening, but the data have still to be interpreted in terms of the biological processes of the retina and visual pathway. The genetics of colour deficiency have also to be unravelled. Why, for example, do protanopia and deuteranopia each affect some one per cent or so of the male population and a much smaller percentage of the female population, whereas tritanopia affects the male and female population equally but only at an estimated frequency of one person in 25,000.[14] I am not competent to discuss the details of these genetic patterns, but a recent study by Kalmus[15] summarizes modern thinking in this field. We must also note that there is a further six per cent of the male population, the so-called anomalous trichromats, who have some loss of colour discrimination and are intermediate in type and degree of defect between

The loci of colours that are confused by the tritanope.   **Figure 31**

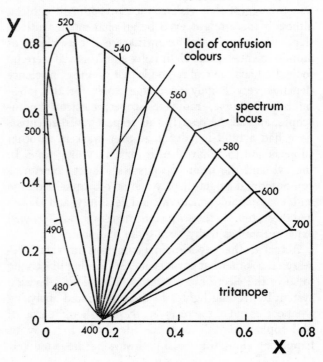

the normal trichromats and the dichromats. However, since Dalton was a dichromat, I am concerning myself here solely with the dichromats.

The possibility that there might be more than one type of colour defect does not seem to have occurred to Dalton. He was in touch with nearly twenty persons whose vision, he said, was like his, yet they could not all have been protanopes. His comment on their individual differences was that 'from a great variety of observations made with many of the above-mentioned persons, it does not appear to me that we differ more from one another than persons in general do'. Yet if his group included some deuteranopes, as was almost inevitable, they would hardly have described a pink geranium as sky blue.

In a moment we must consider the contribution that is being made to solving the problem of Daltonism by direct studies of the retina and visual pathway. Yet you may wonder, as I do, why so little progress has been made on the purely visual side since the time of Dalton and Young. Compare the spectacular developments in atomic and nuclear physics in the same period. I hesitate to suggest that vision is a more difficult subject, although there might even be an element of truth in that. No doubt visual scientists are not as clever as atomic scientists, but Helmholtz and Maxwell were no fools. Perhaps the real reason is that progress in science depends very largely on having tools for the job— bubble chambers, radio telescopes, electron microscopes, and all the rest. In this respect visual scientists have had a built-in advantage over workers in other subjects and they have had it for a very long time. In the eye and the brain we possess a light detector, a computer and a data-display system of exquisite design and incomparable sensitivity and flexibility, and Dalton had these, too. So the scope for progress in purely visual experiments has really been quite marginal.

Actually, the experimental situation in visual research is a somewhat curious one. It is rather like trying to solve the electronic mysteries of a colour television system by feeding light into the camera and analysing what comes out at the receiver. By pure thought a visual philosopher may develop his ideas of what may be happening along the visual pathways but he is unlikely to penetrate much further into the system than Young did, which was not very far. It is only through painstaking research into the minutiae of the biological processes that real progress is being made.

The primary question to be answered is 'How do the retinal receptors work?' Not so long ago we tended to think of them as if they were minute test tubes filled with a light-sensitive liquid which bleached in the light and re-formed itself in the dark. Certainly there is light-sensitive material in the retina and Dartnall,[16] who has been most active in this field in this country, has extracted many different photo-chemical substances from a wide variety of retinae. At least there is no difficulty in postulating substances with absorption maxima ranging in wavelength from 440 to 580 nm such as would be required to give the colour sensitivities represented in Fig. 28. But do they actually occur in the human retina?

The trouble is that the retinal receptors are very small, very light-sensitive and impossible to examine *in situ* in the living human eye. Recently, however, the micro-spectrophotometer has been used by Marks, Dobelle and MacNichol[17] and by Brown and Wald[18] to measure the spectral absorption of individual cones in a human retina kept active for some hours after death. The evidence which this technique is yielding tends to confirm completely Young's concept of three types of colour receptor, but for the moment we must receive the results with some caution. Apart from the biological hurdles to be overcome, there are optical difficulties as well. As Enoch[19] has reminded us, the use of microscope objectives with adequate resolution to image a spot of light on a single receptor necessarily involves numerical apertures giving a much greater cone of light than the retinal receptors can accept. Some of the energy must therefore spill over into neighbouring receptors. It may also be necessary to take account of the energy distribution within the receptor when treated as a waveguide. Comparison between measurements made along the axis of a receptor and when lying on its side may help to clarify some of these issues, but it is as well to be realistic about the problems to be solved. Nevertheless, this is potentially the most direct and convincing technique yet devised for confirming the existence of separate colour receptors in the retina and even for demonstrating that there are three types in the normal retina but only two in the protanope's.

Another tool that is yielding most important information is the electron microscope. If the test-tube concept of a receptor were required to be given a further death-blow, the laminated structure shown in Plate V (facing p. 171) should be sufficient. The functions of this structure are not yet clear, but perhaps it exposes the light-sensitive substance to the more ready absorption of light quanta. Or perhaps it serves to amplify the response when a light quantum has been absorbed.

When the question about the receptors has been answered, the next question to be asked is 'What happens to the signals after they leave the receptors?' Here Pedler[20] has been outstanding in this country in his use of the electron microscope to reveal an immensely complex network of very fine processes running along the synaptic layers. Again, we can only hazard a guess about their visual function, but it looks very much as if they may be acting as a system of information coding or data processing, perhaps concerned with the enhancement of detail and contrast, perhaps, too, with colour discrimination. A schematic network which Pedler has deduced is shown in Fig. 32.

These processes would appear to offer infinite opportunity for the colour signals to become confused, yet in some way which for the moment is beyond our understanding, their identity is retained as they travel across the retina. In fact, I doubt very much whether the classical types of colour defect originate at the synapses, since their characteristics are too clear-cut and too stable to be associated with such a diffuse network. At least protanopia and tritanopia must surely have their origin at the receptor level, if not deuteranopia. On the other hand, it would be foolish to expect all abnormalities of colour vision to fit neatly into the recognized types of dichromat and anomalous trichromat. From time to time we must expect to encounter other aberrations and random variants of the colour process, some of which may well develop from distortions in Pedler's network.

In all this, we must not forget that seeing is a con-

322

tinuous process and that temporal factors are at work. The neurophysiologist has supplied us with much information about the pattern of nerve impulses generated under a variety of conditions of light stimulation of the retina, and recordings made from cells in the lateral geniculate nucleus of the macaque monkey, for example, are yielding highly suggestive clues on the coding of colour information. In a very recent paper by De Valois, Abramov and Jacobs,[21] the responses from

The structural network of the vertebrate retina as deduced by Pedler. *R*—receptors, *H*—horizontal cells, *B*—bipolar cells, *A*—emacrine cells, *CF*—centrifugal fibres, *G*—ganglion cells.

Figure 32

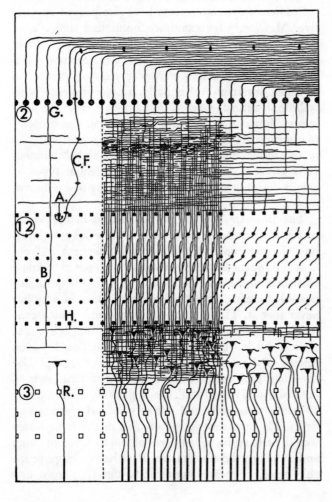

147 cells in the lateral geniculate nucleus have been recorded when the eye has been exposed to flashes of monochromatic light of various wavelengths. The cells were found to divide into two general classes, one class apparently responsible for the transmission of intensity information, the other class for colour. The latter responded by excitation or inhibition according to the wavelength, and were coupled in opponent pairs by their response to red and green, and yellow and blue. This certainly suggests that the colour information may be transmitted to the visual cortex in accord with Hering's opponent colour theory.[22] Failure in the coding system at this point in the visual pathway could be yet another possible cause of Daltonism.

Studies of eye movements have also proved suggestive. McCree,[23] for example, found that under conditions of very steady fixation, he lost much of his power to discriminate between two colours in a bipartite field when they were accurately adjusted to be of equal luminance. Similarly, in experiments with stabilized retinal images, Ditchburn[24] and his colleagues found a progressive reduction in the capacity to discriminate colours as the fine scanning movements of the retinal mosaic were minimized and eliminated. It is unlikely, however, that the congenital types of colour defect arise from any abnormality of eye movements.

The ultimate mystery, of course, is in the visual cortex. It is quite beyond our comprehension to know how the sensations of redness and greenness, yellowness and blueness, are generated. We do not even know what they are. However hard I try, I find it quite impossible to explain what redness is to someone who has never seen it. This is a unique appearance which cannot be described by reference to anything else. Yet Dalton did his best to describe the relation between certain of the colours which he saw. For example, he says that 'pink seems to be composed of nine parts of light blue and one of red'. He is speaking here in terms of colour sensations and not of coloured pigments or lights. My own description of pink in the same terms would perhaps be seven parts of red to three of blue, and although these estimates must have a large probable error, they are significantly different from one another. So these subjective descriptions do have some meaning. Yet having said that, I must immediately qualify my remark by reminding you that Dalton's red may have been like my yellow or my green!

I suppose from the philosophical point of view, this attempt to enter the private visual world of a person with a different visual system from one's own, is the most fascinating part of the whole business. Certainly when I read Dalton's paper I have the impression that this is what really fascinated him, rather than the cause of his abnormality. To me, one of the most interesting questions is whether the visual cortex of a colour defective person could generate redness and greenness and blueness if only the right types of signal were being delivered along the optic nerve. To judge from cases reported in the literature of subjects who have appeared to be colour defective in one eye and normal in the other,[25] the answer is 'Yes', but they may not be typical of subjects who are colour defective in both eyes.

In concluding this paper, I would like to turn from these high-level speculations to more practical issues. Dalton refers to the difficulties his colour defect caused him in his botanical studies, but I doubt whether those of us with normal colour vision are as fully aware as we should be of the many embarrassments which face colour defectives. We take good care of our own skins by demanding that they shall not drive our trains, fly our aeroplanes or pilot our ships. Yet we rarely match these prohibitions by giving positive guidance to colour defective children about their future career.

It might be no bad thing if one outcome of these celebrations were the establishment of a Dalton Society for Dichromats. The first item on its agenda would be to alert school teachers to the fact that in any class of twenty-five boys, two of them are likely to have poor colour vision. These may have trouble in understanding coloured diagrams and illustrations, in deciphering contour maps, sometimes even in reading coloured print, certainly in carrying out some experiments in chemistry. The second item on the agenda would be to give advice to careers masters. Perhaps I have become unusually sensitive on this matter, but one of the more distressing sides of my work is to have to report, as I have had to do on several occasions recently, that a man is colour defective, knowing that this means he will lose his job. Proper vocational guidance could so easily prevent such situations arising.

Finally, there are two points of some curiosity in Dalton's paper to which I must refer. Under a section headed *Miscellaneous observations*, Dalton records:

Colours appear to me much the same by moon-light as they do by candle-light.

Colours viewed by lightning appear the same as by day-light; but whether exactly so, I have not ascertained.

Colours seen by electric light appear to me the same as by day-light. That is, pink appears blue, etc.

That was in 1794 and almost a hundred years had to elapse before electric light as we know it to-day became available. I have to thank my friends at the Science Museum for the solution to this conundrum. Among Joseph Priestley's many contributions to science were experiments on static electricity. He described these in a book entitled *The history and present state of electricity, with original experiments*, a fifth edition of which appeared in the same year, 1794, in which Dalton read his paper. It is clear from this book that 'electric light' was the term commonly used to describe the light from electric sparks and indeed Priestley has a section entitled 'Observations on the Colours of Electric Light' in which he studied with a prism the spectral composition of the light from a spark discharge.

The other curiosity concerns the following extract from a section headed *Characteristic facts of our vision*:

Coats, gowns, etc. appear to us frequently to be badly matched with linings, when others say they are not.

This is odd, because dichromats usually accept matches made by the normal as correct. In fact, this is one of the key observations from which we deduce that dichromatism is a reduced form of trichromatism.

Probably the linings and outer fabric never were an exact colour match but merely had the same dominant hue. I am indebted to Mrs Lesley Ginsburg of the Victoria and Albert Museum for information about the clothes of that period and it is clear that the linings would have been of different material and texture and may have been both lighter and paler than the outer cloth. It is surprising, though, that Dalton found this difference so striking that he described it as a 'bad match'. Perhaps in the less colourful world of the dichromat, lightness and texture acquire a heightened significance. If the hue of the coat and lining were not particularly conspicuous to Dalton because of his colour defect, this may have accentuated their lack of harmony in other respects. This is pure speculation, but colour harmony might be another item on the agenda for our Dalton Society for Dichromats!

Notes

1 Dalton, 'Extraordinary Facts relating to the Vision of Colours: with Observations by Mr John Dalton' (read in October 1794), *Manchester Memoirs*, v (1798) 28–45.

2 W. D. Wright, *Researches on normal and defective colour vision* (London, 1946).

3 T. Young, 'On the Theory of Light and Colours', *Phil. Trans. Roy. Soc.*, xcii (1802) 12–48.

4 Idem., *Lectures on natural philosophy* (London, 1807) ii, 315.

5 H. v. Helmholtz, 'On the Theory of Compound Colours', *Philosophical Magazine* (Ser. 4) iv (1852) 519–34.

6 J. C. Maxwell, 'On the Theory of Compound Colours, and the Relations of the Colours of the Spectrum', *Phil. Trans. Roy. Soc.*, cl (1861) 57–84.

7 H. Grassmann, 'On the Theory of Compound Colours', *Phil. Mag.* (Ser. 4) vii (1854) 254–64.

8 W. D. Wright, 'A Colorimetric Equipment for Research on Vision', *J. Sci. Inst.*, xvi (1939) 10–19.

9 L. C. Thomson and W. D. Wright, 'The Convergence of the Tritanopic Confusion Loci and the Derivation of the Fundamental Response Functions', *J. Opt. Soc. Am.*, xliii (1953) 890–4.

10 F. H. G. Pitt, 'Characteristics of Dichromatic Vision', *Med. Res. Counc. Spec. Rep. Ser.*, no. 200 (1935).

11 H. v. Helmholtz, *Handbuch der Physiologischen Optik* (Leipzig, 1867). English trans. by J. P. C. Southall, *Physiological Optics* (Opt. Soc. Am., 1924).

12 F. H. G. Pitt, 'The Nature of Normal Trichromatic and Dichromatic Vision', *Proc. Roy. Soc. B.*, cxxxii (1944) 101–17.

13 W. D. Wright, *The Measurement of colour* (London, 3rd edn, 1964).

14 Idem., 'The Characteristics of Tritanopia', *J. Opt. Soc. Am.*, xlii (1952) 509–21.

15 H. Kalmus, *Diagnosis and genetics of defective colour vision* (Oxford, 1965).

16 H. J. A. Dartnall, *The visual pigments* (Methuen: London, 1957); H. J. A. Dartnall and J. N. Lythgoe, 'The Spectral Clustering of Visual Pigments', *Vision Res.*, v (1965) 81–100.

17 W. B. Marks, W. H. Dobelle and E. F. MacNichol, 'Visual Pigments of Single Primate Cones', *Science*, cxliii (1964) 1181–3; W. B. Marks, 'Visual Pigments of Single Cones', *CIBA Foundation symposium on colour vision* (London, 1965) 208–16.

18 P. K. Brown and G. Wald, 'Visual Pigments in Single Rods and Cones of the Human Retina', *Science*, cxliv (1964) 45–52.

19 J. M. Enoch, 'Retinal Microspectrophotometry', *J. Opt. Soc. Am.*, lvi (1966) 833–5.

20 C. M. H. Pedler 'Rods and Cones—A French Approach',

Notes   *CIBA Foundation symposium on colour vision* (London, 1965) 52–83; 'New Light on the Retina', *Spectrum*, no. 16 (1965) 9–10.
21 R. L. De Valois, I. Abramov and G. H. Jacobs, 'Analysis of Response Patterns of LGN Cells', *J. Opt. Soc. Am.*, lvi (1966) 966–77.
22 E. Hering, *Outline of a theory of the light sense*, trans. by L. M. Hurvich and D. Jameson (Harvard Univ. Press, 1964).
23 K. J. McCree, 'Colour Confusion Produced by Voluntary Fixation', *Optica Acta*, vii (1960) 281–90; 'Small-field Tritanopia and the Effects of Voluntary Fixation', *Optica Acta*, vii (1960) 317–23.
24 R. W. Ditchburn, 'Information and Control in the Visual System', *Nature*, cxcviii (1963) 630–2.
25 Y. Hsia and C. H. Graham, 'Colour Blindness', chap. 14, *Vision and Visual Perception*, ed. C. H. Graham (New York, 1965).

Dalton's
Influence on
Chemistry

When I was invited to present this paper, I had the
mistaken understanding that probably there would not
be more than one or two given and hence in submitting
a title I tried to make it general so that I could have
some leeway in preparing it. Finally the programme
arrived at my desk and I found great difficulty in trying
to avoid the subjects of others on the programme. Not
being a historian of science in any professional way, I
shall mention the historical events rather briefly and
outline the great advances that have occurred in the
approximately 160 years since Dalton proposed the
atomic theory in modern form. I hope that I do not
intrude too seriously into the proper domains of my
colleagues and in any case probably all of us will present
some personal view in regard to the work of John Dalton and the effect that he has had upon science.

Dalton started his scientific career as a meteorologist
and his atomic theory grew out of these studies in a
natural way. The atmosphere consists of gases, mostly
oxygen and nitrogen (azote to Dalton and his colleagues of that time), with a minor variable constituent,
namely water vapour, which quite obviously enters the
air by evaporation of the liquid and leaves the air as rain
unless we assume that conservation of water does not
exist, a point of view not always so obvious to people
of the past. Dalton's studies elucidated the situation in
regard to this problem. Lavoisier and others thought
that water in the air combined with the oxygen and
nitrogen to form a chemical compound as they were

understood at that time. Dalton regarded this situation as that of a mixture and he showed by experiments that the air consisted of a mixture of about 4 parts of nitrogen to 1 part oxygen, and that the amount of water varied from zero parts up to a maximum and that this maximum increased with the temperature. Also he found that the quantity of water vapour taken up by a gas was independent of the kind of gas. (We can all think of gases for which this conclusion would not hold, but it should certainly be true for many permanent gases available to Dalton.) From these studies he formulated the law of partial pressures. These studies led on to the diffusion of gases into each other, and the observation that gases of different densities do not separate into different layers in the earth's gravitational field.

Dalton discovered the law of multiple proportions using the compounds of carbon and hydrogen, carbon and oxygen, and nitrogen and oxygen. Though the analytical data were not very good it was possible in these cases to show that this law held, and of course it was consistent with the atomic theory and the formulae proposed by Dalton.

Henry's law was developed at approximately the same time. Again gases become mixed homogeneously with liquids and the amount of gas dissolved is proportional to the pressure of the gas. There are differences of course in the solubility of the gases in different liquids. Dalton followed this work of Henry closely during these early years of the nineteenth century. He came close to discovering Henry's law but his crediting it to Henry probably means that he did not really discover this law. Dalton was an honest man and carefully credited the work of other scientists to them. Dalton correctly realized that the process was a physical one and not directly related to chemical processes which were being investigated at the same time.

Such studies led quite naturally to the consideration of some sort of ultimate particles as the underlying structure of gases. But apparently his particles were almost stationary, moving between each other at low velocities.

Of course if one assumes that gases consist of particles, then either different gases consist of particles of different masses or of different numbers of particles per unit volume. Dalton in 1803 first became aware of this problem and his conclusions are consistent with the assumption that gases vary in both ways. His table of atomic and molecular weights is well known and in fact has been published in many chemical texts and histories of the subject. As we know, he adopted the atomic weight of hydrogen as 1 and tried to base the atomic weights of other elements and the molecular weights of compounds on this basis. Hydrogen of course was chosen because it appeared to be the gas of lowest density known at that time and this proves still to be true today, except for our knowledge of atomic hydrogen, electrons and neutrons, and other particles of modern physics which are not studied in ways at all similar to those used by Dalton.

Dalton's idea of the pressure exerted by the gas depended upon the theory of heat at that time, namely the existence of a substance known as caloric, which he imagined surrounded each one of the atoms and molecules with an envelope which made contact with neighbouring atoms and molecules. The particles of gas were assumed to be arranged somewhat like our idea of atoms in crystals. Of course the idea of caloric was not due to John Dalton but was in fact a general idea of the times.

A curious situation existed in this decade of the nineteenth century in that for many years previous to this the beginnings of a kinetic theory of gases had been proposed by Bernoulli in 1739. He had devised essentially the well known formula for explaining Boyle's law in terms of the kinetic thoery of gases, namely that $P = \frac{1}{3} nmv^2$. In fact, the idea that the pressure of a gas was due to moving particles was proposed by Hooke approximately 100 years earlier and Boyle's law was proposed in 1662. It is curious that Dalton did not make use of these ideas and it is possible to be critical of Dalton on this ground. However, it should be pointed out that no other chemists of the day made use of them either, and in fact physicists did not develop the ideas effectively either at that time. As a matter of fact, they were all confused by the idea of caloric and of course by the hypothesis of phlogiston. In a way, heat is a substance. It has mass and a very small density, not at all measurable by direct means then or since. It is a gas that is very permeable and flows through all substances and even through a vacuum. In effect, it is a substance that is superimposed upon the more obvious substances that are susceptible to human senses and more direct physical measurements. In fact, we have developed most complicated ways of discussing these subjects. Particles move as particles or waves, light is waves or particles, molecules vibrate and these vibrations are governed by quantum mechanics, electrons move about atoms or travel as waves throughout a solid, etc. Heat or caloric is stored in all these forms and as chemical energy. Heat or caloric is a substance with mass of course, but it is not a substance easily followed by the methods of the early nineteenth century or even those of today.

The problem of atomic weights and molecular formulae was a difficult one for Dalton and for other students of the subject at that time. Dalton used a rule of greatest simplicity, Occam's razor in fact. He had the great genius to originate the concept that chemical substances were composed of smaller particles, atoms, and these were combined in various ways to give chemical compounds. He applied the idea that one combination of A and B elements and atoms would be to give a molecule having the formula AB. Then he had the idea that other molecules could be represented by AB^2 or A^2B or more complicated forms if necessary, but always he tried to use these most simple formulae to explain the molecular structure of chemical compounds. During these years the idea of equivalent weights was developed, and as a matter of fact, for many years chemists relied upon equivalent weights and oftentimes were not too enthusiastic about the use of atomic weights.

Higgins previously had come close to proposing the atomic theory, but quite definitely failed to ascribe definite masses to his particles. To me the essential contribution of Dalton consists in the postulate of definite atoms having definite masses combining to form molecules of definite numbers of atoms of different kinds with the masses of the molecules equal to the sum of the masses of their atoms. That his formulae and atomic weights were mostly incorrect is of minor importance.

An important development of the first decade of the nineteenth century was Gay-Lussac's law of combining volumes. When gases react chemically, the proportions by volume measured at the same temperature and pressure bear simple whole number relations to each other and the volumes of the products if gaseous measured under the same conditions also bear simple whole number relations to the volumes of the reacting gases. Dalton never believed that this law was correct.

Following this, Avogadro in 1811 proposed his famous hypothesis, namely that equal volumes of gases measured at the same temperature and pressure contain the same number of molecules. Dalton again did not accept Avogadro's hypothesis and his difficulty in accepting it was due to his idea of the rule of greatest simplicity. It was necessary to assume, as we learned much later, that elementary gases must consist of molecules containing more than one atom—hydrogen two atoms, oxygen two atoms, chlorine two atoms, and so forth—and without this hypothesis it is difficult to understand Gay-Lussac's law of combining volumes and Avogadro's hypothesis. Hence Dalton really never accepted these during the last thirty-five years of his life.

It is of interest to consider Dalton's atomic and molecular weights of 1808 in comparison with the modern values based upon analytical data of high precision. Table 1 lists some compounds considered by Dalton together with his molecular weights and the modern values.

Dalton and modern molecular weights and numbers of atoms per unit volume compared.

Table 1

Mod.	Dal.	Molecular Weight Dal.	Mod.	Ratio of elements by weight Dal.	Mod.	Relative no. of molecules per unit vol. Dal.
H_2	H	1	2		1	1	1
NH_3	NH	6	17	N/H 5	4·67	1·31
H_2O	OH	8	18	O/H 7	8	1·125
CO	CO	12	28	O/C 1·4	1·33	1·167
NO	NO	12	30	O/N 1·4	1·14	1·25
C_2H_4	CH	6	28	C/H 5	6	2·33
N_2O	N_2O	17	44	N/O 1·43	1·75	1·30
NO_2	NO_2	19	46	O/N 2·80	2·29	1·21
CO_2	CO_2	19	44	O/C 2·80	2·67	1·16
CH_4	CH_2	7	16	C/H 2·50	3·00	1·14
SO_3	SO_3	36	80	O/S 1·4	1·5	1·11
H_2S	HS	16	34	S/H 15	16	1·06

A consideration of the ratios of weights of elements required by his formulae and those required by modern formulae shows the great errors in his data. In fact, it is surprising that he estimated the formulae as well as he did in many cases. The last column gives the relative number of molecules per unit volume with hydrogen gas equal to 1, assuming his formula for the substance and our modern data for the relative densities. Dalton's 'rule of greatest simplicity' did not lead to simple ratios of numbers of gaseous molecules per unit volume. Avogadro's hypothesis made all of these equal to unity.

During a half century following the enunciation of Avogadro's hypothesis great confusion reigned in the field of chemistry. It was in this period that the use of chemical symbols developed, the ideas of combining weights, the existence of large numbers of carbon compounds, much experimentation on the analytical side, rather exact measurements of chemical composition of many substances, the beginnings of thermodynamics, and the kinetic theory of gases, were all developed, and in many ways there was inadequate interaction between the various disciplines.

Also, enormous confusion reigned in regard to the values of atomic weights and even what substances in some cases were elements and which were compounds. It was not until 1858 that Cannizzaro, another Italian chemist, published a paper pointing out that Avogadro's hypothesis of 1811 solved many of the difficult problems in regard to molecular and atomic weights, and in fact that this hypothesis cleared up the great confusion. Not until two years later at the Karlsruhe Congress where this subject was discussed did chemists realize the validity of Avogadro's theory. It is unfortunate that Dalton did not have the genius to guide chemists during this time by accepting Gay-Lussac's law and Avogadro's hypothesis. But it should be pointed out in all fairness that no other chemist was able to see through this maze of difficulties in a clear fashion either. We may think that it was the fault of Dalton but it was the fault of all other people working in this field during these years as well.

Today, it is difficult to appreciate the problem presented to chemists at the beginning of the nineteenth century. To us the existence of atoms and molecules and the relationships between them are so obvious, so natural, so real. But chemistry is a difficult science and it developed late in the historical sequence. Astronomy became a modern science with Tycho Brahe (1546–1601), Kepler (1571–1630), and Copernicus (1473–1543). Physics entered the modern phase with Galileo Galilei (1564–1642) and Sir Isaac Newton (1642–1727). But chemistry entered its modern phase only in the latter years of the eighteenth and the first half of the nineteenth century with John Dalton and his contemporaries. Descriptive and systematic biology became modern with Linnaeus (1707–78) but exact and quantitative biology which is a most difficult science is only developing in this century. The quantitative chemical facts could only develop after effective balances had been devised, and the lack of agreement between Dalton's atomic weights and what they should have been on the basis of his assumed structures shows that the analytical data were of very inferior quality in that first decade of the nineteenth century. Thus we must credit him with great insight in proposing the atomic theory at all.

The scientific discoveries of any particular man would have been made by some other person had he not made them. At the present time one can expect that any important discovery would have been made within a few years had the particular man, who did make it, not done so. In evaluating the importance of Dalton's proposal of the modern atomic and molecular concept, it is well to speculate briefly on the question of who would have advanced the modern atomic concept and when it might have occurred if Dalton had not done so. The papers presented at this meeting show how sceptical of Dalton's ideas other chemists were and how difficult it was for them to accept and extend his ideas. It seems improbable that men who were critical and doubtful in regard to these ideas would have originated the atomic theory themselves. Possibly as suggested in my presence at lunch during the meeting Wollaston would have proposed an atomic theory or possibly Higgins' ideas would have been developed by someone. I think it probable that considerable delay in the development of chemistry might have occurred. Possibly the great delay until 1860 in getting Avogadro's hypothesis accepted would have absorbed any delay in the proposal of the Dalton theory.

As an aside, is it not surprising that men evolving under conditions similar to those under which the anthropoid apes live at the present time should have acquired the capacity to produce music, calculus, ideas regarding atoms and molecules and Newton's laws of motion, or even the ability to drive cars on the streets of Manchester? Possibly we should pause to genuflect before the human animal but understanding him involves much chemistry and this owes much to Dalton.

Scientific Developments from Dalton's Theory

Dalton's proposal of the atomic theory in which atoms of elements having definite fixed masses were combined in molecules to form the ultimate constituents of compounds, together with Avogadro's hypothesis and the many experimental facts that developed during the first half of the nineteenth century, established chemistry on a firm foundation and led to immensely interesting developments in related sciences.

From these developments it was possible to determine the correct atomic weights on the assumption that all atoms of a given element were identical and in particular had the same mass. It was possible to determine the correct formulae of chemical compounds in the gaseous state and also to derive the correct minimal formulae for compounds that could not be studied in the gaseous state. The concepts of atoms and molecules were clearly established at this time and little modification of the concepts has occurred since.

During the first half of the nineteenth century many compounds of carbon had been studied and certainly a good orientation of our knowledge of the great complexity of carbon chemistry had been established. With the events of 1860 the correct chemical formulae were derived. It was no longer possible to follow Dalton's rule of greatest simplicity, and the immense complexity of the compounds of carbon has continued to grow throughout all the years since. The organic chemistry which was applied in these days to all compounds of carbon because they were found in living things became enormously extended during the latter years of the nineteenth century and especially during the years of this century. Today, organic chemistry has become divided into the chemistry of carbon compounds and biochemistry. Dalton's much simpler ideas were extended into the field of structural chemistry which has proved to be so very useful in understanding this complex chemistry.

In 1868 the chemistry of all the elements had been extended to such a point that Mendeleev and Meyer were able to classify the elements into the periodic system. It was possible to conclude that the periods were not of equal length. Mendeleev showed that the first period consisted only of hydrogen at that time, the two next periods of 7 elements each at that time, the next two periods to which he correctly assigned 17 elements each, and he also recognized the great complexity of the long period of the elements. This extension of the idea of the atomic theory was carried on in this century to be explained by the development of the electrical structure of atoms and of Bohr's theory of the atom with its many extensions and many details.

It does seem to me that a retrograde step has been taken in this development in recent years, in that we do not properly place thorium and uranium in our table but classify them as part of an actinide group analogous to the lanthanide group, whereas I believe the earlier authors correctly realized that it should be the uraninite group.

During the 60's, Bunsen and Kirchhoff were able to identify the spectra of atoms and very rapidly the extension of this to astronomical studies occurred so that it was now proven that the elements existed in the stars as well.

The discovery of X-rays and their application to the study of crystals have made possible a very exact knowledge of the arrangement of atoms in crystals due to the pioneering work of the Braggs, and again have substantiated the ideas developed during the nineteenth century in regard to the chemical formulae of compounds in the solid state.

The study of electrochemistry started by Galvani and Volta and developed especially by Faraday first showed that the structure of chemical substances was closely related to electricity and the establishment of the electrochemical equivalents showed that electricity was reasonably assumed to exist in discrete quantities if matter was atomic in character. The discovery of the electron and positively charged particles at the beginning of the twentieth century confirmed this postulate definitely and laid the basis for our modern ideas in regard to the structures of atoms and molecules.

Dalton's atoms remained identical in mass and structure until the years of the twentieth century when radioactivity was discovered and the existence of radioactive elements identical in chemical properties to ordinary elements but differing in their radioactive properties were discovered. This was followed by the discovery by Sir J. J. Thomson and others that the ordinary elements consist of mixtures of atoms of different mass. Thus the original concept that all atoms of a given element were identical was destroyed. The work that has been done in this century on determining the masses of these individual atoms constitutes an enormous extension of the primitive ideas of Dalton in regard to the masses of atoms. We even find that there are slight differences in the chemical properties of these isotopes and we find that indeed Dalton's elements are mixtures. But his first statement in regard to this has

Table 2 Atomic weights of Dalton in 1808: H,1; N,5; C,5; O,7; S,15.

	Modern Symbol	Dalton's Atomic Weight	Modern (Mean) Atomic Weight	Isotopes and Atomic Weights	
Hydrogen	H	1	1·00797	H^1	1·007825
				H^2	2·01410
				H^3	3·01603
Azote	N	5	14·0067	N^{14}	14·00307
				N^{15}	15·00012
Carbon	C	5	12·01115	C^{12}	12·00000
				C^{13}	13·00335
Oxygen	O	7	15·9994	O^{16}	15·99491
				O^{17}	16·99914
				O^{18}	17·99916
Phosphorus	P	9	30·9738	P^{31}	30·97376
Sulphur	S	13	32·064	S^{32}	31·97207
				S^{33}	32·97146
				S^{34}	33·96786
				S^{36}	35·96709

held up to be remarkably true over the century and a half since he proposed his theory. It might have been difficult to have established the law of definite proportions had deuterium been approximately as abundant as its lighter isotope, for in this case substantial variations in the proportion by weight of hydrogen in its compounds would have been observed. Or, it may be that isotopes would have been discovered earlier than they were had this been the case. The masses of these isotopes through the theory of relativity enable us to assign energies to them and to make calculations in regard to this. I think it is interesting to set down at this point the atomic weights for a few elements as they are known today and as they were given by Dalton approximately 160 years ago.

During recent years we have developed rather definite ideas in regard to the relative abundances of the elements in nature, both in our own solar system and those of the distant stars. To a first approximation the abundances in all stars are remarkably similar though differences are observed. On the basis of the modern physics we have been able to outline the processes that produced the origin of the elements.

Modern physics in this century has elucidated certain problems discussed during the early years of the nineteenth century. Dalton sometimes wrote his atomic weights as whole numbers though he could hardly have argued that they were indeed definitely whole number multiples of the atomic weight of hydrogen. However, Prout made exactly this assumption which of course was not confirmed by subsequent work of the nineteenth century. Only the discovery of isotopes has shown that Prout's hypothesis is correct and in a way all atoms are multiples of the hydrogen atom, providing we note that neutrons do decay into a proton and an electron. Of course we note the immense developments of physical science that were necessary before this conclusion could be definitely and correctly formulated. We may mention the discovery of the electron, proton, nuclear atom, and the relation between energy and mass of the relativity theory in order to account for the small but definite deviations from the exact integral multiples of the atomic weight of hydrogen.

Also, the Newtonian short-range forces which con-

J D—AA

cerned scientists of the eighteenth century are definitely understood today in principle, even though exact numerical calculations cannot be secured except for the hydrogen atom and other one-electron atoms, and as a result of most complex calculations by some of our most competent theoretical physicists for helium and the hydrogen molecule. These calculations show that we are aware of all the forces involved in the formation of atoms and molecules. There are no further rules of the mechanics of the external electrons of atoms and molecules to be discovered. But what an immense history of chemical, physical, and indeed mathematical facts and methods were needed to do this—the electron, nuclear atom, relativity theory, quantum mechanics, the spin and magnetic moments of the electron and proton. The problem of Newton's short-range forces could not have been solved by many men of the calibre of Newton during the eighteenth and nineteenth centuries. Only the physical discoveries of all science up to and including the first two decades of this century made this possible. It is not possible to attack certain problems until the correct time in the development of a scientific problem.

It is interesting indeed that somewhere in space there exists antimatter which has gross physical and chemical properties identical to those of the matter of the earth, solar system, and our galaxy. Whereas our matter consists of negative electrons, positive protons and neutrons which decay into negative electrons and positive protons, antimatter consists of positive electrons, negative protons and neutrons which decay into these positive electrons and negative protons. Each has its appropriate neutrinos as well. I doubt if antimatter exists in our galaxy as stars and solid chunks of matter or dust. It undoubtedly is produced by high energy particles in small amounts and for short periods of time within our galaxy, for we observe the effects of these in our meteorites and we know that they should be produced by energetic particles because of our observations in our high energy laboratories. Yet it may be that we look out from our galaxy on other galaxies which consist of such antimatter. But I do not believe that an anti-Dalton exists or ever has existed. If this were the case, there would be an anti-British nation and antisilk rubbed on antiglass would produce positive electricity and hence electrons would be assigned a negative charge and the name electron would require the existence of an anti-Greek nation. Well, you see where we are going. We would only know of matter when we produced it in our laboratories, and of course we would call it antimatter. It gets very confusing. Yet galaxies may exist in which intelligent beings with similar though not identical chemistry to our own are discussing atomic theories.

In these few words I have outlined part of the magnificent structure that has been built on Dalton's theory of atoms which he stated in the first years of the nineteenth century. It is seldom that any discovery of this kind has been able to grow into such a magnificent structure of knowledge as is true in this case.

I have given some thought to the question as to whether this is the approximate end of the development of Dalton's ideas. It is of course certain that very many details in regard to the magnificent structure will be developed in the future. But the question arises as to whether anything qualitatively new comparable to the developments of the past will occur in this field again.

I must admit that I am a very poor prophet and I think this is probably characteristic of most other people, if not in fact a characteristic of all scientists. We see ahead only a very slight distance. I remember my own predictions in regard to the usefulness of heavy hydrogen. I thought it might be useful to about the extent that the inert gases are used in electrical signs or something of the sort; that it might be useful for tracer techniques in biochemistry, as indeed it is. But I did not foresee that it would be the basis of the hydrogen bomb nor that it would be very useful in securing vast amounts of power in the future. So in discussing briefly whether there is a possibility of more enormous developments from the theory of atoms and molecules I have a definitely modest opinion of my own abilities as a prophet.

First of all, I do not regard the many strange particles that are being developed by high energy physics as truly a legitimate extension of Dalton's ideas of atoms. We perhaps will include the antimatter particles corresponding to protons, neutrons, neutrinos, and electrons, as a legitimate extension of this theory, as I have mentioned previously. But particles that can be produced only in high energy accelerators and which exist only in extragalactic and interstellar regions of space are hardly quantities which would be of concern to John Dalton or his successors during the last 160 years, and they definitely do not concern the many diligent and intelligent chemists of today. Possibly others would disagree with this and of course they did develop as a result of studies upon Dalton's atoms and molecules.

During the years of this century great efforts have been made to understand the forces that hold the particles of atoms and molecules together, as mentioned above. This involves the forces between positive and negative charges and quantum mechanics which must be used to describe their interactions. It also includes a discussion of the quantum mechanics of the particles of the nucleus. Great progress has been made in understanding these forces and energies involved in these structures of atoms and molecules. However, the mechanics of these processes are very difficult indeed and at least up to the present time it has not been possible to devise methods for calculating the structure and energies of atoms and complex molecules with high precision. We must depend to a large extent upon guidance from empirical facts. This is largely true of all the processes involved in the science of chemistry and its very important extension into biochemistry. Observations of details are far more important in understanding these processes than are the theories based upon exact calculation, even though the theories are very useful indeed. It will also be true probably that measured values of thermodynamic properties will remain far more important in quantitative thinking about problems than will those that are deduced by quantum mechanics and statistical mechanics, even though the latter are very illuminating in regard to the fundamental meaning of the observed facts.

Many details of the structure and properties of chemical substances and the application of chemistry to practical purposes will be explored. One very outstanding chemical problem will be successfully studied during the coming years, namely the fundamental chemical processes of living organisms. Also, we will acquire much more exact knowledge regarding the origin of life.

However, it is my belief that the discovery of atoms and molecules will remain for all time as the most fundamental discovery of chemistry.

Harold C Urey

*Dalton's
Influence on
Chemistry*

Short Bibliography	For a full bibliography the reader is referred to *John Dalton, 1766–1844, a bibliography of works by and about him*, compiled with an introduction by A. L. Smyth, FLA, (Manchester, 1966).
Biography	GREENAWAY, FRANK, *John Dalton and the atom* (London, 1966)
Biographies of Contemporaries	GIBBS, F. W., *Joseph Priestley; adventurer in science and champion of truth* (London, 1965) GUERLAC, H., *Lavoisier: the critical year* (Cornell, 1961) MCKIE, D., *Antoine Lavoisier, scientist, economist, social reformer* (London, 1952) SMEATON, W. A., *Fourcroy, chemist and revolutionary, 1755–1803* (London, 1962) SÖDERBAUM, H. G., *J. J. Berzelius; autobiographical notes* (Baltimore, 1934) trs Olaf Larsell TRENEER, ANNE, *The mercurial chemist: a life of Sir Humphry Davy* (London, 1963)
General Histories	PARTINGTON, J. R., *A history of chemistry* (London, 1964) iv TATON, R., (ed.), *Histoire generale des sciences* (Paris, 1961) ii, iii (1) WOLF, A., *A history of science, technology and philosophy in the eighteenth century* (London, 1962)
Important Papers	Important papers relating to Dalton have been published at various times by F. Greenaway (*Manchester Memoirs*); H. Guerlac (*Isis*); A. N. Meldrum (*Manchester Memoirs*); L. K. Nash (*Isis*); A. W. Thackray (*Manchester Memoirs, Isis* and *British Journal for the History of Science*).